CIE BIOLOGY 2

Cambridge International Examination

A Level Year 2 | **Student Workbook**

CIE BIOLOGY 2

Cambridge International Examination

A Level Year 2 **Student Workbook**

Meet the Writing Team

Tracey Greenwood
I have been writing resources for students since 1993. I have a Ph.D in biology, specialising in lake ecology and I have taught both graduate and undergraduate biology.

Tracey
Senior Author

Lissa Bainbridge-Smith
I worked in industry in a research and development capacity for 8 years before joining BIOZONE in 2006. I have an M.Sc from Waikato University.

Lissa
Author

Kent Pryor
I have a BSc from Massey University majoring in zoology and ecology and taught secondary school biology and chemistry for 9 years before joining BIOZONE as an author in 2009.

Kent
Author

Richard Allan
I have had 11 years experience teaching senior secondary school biology. I have a Masters degree in biology and founded BIOZONE in the 1980s after developing resources for my own students.

Richard
Founder & CEO

First edition 2016
ISBN 978-1-927309-32-2

Copyright © 2016 Richard Allan
Published by BIOZONE International Ltd

Printed by REPLIKA PRESS PVT LTD using paper produced from renewable and waste materials

Purchases of this workbook may be made direct from the publisher:

BIOZONE

BIOZONE Learning Media (UK) Ltd
United Kingdom, Europe, Middle East
Telephone: +44 1283 530 366
Fax: +44 1283 831 900
Email: sales@biozone.co.uk
Web: www.biozone.co.uk

BIOZONE International Ltd
Head office, New Zealand
Telephone: +64 7 856 8104
Fax: +64 7 856 9243
Email: sales@biozone.co.nz
Web: www.biozone.co.nz

BIOZONE Corporation
USA and Canada
FREE phone: 1-855-246-4555
FREE fax: 1-855-935-3555
Email: sales@thebiozone.com
Web: www.thebiozone.com

Cover photograph

The Chinese water dragon (*Physignathus cocincinus*) is native to the lowland and highland forests of southern China and southeastern Asia. They can grow up to one metre long and live for ten to fifteen years. They are active during the day and spend much of their time in trees, although they are semi-aquatic and able to remain submerged for up to 25 minutes.

PHOTO: fivespots www.dollarphotoclub.com

Thanks to:

The staff at BIOZONE, including Julie Fairless and Nell Travaglia for design and graphics support, Paolo Curray for IT support, Debbie Antoniadis and Tim Lind for office handling and logistics, and the BIOZONE sales team.

Contents

Activity is marked: ● to be done;   ✓ when completed

Contents

Activity is marked: ⬜ to be done; ✓ when completed

Using This Workbook

This first edition of CIE Biology 2 has been specifically written to meet the content and skills requirements of A Level CIE Biology. Learning outcomes in the introduction to each chapter provide you with a concise guide to the knowledge and skills requirements for each module. Each learning outcome is matched to the activity or activities addressing it. Practical skills are identified in the chapter introductions by a code (PRAC) and supported by activities designed to provide background and familiarity with apparatus, techniques, experimental design, and interpretation of results. A wide range of activities will help you to build on what you already know, explore new topics, work collaboratively, and practise your skills in data handling and interpretation. We hope that you find the workbook valuable and that you make full use of its features.

▶ The outline of the chapter structure below will help you to navigate through the material in each chapter.

Introduction
- A check list of the knowledge and skills requirements for the chapter.
- A list of key terms.

Activities
- The KEY IDEA provides your focus for the activity.
- Annotated diagrams help you understand the content.
- Questions review the content of the page.

Review
- Create your own summary for review.
- Hints help you to focus on what is important.
- Your summary will consolidate your understanding of the content in the chapter.

Literacy
- Activities are based on, but not restricted to, the introductory key terms list.
- Several types of activities test your understanding of the concepts and biological terms in the chapter.

Linkages are made between ideas in separate activities

Structure of a chapter

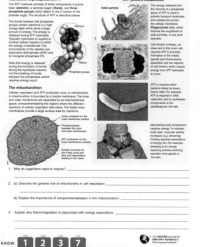

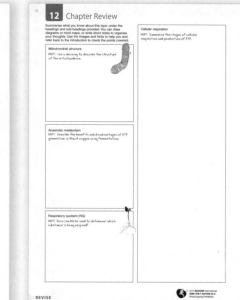

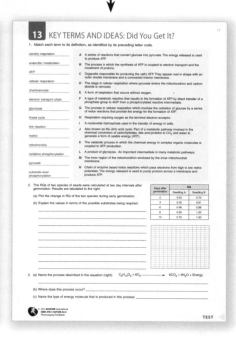

Using the Tab System

The tab system is a useful system for quickly identifying related content and online support. Links generally refer to activities that build on the information in the activity in depth or extent. In the example below, the weblink 1 describes some of the roles of ATP in cells. Activity 2 explains how ATP is recharged from ADP. Sometimes, a link will reflect on material that has been covered earlier as a reminder for important terms that have already been defined or for a formula that may be required to answer a question. The weblinks code is always the same as the activity number on which it is cited. On visiting the weblink page (below), find the number and it will correspond to one or more external websites providing a video or animation of some aspect of the activity's content. Occasionally, the weblink may provide a bank of photographs where images are provided in colour, e.g. for plant and animal histology.

Activities are coded

COMP = comprehension of text

DATA = data handling and interpretation

KNOW = content you need to know

PRAC = a paper practical or a practical focus

REFER = reference - use this for information

REVISE = review the material in the section

SKILL = a specific skill to be demonstrated

TEST = test your understanding

EXT = extension material

KNOW | WEB **1** | LINK **2** | LINK **3**

Weblinks
Bookmark the weblinks page:
www.biozone.co.uk/weblink/CIE-2-9322

Access the external URL for the activity by clicking the link

Link
Connections are made between activities in different sections of the syllabus that are related through content or because they build on prior knowledge.

www.biozone.co.uk/weblink/CIE-2-9322

This WEBLINKS page provides links to **external websites** with supporting information for the activities. These sites are distinct from those provided in the BIOLINKS area of BIOZONE's web site. For the most part, they are narrowly focussed animations and video clips directly relevant to some aspect of the activity on which they are cited. They provide great support to help your understanding of basic concepts.

Chapter in the workbook

Activity in the workbook

Hyperlink to the external website page.

Bookmark weblinks by typing in the address: it is not accessible directly from BIOZONE's website
Corrections and clarifications to current editions are always posted on the weblinks page

▶ Understanding the activity coding system and making use of the online material identified will enable you to get the most out of this resource. The chapter content is structured to build knowledge and skills but this structure does not necessarily represent a strict order of treatment. Be guided by your teacher, who will assign activities as part of a wider programme of independent and group-based work.

Look out for these features and know how to use them:

The **chapter introduction** provides you with a summary of the knowledge and skills requirements for the topic, phrased as a set of learning outcomes. Use the check boxes to identify and mark off the points as you complete them. The chapter introduction also provides you with a list of key terms for the chapter, from which you can construct your own glossary as you work through the activities.

The **activities** form most of this workbook. They are numbered sequentially and each has a task code identifying the skill emphasised. Each activity has a short introduction with a key idea identifying the main message of the page. Most of the information is associated with pictures and diagrams, and your understanding of the content is reviewed through the questions. Some of the activities involve modelling and group work.

Free response questions allow you to use the information provided to answer questions about the content of the activity, either directly or by applying the same principles to a new situation. In some cases, an activity will assume understanding of prior content.

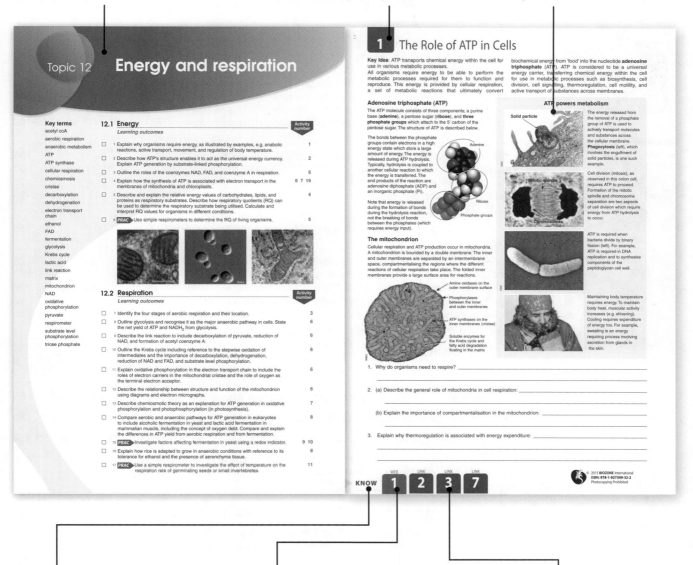

A **TASK CODE** on the page tab identifies the type of activity. For example, is it primarily information-based (KNOW), or does it involve modelling (PRAC) or data handling (DATA)? A full list of codes is given on the following page but the codes themselves are relatively self explanatory.

WEB tabs at the bottom of the activity page alert the reader to the **Weblinks** resource, which provides external, online support material for the activity, usually in the form of an animation, video clip, photo library, or quiz. Bookmark the Weblinks page (see next page) and visit it frequently as you progress through the workbook.

LINK tabs at the bottom of the activity page identify activities that are related in that they build on content or apply the same principles to a new situation.

Summary of Practical and Mathematical Skills at A level

▶ The practical and mathematical skills for CIE A Level are outlined below and supported in the activities indicated.

Paper 5: Assessed practical skills

A Level requirements supported as noted. All points also supported in CIE1.

Activity number

Defining the problem

☐ 1 Define problems in a practical context, including expressing the aim of an experiment as a testable prediction or hypothesis, identifying independent, dependent, and controlled variables.
4 6 10 11 18 25 26

Methods

☐ 2 Describe experimental methods involving a range of apparatus, materials, and techniques. Demonstrate understanding of how to collect accurate, precise data, make suitable volumes and concentrations, and set up controls.
4 6 10 11 18 25 26

☐ 3 Describe methodology and use of apparatus to collect results.
4 6 10 11 18 25 26 155

☐ 4 Describe how to evaluate results using descriptive statistics, including standard deviation (s), standard error (SE), and 95% confidence intervals (95% CI).
104 105 106

☐ 5 Demonstrate understanding of risk management in experimental work.
4 6 11 150 155

Analysis, conclusions, and evaluation

☐ 6 Analyse provided data, including:
• recognising different types of variables and different types of data. — 4 6 25 26
• evaluation of error, confidence limits, and statistical tests as appropriate. — 105 106 107
• use of tables and graphs to identify key points in data (including variability). — 10 11 25 26 105 106
• use of appropriate calculations to simplify, explain, or compare data. — 150 156
• use of s, SE, or graphs with SE bars to evaluate differences between means. — 104 105 106
• use of appropriate statistical methods to assess variability in data. — 86 87 107 108 109 158-162

☐ 7 For provided data:
• identify and explain anomalous values in tables and graphs. — 105
• evaluate methodology, including replication, range and interval of data. — 4 6 10 11 25 26 105
• evaluate the method of measurement for the dependent variable. — 4 10 11 25 26
• evaluate how well the independent variable in all treatments was controlled. — 4 10 11 25 26

☐ 8 Make informed judgements about your confidence in the results, the validity of the investigation, and the reliability of the data as a test for the hypothesis.
4 10 11 25 26 106 155

☐ 9 For provided data:
• make conclusions that include key points of the raw and processed data. — 4 6 10 11 25 26
• decide whether a given hypothesis is supported by the data. — 4 6 10 11 25 26 150
• give scientific explanations of the data and conclusions. — 4 10 11 18 25 26 109 150 155 156
• make further predictions and hypotheses based on your conclusions. — 4 6 11 26
• make suggestions about possible improvements to the investigation. — 4 6 10 11 26 155

Mathematical skills

A Level requirements supported as noted. For AS Level requirements, see CIE1

Activity number

☐ 1 Demonstrate an understanding of simple probability, e.g. as in genetic inheritance.
76 80 83-85

☐ 2 Understand the principles of sampling as applied to biological situations and data.
146 147 148

☐ 3 Understand the importance of chance when interpreting data. — 86 87 105 108 109 146 150 158 159

☐ 4 Use the Lincoln index (*aka* Lincoln-Petersen index) to calculate an estimate population size using mark-release-recapture data using a provided formula.
157

☐ 5 Calculate Simpson's index of diversity (D) using a provided formula.
149 150

☐ 6 Calculate and understand (sample) standard deviation and standard error (SE).
104 105 106

☐ 7 Understand the benefits of using SE and 95% confidence intervals (95% CI) to make statements about data and to use as error bars on graphs.
106

☐ 8 Distinguish between correlation and causation.
160

☐ 9 Use Spearman's rank correlation to test for correlation in non-normal data. Use Pearson's linear correlation to test for correlation in normally distributed data.
161 162

☐ 10 Use the chi-squared (χ^2) test for goodness of fit, e.g. to test the significance of departures from expected phenotypic ratios in genetic crosses. Student's could also use the χ^2 test for independence, e.g. to test the significance of species associations in studies of distribution and abundance.
86 87 158 159

☐ 11 Use the Student's t test to compare two populations.
108 109

☐ 12 Use a spreadsheet programme to analyse and present data, make calculations, and carry out statistical tests.
86 87 105 106 109 158-162

Topic 12 — Energy and respiration

Key terms

acetyl coA

aerobic respiration

anaerobic metabolism

ATP

ATP synthase

cellular respiration

chemiosmosis

cristae

decarboxylation

dehydrogenation

electron transport chain

ethanol

FAD

fermentation

glycolysis

Krebs cycle

lactic acid

link reaction

matrix

mitochondrion

NAD

oxidative phosphorylation

pyruvate

respirometer

substrate level phosphorylation

triose phosphate

12.1 Energy

Learning outcomes

		Activity number
☐	1 Explain why organisms require energy, as illustrated by examples, e.g. anabolic reactions, active transport, movement, and regulation of body temperature.	1
☐	2 Describe how ATP's structure enables it to act as the universal energy currency. Explain ATP generation by substrate-linked phosphorylation.	2
☐	3 Outline the roles of the coenzymes NAD, FAD, and coenzyme A in respiration.	7
☐	4 Explain how the synthesis of ATP is associated with electron transport in the membranes of mitochondria and chloroplasts.	7 19
☐	5 Describe and explain the relative energy values of carbohydrates, lipids, and proteins as respiratory substrates. Describe how respiratory quotients (RQ) can be used to determine the respiratory substrate being utilised. Calculate and interpret RQ values for organisms in different conditions.	5
☐	6 **PRAC** Use simple respirometers to determine the RQ of living organisms.	6

Dartmouth College   Masur

12.2 Respiration

Learning outcomes

		Activity number
☐	7 Identify the four stages of aerobic respiration and their location.	3
☐	8 Outline glycolysis and recognise it as the major anaerobic pathway in cells. State the net yield of ATP and $NADH_2$ from glycolysis.	7
☐	9 Describe the link reaction to include decarboxylation of pyruvate, reduction of NAD, and formation of acetyl coenzyme A.	7
☐	10 Outline the Krebs cycle including reference to the stepwise oxidation of intermediates and the importance of decarboxylation, dehydrogenation, reduction of NAD and FAD, and substrate level phosphorylation.	7
☐	11 Explain oxidative phosphorylation in the electron transport chain to include the roles of electron carriers in the mitochondrial cristae and the role of oxygen as the terminal electron acceptor.	7
☐	12 Describe the relationship between structure and function of the mitochondrion using diagrams and electron micrographs.	7
☐	13 Describe chemiosmotic theory as an explanation for ATP generation in oxidative phosphorylation and photophosphorylation (in photosynthesis).	8
☐	14 Compare aerobic and anaerobic pathways for ATP generation in eukaryotes to include alcoholic fermentation in yeast and lactic acid fermentation in mammalian muscle, including the concept of oxygen debt. Compare and explain the differences in ATP yield from aerobic respiration and from fermentation.	9
☐	15 **PRAC** Investigate factors affecting respiration in yeast using a redox indicator.	10 11
☐	16 Explain how rice is adapted to grow in anaerobic conditions with reference to its tolerance for ethanol and the presence of aerenchyma tissue.	9
☐	17 **PRAC** Use a simple respirometer to investigate the effect of temperature on the respiration rate of germinating seeds or small invertebrates.	4

1 The Role of ATP in Cells

Key Idea: ATP transports chemical energy within the cell for use in various metabolic processes.

All organisms require energy to be able to perform the metabolic processes required for them to function and reproduce. This energy is provided by cellular respiration, a set of metabolic reactions that ultimately convert biochemical energy from 'food' into the nucleotide **adenosine triphosphate** (ATP). ATP is considered to be a universal energy carrier, transferring chemical energy within the cell for use in metabolic processes such as biosynthesis, cell division, cell signalling, thermoregulation, cell motility, and active transport of substances across membranes.

Adenosine triphosphate (ATP)

base sugar phosphate

The ATP molecule consists of three components; a purine base (**adenine**), a pentose sugar (**ribose**), and **three phosphate groups** which attach to the 5' carbon of the pentose sugar. The structure of ATP is described below.

The bonds between the phosphate groups contain electrons in a high energy state which store a large amount of energy. The energy is released during ATP hydrolysis. Typically, hydrolysis is coupled to another cellular reaction to which the energy is transferred. The end products of the reaction are adenosine diphosphate (ADP) and an inorganic phosphate (Pi).

Note that energy is released during the formation of bonds during the hydrolysis reaction, not the breaking of bonds between the phosphates (which requires energy input).

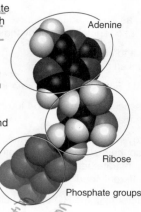

Adenine

Ribose

Phosphate groups

ATP products
Cellular respiration

The mitochondrion

Cellular respiration and ATP production occur in mitochondria. A mitochondrion is bounded by a double membrane. The inner and outer membranes are separated by an intermembrane space, compartmentalising the regions where the different reactions of cellular respiration take place. The folded inner membranes provide a large surface area for reactions.

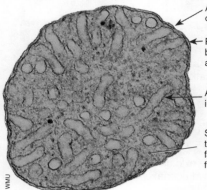

→ Amine oxidases on the outer membrane surface

→ Phosphorylases between the inner and outer membranes

→ ATP synthases on the inner membranes (cristae)

→ Soluble enzymes for the Krebs cycle and fatty acid degradation floating in the matrix

ATP powers metabolism

cell division
DNA replication
binary fission

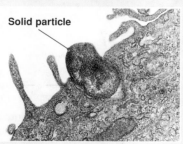

Solid particle

The energy released from the removal of a phosphate group of ATP is used to actively transport molecules and substances across the cellular membrane. **Phagocytosis** (left), which involves the engulfment of solid particles, is one such example.

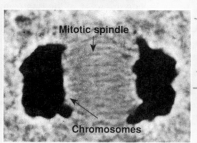

Mitotic spindle

Chromosomes

Cell division (mitosis), as observed in this onion cell, requires ATP to proceed. Formation of the mitotic spindle and chromosome separation are two aspects of cell division which require energy from ATP hydrolysis to occur.

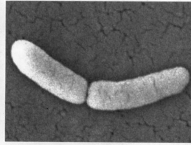

ATP is required when bacteria divide by binary fission (left). For example, ATP is required in DNA replication and to synthesise components of the peptidoglycan cell wall.

Maintaining body temperature requires energy. To maintain body heat, muscular activity increases (e.g. shivering). Cooling requires expenditure of energy too. For example, sweating is an energy requiring process involving secretion from glands in the skin.

1. Why do organisms need to respire? *Respiration provides the source of ATP which is required for metabolic processes*

2. (a) Describe the general role of mitochondria in cell respiration: *site for Krebs cycle and ETS stages of cell respiration and ATP production*

   (b) Explain the importance of compartmentalisation in the mitochondrion: *It provides functional efficiency pH blood*

3. Explain why thermoregulation is associated with energy expenditure: *Maintaining body temp*

© 2016 **BIOZONE** International
ISBN: 978-1-927309-32-2
Photocopying Prohibited

2 ATP and Energy

Key Idea: ATP is the universal energy carrier in cells. Energy is stored in the covalent bonds between phosphate groups. The molecule ATP (adenosine triphosphate) is the universal energy carrier for the cell. ATP can release its energy quickly by hydrolysis of the terminal phosphate. This reaction is catalysed by the enzyme ATPase. Once ATP has released its energy, it becomes ADP (adenosine diphosphate), a low energy molecule that can be recharged by adding a phosphate. The energy to do this is supplied by the controlled breakdown of respiratory substrates in cellular respiration.

How does ATP provide energy?

ATP releases its energy during hydrolysis. Water is split and added to the terminal phosphate group resulting in ADP and Pi. For every mole of ATP hydrolysed **30.7 kJ** of energy is released. Note that energy is released during the formation of chemical bonds, not from the breaking of chemical bonds.

$$ATP \xrightarrow{ATPase} ADP + Pi$$

The reaction of A + B is endergonic. It requires energy to proceed and will not occur spontaneously.

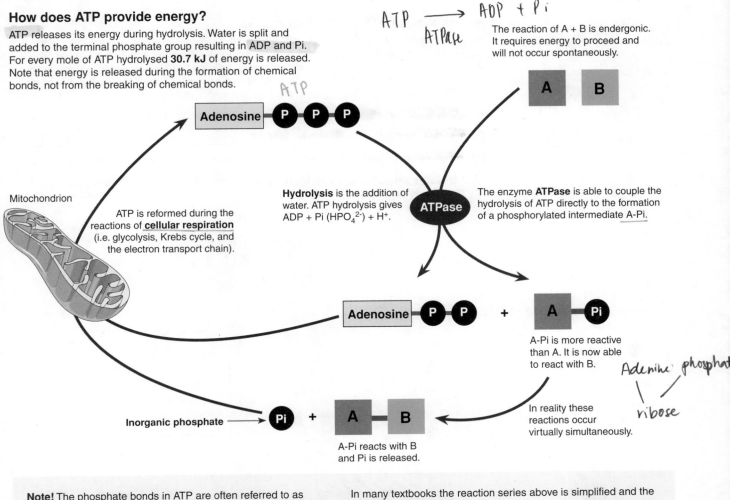

ATP

Adenosine — P P P

Mitochondrion

ATP is reformed during the reactions of **cellular respiration** (i.e. glycolysis, Krebs cycle, and the electron transport chain).

Hydrolysis is the addition of water. ATP hydrolysis gives ADP + Pi (HPO_4^{2-}) + H^+.

ATPase

The enzyme **ATPase** is able to couple the hydrolysis of ATP directly to the formation of a phosphorylated intermediate A-Pi.

A B

Adenosine — P P + A — Pi

A-Pi is more reactive than A. It is now able to react with B.

Adenine phosphate
ribose

Inorganic phosphate → Pi + A — B

A-Pi reacts with B and Pi is released.

In reality these reactions occur virtually simultaneously.

Note! The phosphate bonds in ATP are often referred to as high energy bonds. This can be misleading. The bonds contain *electrons in a high energy state* (making the bonds themselves relatively weak). A small amount of energy is required to break the bonds, but when the intermediates recombine and form new chemical bonds a large amount of energy is released. The final product is less reactive than the original reactants.

In many textbooks the reaction series above is simplified and the intermediates are left out:

A + B ————————→ AB

ATP   ADP + Pi

---

1. (a) How does ATP supply energy to power metabolism? _The hydrolysis of ATP is couple to the formation_ _____

_____

(b) In what way is the ADP/ATP system like a rechargeable battery? _____

_____

2. What is the immediate source of energy for reforming ATP from ADP? _Glucose_ _____

3. Which enzyme catalyses the hydrolysis of ATP?: _ATPase_ _____

4. Explain why highly active cells (e.g. sperm cells) have large numbers of mitochondria: _Highly active cells_ _require a lot of energy and therefore large num of mitochondria so that enough ATP can be produced._

LINK LINK LINK WEB
7 3 1 2 KNOW

3 ATP Production in Cells

Key Idea: Cellular respiration is the process by which the energy in glucose is transferred to ATP.

Cellular respiration can be **aerobic** (requires oxygen) or **anaerobic** (does not require oxygen). Some plants and animals can generate ATP anaerobically for short periods of time. Other organisms (anaerobic bacteria) use only anaerobic respiration and live in oxygen-free environments. Cellular respiration occurs in the cytoplasm and mitochondria. The overall process is summarised by the word equation: glucose + oxygen → carbon dioxide + water + ATP.

An overview of ATP production in cells

Respiration involves three metabolic stages (plus a link reaction) summarised below. The first two stages are the catabolic pathways that decompose glucose and other organic fuels. In the third stage, the electron transport chain accepts electrons from the first two stages and passes these from one electron acceptor to another. The energy released at each stepwise transfer is used to make ATP. The final electron acceptor in this process is molecular oxygen.

1 **Glycolysis**. In the cytoplasm, glucose is broken down into two molecules of pyruvate.

2 **The link reaction**. In the mitochondrial matrix, pyruvate is split and added to coenzyme A.

3 **Krebs cycle**. In the mitochondrial matrix, a derivative of pyruvate is decomposed to CO_2.

4 **Electron transport and oxidative phosphorylation**. This occurs in the inner membranes of the mitochondrion and accounts for almost 90% of the ATP generated by respiration.

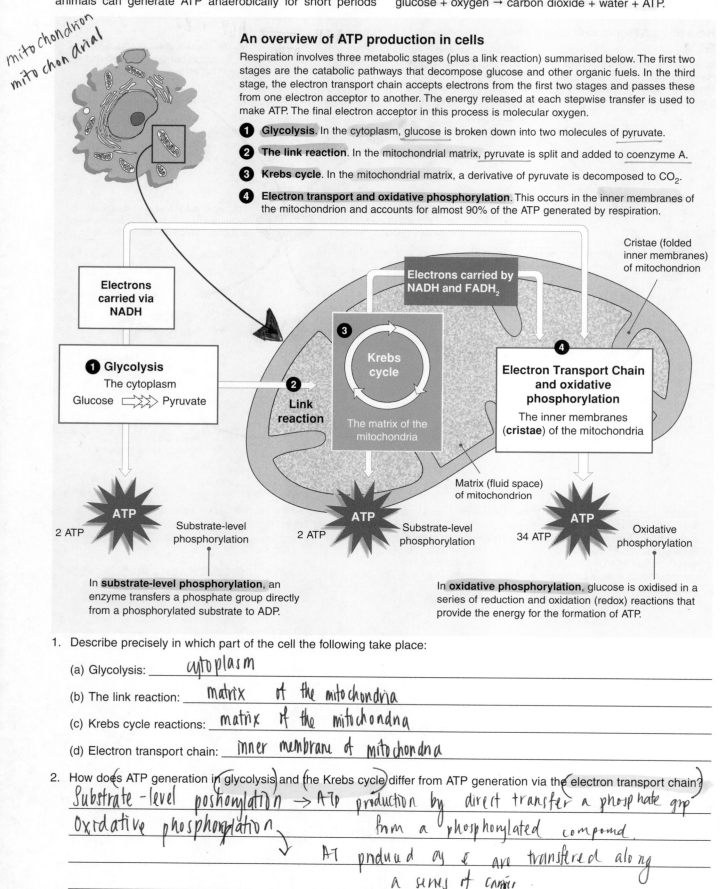

mitochondrion
mitochondrial

In **substrate-level phosphorylation**, an enzyme transfers a phosphate group directly from a phosphorylated substrate to ADP.

In **oxidative phosphorylation**, glucose is oxidised in a series of reduction and oxidation (redox) reactions that provide the energy for the formation of ATP.

1. Describe precisely in which part of the cell the following take place:

   (a) Glycolysis: _cytoplasm_

   (b) The link reaction: _matrix of the mitochondria_

   (c) Krebs cycle reactions: _matrix of the mitochondria_

   (d) Electron transport chain: _inner membrane of mitochondria_

2. How does ATP generation in glycolysis and the Krebs cycle differ from ATP generation via the electron transport chain?

   Substrate-level phosphorylation → ATP production by direct transfer a phosphate grp
   Oxidative phosphorylation   from a phosphorylated compound
   _   ATP produced as e⁻ are transferred along_
   _   a series of carriers_

4 Measuring Respiration Rate

Key Idea: Oxygen consumption and CO_2 production in respiring organisms can be measured with a respirometer. A respirometer measures the amount of oxygen consumed and the amount of carbon dioxide produced during cellular respiration. Respirometers are quite simple pieces of apparatus but can give accurate results if set up carefully.

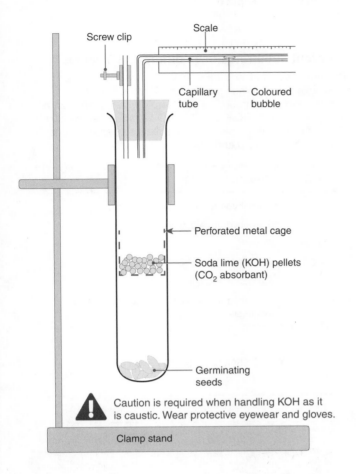

Caution is required when handling KOH as it is caustic. Wear protective eyewear and gloves.

Measuring respiration with a simple respirometer

The diagram on the left shows a **simple respirometer**. It measures the change in gases as respiration occurs.

▸ Respiring organisms, in this case germinating seeds, are placed into the bottom of the chamber.

▸ Soda lime or potassium hydroxide is added to absorb any carbon dioxide produced during respiration. Therefore the respirometer measures oxygen consumption.

▸ Once the organisms have been placed into the chamber the screw clip is closed. The start position of the coloured bubble is measured (this is the time zero reading).

▸ The coloured bubble in the capillary tube moves in response to the change in oxygen consumption. Measuring the movement of the liquid (e.g. with a ruler) allows the change in volume of gas to be estimated.

▸ Care needs to be taken when using a simple respirometer because changes in temperature or atmospheric pressure may change the readings and give a false measure of respiration.

▸ **Differential respirometers** (not shown) use two chambers (a control chamber with no organisms and a test chamber) connected by a U-tube. Changes in temperature or atmospheric pressure act equally on both chambers. Observed changes are only due to the activities of the respiring organism.

1. Why does the bubble in the capillary tube move?

_____

_____

_____

2. A student used a simple respirometer (like the one above) to measure respiration in maggots. Their results are presented in the table (right). The maggots were left to acclimatise for 10 minutes before the experiment was started.

(a) Calculate the rate of respiration and record this in the table. The first two calculations have been done for you.

(b) Plot the rate of respiration on the grid, below right.

(c) Describe the results in your plot: _____

_____

_____

_____

Time / minutes	Distance bubble moved / mm	Rate/ mm min⁻¹
0	0	0
5	25	5
10	65	
15	95	
20	130	
25	160	

(d) Why was there an acclimatisation period before the experiment began?

_____

_____

3. Why would it have been better to use a differential respirometer? _____

_____

_____

_____

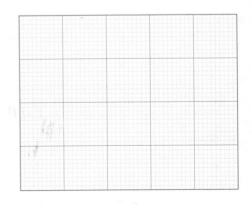

© 2016 **BIOZONE** International
ISBN: 978-1-927309-32-2
Photocopying Prohibited

LINK 11 LINK 5 WEB 4 **DATA**

5 Respiratory Quotient

Key Idea: The respiratory quotient is the ratio of the amount of carbon dioxide produced during cellular respiration to the amount of oxygen consumed.
The ratio of carbon dioxide produced to the amount of oxygen being consumed during cellular respiration in a set period of time is called the **respiratory quotient** (RQ). It is often calculated to provide a useful indication about the respiratory substrate being respired.

Calculating RQ

The RQ is the amount of carbon dioxide (CO_2) produced, divided by the amount of oxygen (O_2) used in a set period of time. The equation for calculating RQ is very simple and is given below.

$$RQ = \frac{CO_2 \text{ produced}}{O_2 \text{ consumed}}$$

For the equation below, the RQ value would be 1:
$(6CO_2 \div 6O_2)$

$$6O_2 + C_6H_{12}O_6 \longrightarrow 6CO_2 + 6H_2O$$

Different substrates have different RQ values

Different respiratory substrates have different RQ values (see table below). When pure carbohydrate is oxidised in cellular respiration, the RQ is 1.0. More oxygen is required to oxidise fatty acids (RQ = 0.7). The RQ for protein is about 0.9. Organisms usually respire a mix of substrates, and produce RQ values of between 0.8 and 0.9.

RQ	Substrate
> 1.0	Carbohydrate with some anaerobic respiration
1.0	Carbohydrate e.g. glucose
0.9	Protein
0.7	Fat
0.5	Fat with associated carbohydrate synthesis
0.3	Carbohydrate with associated organic acid synthesis

1. This equation shows aerobic respiration of compound A: $C_{55}H_{100}O_6 + 77O_2 \rightarrow 55CO_2 + 50H_2O$

   (a) Calculate the RQ value: _____

   (b) Based on the RQ value, what substrate is being respired? _____

2. The table (right) shows the results of an experiment to measure the rates of oxygen consumption and carbon dioxide production of crickets 1 hour and 48 hours after feeding at different temperatures:

   (a) Calculate the RQ at 20°C, 1 hour after feeding:

   _____

   (b) Calculate the RQ at 20°C, 48 hours after feeding:

   _____

   (c) Explain the difference between the two results: _____

   _____

   (d) Did increasing the temperature to 30°C have any effect on RQ value? Explain your answer: _____

   _____

   _____

Time after last feed / hours	Temperature / °C	Rate of O_2 consumption / cm^3 g^{-1} h^{-1}	Rate of CO_2 production / cm^3 g^{-1} h^{-1}
1	20	2.82	2.82
48	20	2.82	1.97
1	30	5.12	5.12
48	30	5.12	3.57

3. The graph (right) shows the RQ values for germinating wheat seeds. Study the graph state the most likely respiratory substances at:

   Point A: _____

   Point B: _____

   Point C: _____

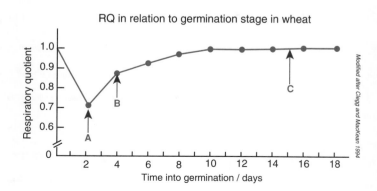

RQ in relation to germination stage in wheat

Modified after Clegg and MacKean 1994

6 Determining Respiratory Quotient

Key Idea: Measurements of the volume of gas exchange using a respirometer, with and without the removal of carbon dioxide, can be used to calculate the respiratory quotient. When organisms respire, they use oxygen and produce carbon dioxide. By placing an organism in a sealed container and removing the carbon dioxide, it is possible to measure the amount of oxygen being used by recording how much the volume of gas in the container changes. Then, by leaving the carbon dioxide in place it is possible to measure the carbon dioxide produced. These two figures can be used to calculate the respiratory quotient and possibly determine the substrate being respired.

Aim

To identify the respiratory substrate of blow-fly maggots by measuring the amount of oxygen used and carbon dioxide (CO_2) produced in a differential respirometer.

Hypothesis

If the maggots respire carbohydrate, then the respiratory quotient will be around 1.0.

The method

Two test tubes were set up as per the diagram right. Test tube B acts as a thermobarometer and minimises any volume changes due to changes in air temperature or pressure. It is connected to test tube A by a capillary tube containing coloured water. Test tube A contains the maggots and potassium hydroxide (KOH) to remove the CO_2. The syringe was used to add air to the system to move the water in the capillary tube as necessary. In the first experiment, the system was sealed and the amount of movement in the capillary tube was measured every minute for five minutes. In the second experiment, the KOH was removed from test tube A and the procedure was repeated. The capillary tube was calibrated to measure 0.002 mL per division.

The volume of oxygen was measured using the capillary tube and scale in the first experiment. The volume of CO_2 is the volume moved in experiment 1 minus the volume moved in experiment 2. The results are shown in the table below.

Test tube A   **Test tube B**

Maggots in mesh basket

Syringe

Glass beads

Filter paper helps CO_2 dissolve in the KOH

Capillary U-tube containing coloured water (manometer)

KOH absorbs CO_2

⚠ Caution is required when handling KOH as it is caustic. Wear protective eyewear and gloves.

Experiment 1: Test tube with KOH		
Time / min	Manometer reading / divisions moved	Volume / mL
0	0.0	
1	2.0	
2	2.5	
3	2.0	
4	1.5	
5	1.5	
Mean		

Experiment 2: Test tube without KOH		
Time / min	Manometer reading / divisions moved	Volume / mL
0	1.0	
1	1.0	
2	0.75	
3	0.75	
4	1.0	
5	0.5	
Mean		

1. Complete the tables above:

2. Calculate average oxygen consumption in mL per minute: _____

_____

3. Calculate the average carbon dioxide produced in mL per minute: _____

_____

4. Calculate the RQ for the maggots: _____

_____

5. Use the information on page 6 *Respiratory Quotient* to determine the substrate the maggots are respiring:

_____

_____

LINK
5

LINK
4

WEB
6

DATA ◄

7 The Biochemistry of Respiration

Key Idea: During cellular respiration, the energy in glucose is transferred to ATP in a series of enzyme controlled steps. The oxidation of glucose is a catabolic, energy yielding pathway. The breakdown of glucose and other organic fuels (such as fats and proteins) to simpler molecules releases energy for ATP synthesis. Glycolysis and the Krebs cycle supply electrons to the electron transport chain, which drives oxidative phosphorylation. Glycolysis nets two ATP. The conversion of pyruvate (the end product of glycolysis)

to acetyl CoA links glycolysis to the Krebs cycle. One "turn" of the cycle releases carbon dioxide, forms one ATP, and passes electrons to three NAD^+ and one FAD. Most of the ATP generated in cellular respiration is produced by oxidative phosphorylation when $NADH + H^+$ and $FADH_2$ donate electrons to the series of electron carriers in the electron transport chain. At the end of the chain, electrons are passed to molecular oxygen, reducing it to water. Electron transport is coupled to ATP synthesis.

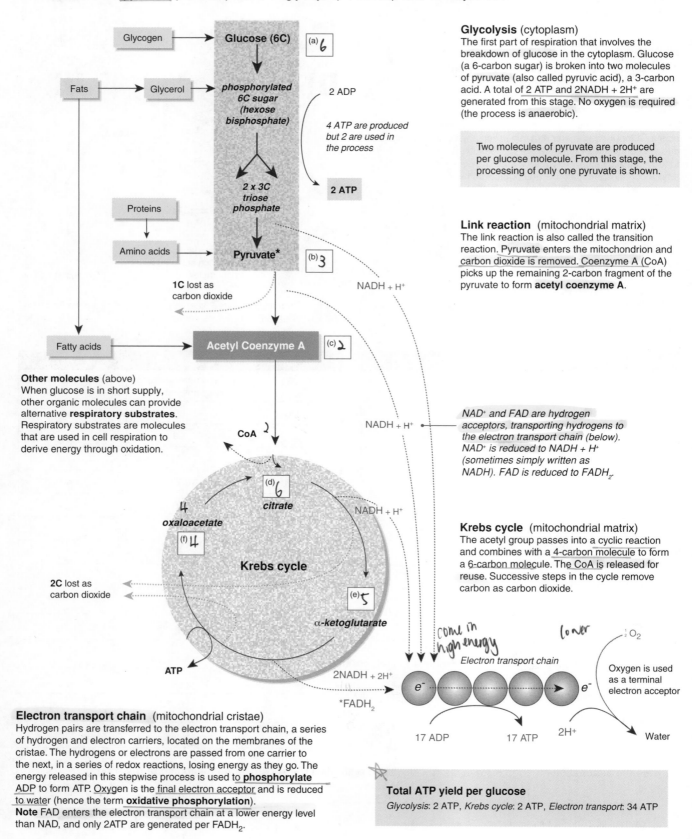

Glycolysis (cytoplasm)
The first part of respiration that involves the breakdown of glucose in the cytoplasm. Glucose (a 6-carbon sugar) is broken into two molecules of pyruvate (also called pyruvic acid), a 3-carbon acid. A total of 2 ATP and $2NADH + 2H^+$ are generated from this stage. No oxygen is required (the process is anaerobic).

Two molecules of pyruvate are produced per glucose molecule. From this stage, the processing of only one pyruvate is shown.

Link reaction (mitochondrial matrix)
The link reaction is also called the transition reaction. Pyruvate enters the mitochondrion and carbon dioxide is removed. Coenzyme A (CoA) picks up the remaining 2-carbon fragment of the pyruvate to form **acetyl coenzyme A**.

NAD^+ and FAD are hydrogen acceptors, transporting hydrogens to the electron transport chain (below). NAD^+ is reduced to $NADH + H^+$ (sometimes simply written as NADH). FAD is reduced to $FADH_2$.

Krebs cycle (mitochondrial matrix)
The acetyl group passes into a cyclic reaction and combines with a 4-carbon molecule to form a 6-carbon molecule. The CoA is released for reuse. Successive steps in the cycle remove carbon as carbon dioxide.

Other molecules (above)
When glucose is in short supply, other organic molecules can provide alternative **respiratory substrates**. Respiratory substrates are molecules that are used in cell respiration to derive energy through oxidation.

Electron transport chain (mitochondrial cristae)
Hydrogen pairs are transferred to the electron transport chain, a series of hydrogen and electron carriers, located on the membranes of the cristae. The hydrogens or electrons are passed from one carrier to the next, in a series of redox reactions, losing energy as they go. The energy released in this stepwise process is used to **phosphorylate ADP** to form ATP. Oxygen is the final electron acceptor and is reduced to water (hence the term **oxidative phosphorylation**).
Note FAD enters the electron transport chain at a lower energy level than NAD, and only 2ATP are generated per $FADH_2$.

Oxygen is used as a terminal electron acceptor

Total ATP yield per glucose
Glycolysis: 2 ATP, *Krebs cycle*: 2 ATP, *Electron transport*: 34 ATP

© 2016 **BIOZONE** International
ISBN: 978-1-927309-32-2
Photocopying Prohibited

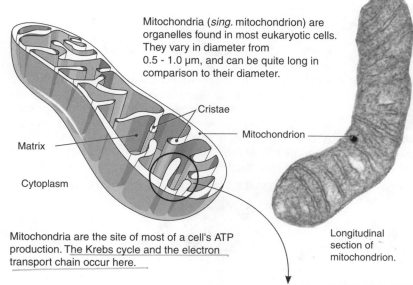

Mitochondria (*sing.* mitochondrion) are organelles found in most eukaryotic cells. They vary in diameter from 0.5 - 1.0 μm, and can be quite long in comparison to their diameter.

Cristae

Matrix

Mitochondrion

Cytoplasm

Longitudinal section of mitochondrion.

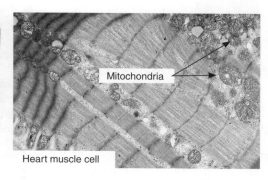

Mitochondria

Heart muscle cell

Mitochondria are the site of most of a cell's ATP production. The Krebs cycle and the electron transport chain occur here.

Cells that require a lot of ATP for cellular processes have a lot of mitochondria. Sperm cells contain a large number of mitochondria near the base of the tail. Liver cells have around 2000 mitochondria per cell, taking up 25% of the cytoplasmic space. Heart muscle cells (above) may have 40% of the cytoplasmic space taken up by mitochondria.

Location of cellular respiration

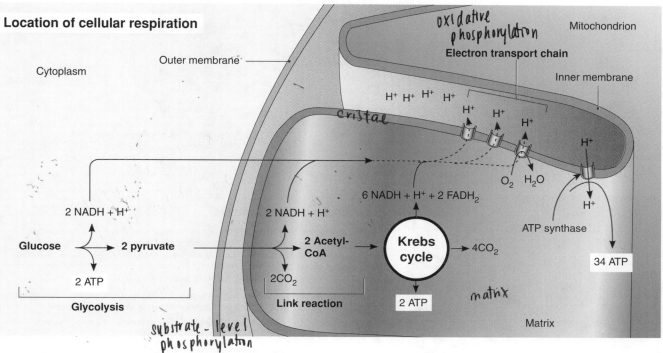

oxidative phosphorylation

Mitochondrion

Outer membrane

Cytoplasm

Electron transport chain

Inner membrane

H^+ H^+ H^+ H^+

cristae

H^+ H^+ H^+

H^+

O_2 H_2O

H^+

6 NADH + H^+ + 2 $FADH_2$

2 NADH + H^+

2 NADH + H^+

ATP synthase

H^+

Glucose → 2 pyruvate

2 Acetyl-CoA

Krebs cycle

4CO_2

34 ATP

2 ATP

$2CO_2$

2 ATP

matrix

Glycolysis

Link reaction

Matrix

substrate-level phosphorylation

1. In the longitudinal section of a mitochondrion (above), label the matrix and cristae.

2. Explain the purpose of the link reaction: _Prepare pyrute for entry in the Krebs cycle. Carbon dioxide is removed and coenzyme A is added link glycolysis to Krebs cycle._

3. On the diagram of cell respiration (previous page), state the number of carbon atoms in each of the molecules (a)-(f):

4. How many ATP molecules **per molecule of glucose** are generated during the following stages of respiration?

   (a) Glycolysis: _2_____ (b) Krebs cycle: _2_____ (c) Electron transport chain: _34_____ (d) Total: _38_____

5. Explain what happens to the carbon atoms lost during respiration: _____

6. Explain what happens during oxidative phosphorylation: _ADP is phosphorylated to ATP._

   Electrons passed along the ETC are used to pump H ion across the inner membrane of the mitochondria. The flow of hydrogen ions back across the membrane is couple to the phosphorylation of ADP to ATP. Oxygen is the final ē acceptor, reducing hydrogen to water. Because O is the final acceptor the process is called oxidative phosphorylation.

8 Chemiosmosis

Key Idea: Chemiosmosis is the process in which electron transport is coupled to ATP synthesis.

Chemiosmosis occurs in the membranes of mitochondria, the chloroplasts of plants, and across the plasma membrane of bacteria. It involves establishing and using a proton gradient to drive ATP synthesis. Chemiosmosis has two key components: an **electron transport chain** sets up a proton gradient as electrons pass along it to a final electron acceptor, and an enzyme, **ATP synthase**, uses the proton gradient to

catalyse ATP synthesis. In respiration, electron carriers on the inner mitochondrial membrane oxidise $NADH + H^+$ and $FADH_2$. The energy released from this process is used to move protons against their concentration gradient, from the matrix into the intermembrane space. The return of protons to the matrix via ATP synthase is coupled to ATP synthesis. A similar process occurs Similarly, in the chloroplasts of green plants, ATP is produced when protons pass from the thylakoid lumen to the chloroplast stroma via ATP synthase.

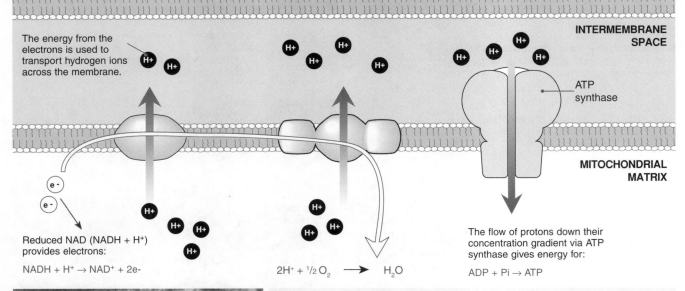

INTERMEMBRANE SPACE

The energy from the electrons is used to transport hydrogen ions across the membrane.

ATP synthase

MITOCHONDRIAL MATRIX

Reduced NAD (NADH + H⁺) provides electrons:

$NADH + H^+ \rightarrow NAD^+ + 2e-$

$2H^+ + \frac{1}{2}O_2 \longrightarrow H_2O$

The flow of protons down their concentration gradient via ATP synthase gives energy for:

$ADP + Pi \rightarrow ATP$

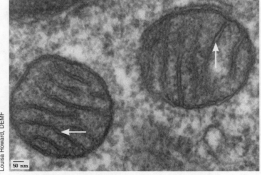

The intermembrane spaces can be seen (arrows) in this transverse section of mitochondria.

The evidence for chemiosmosis

The British biochemist Peter Mitchell proposed the chemiosmotic hypothesis in 1961. He proposed that, because living cells have membrane potential, electrochemical gradients could be used to do work, i.e. provide the energy for ATP synthesis. Scientists at the time were sceptical, but the evidence for chemiosmosis was extensive and came from studies of isolated mitochondria and chloroplasts. Evidence included:

▸ The outer membranes of mitochondria were removed leaving the inner membranes intact. Adding protons to the treated mitochondria increased ATP synthesis.

▸ When isolated chloroplasts were illuminated, the medium in which they were suspended became alkaline.

▸ Isolated chloroplasts were kept in the dark and transferred first to a low pH medium (to acidify the thylakoid interior) and then to an alkaline medium (low protons). They then spontaneously synthesised ATP (no light was needed).

1. Summarise the process of chemiosmosis: _____

_____

_____

2. Why did the addition of protons to the treated mitochondria increase ATP synthesis?_____

_____

_____

3. Why did the suspension of isolated chloroplasts become alkaline when illuminated?_____

_____

4. (a) What was the purpose of transferring the chloroplasts first to an acid then to an alkaline medium? _____

_____

   (b) Why did ATP synthesis occur spontaneously in these treated chloroplasts? _____

_____

© 2016 **BIOZONE** International
ISBN: 978-1-927309-32-2
Photocopying Prohibited

9 Anaerobic Pathways

Mammalian muscle.
lactic acid.
yeast

Key Idea: Glucose can be metabolised aerobically and anaerobically to produce ATP. The ATP yield from aerobic processes is higher than from anaerobic processes.

Aerobic respiration occurs in the presence of oxygen. Organisms can also generate ATP anaerobically (without oxygen) by using a molecule other than oxygen as the terminal electron acceptor for the pathway. In <u>alcoholic</u> fermentation, the electron acceptor is ethanal. In lactic acid fermentation, which occurs in mammalian muscle even when oxygen is present, the electron acceptor is pyruvate itself.

Lactic acid fermentation

Mammalian skeletal muscle produces ATP without the requirement for oxygen by using lactic acid fermentation. In this pathway, pyruvate is reduced to lactic acid, which dissociates to form lactate and H^+. The conversion of pyruvate to lactate is reversible and this pathway operates alongside the aerobic system all the time to enable greater intensity and duration of activity. Lactate can be metabolised in the muscle itself or it can enter the circulation and be taken up by the liver to replenish carbohydrate stores. This 'lactate shuttle' is an important mechanism for balancing the distribution of substrates and waste products.

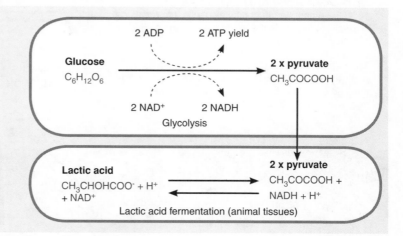

2 ADP → 2 ATP yield

Glucose
$C_6H_{12}O_6$ → **2 x pyruvate** $CH_3COCOOH$

2 NAD^+ → 2 NADH

Glycolysis

Lactic acid
$CH_3CHOHCOO^- + H^+$ + NAD^+ ⇌ **2 x pyruvate** $CH_3COCOOH$ + $NADH + H^+$

Lactic acid fermentation (animal tissues)

Excess post-exercise oxygen consumption

The graph below illustrates the principle of excess post-exercise oxygen consumption (EPOC, commonly called **oxygen debt**). In the graph, the energy demands of aerobic exercise require 3 dm³ of oxygen per minute. The rate of oxygen uptake increases immediately exercise starts, but the full requirement is not met until six minutes later. The **oxygen deficit** is the amount of oxygen needed (for aerobic energy supply) but not supplied by breathing. During the first six minutes, energy is supplied largely from anaerobic pathways (creatine phosphate and glycolysis). After exercise, oxygen uptake per minute does not drop immediately to resting level. The extra oxygen that is taken in despite the drop in energy demand is the **oxygen debt**. The oxygen debt is used to replace oxygen reserves, restore creatine phosphate, and oxidise the lactate or convert it to glucose.

Oxygen uptake during exercise and recovery

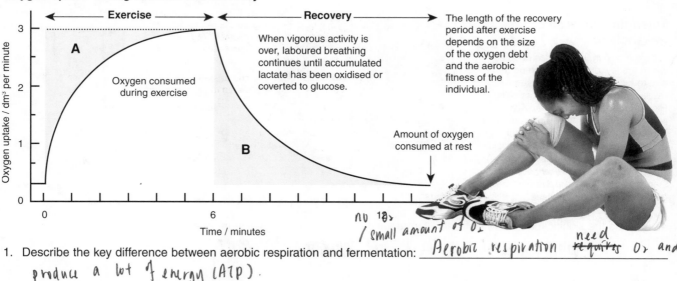

← Exercise → ← Recovery →

A — Oxygen consumed during exercise

When vigorous activity is over, laboured breathing continues until accumulated lactate has been oxidised or coverted to glucose.

B

Amount of oxygen consumed at rest

The length of the recovery period after exercise depends on the size of the oxygen debt and the aerobic fitness of the individual.

Oxygen uptake / dm³ per minute (y-axis: 0, 1, 2, 3)
Time / minutes (x-axis: 0, 6)

no 18>
/ small amount of O₂

1. Describe the key difference between aerobic respiration and fermentation: _Aerobic respiration requires O₂ and produce a lot of energy (ATP)._

2. (a) Refer to page 8 and determine the efficiency of fermentation compared to aerobic respiration: $\frac{2}{38} = 5.3$ %

   (b) Why is the efficiency of these anaerobic pathways so low? _Only a small amount of the energy of a glucose molecule is released in anaerobic respiration. The remainder stays locked up in the molecule_

3. Study the graph and explanatory paragraph above, then identify and describe what is represented by:

   (a) The shaded region **A**: _____

   _____

   (b) The shaded region **B**: _____

   _____

Alcoholic fermentation

In alcoholic fermentation, the H^+ acceptor in the absence of oxygen is ethanal, which is reduced to ethanol with the release of carbon dioxide (CO_2). Yeasts respire aerobically when oxygen is available and substrate is limited but can use alcoholic fermentation when oxygen is absent and/or sugars are in excess supply. At ethanol levels above 12-15%, the ethanol produced by alcoholic fermentation is toxic and this limits the ability of yeast to use this pathway indefinitely.

The root cells of plants also use fermentation as a pathway when oxygen is unavailable, but the ethanol must be converted back to respiratory intermediates and respired aerobically.

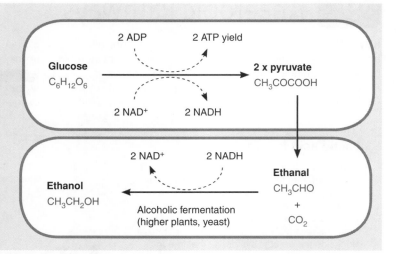

The alcohol and CO_2 produced from alcoholic fermentation form the basis of the brewing and baking industries. In baking, the dough is left to ferment and the yeast metabolises sugars to produce ethanol and CO_2. The CO_2 causes the dough to rise.

Yeasts are used to produce almost all alcoholic beverages (e.g. wine and beers). The yeast used in the process breaks down the sugars into ethanol (alcohol) and CO_2. The alcohol produced is a metabolic by-product of fermentation by the yeast.

It was once thought that lactic acid was a toxic by-product of anaerobic metabolism in muscle and this caused fatigue. However, research has shown that the lactate shuttle in vertebrate skeletal muscle works alongside the aerobic system to enable maximal muscle activity.

Tolerating anaerobic metabolism

Rice is grown in flooded rice paddies, which are low oxygen environments and reduce the amount of oxygen available to the rice plant's root cells. Rice root cells respire anaerobically, which produces ethanol. The ethanol is removed by the enzyme alcohol dehydrogenase. Additionally, the roots contain large air spaces (aerenchyma), which allow air to move between the stem and root cells, supplying oxygen from above the water surface.

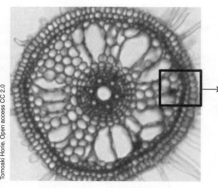

Transverse section through a rice root

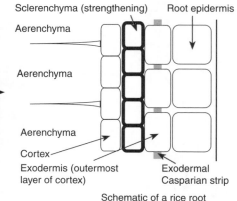

Schematic of a rice root

4. What is the significance of the lactic acid fermentation pathway in mammalian muscle being reversible?

allow greater intensity and duration of activity.

5. In the baking industry, what do you think happens to the alcohol produced by the yeast fermentation:

evaporated during the baking process

6. Why can't alcoholic fermentation go on indefinitely? _The build up of ethanol, which is toxic to cells, inhibits further metabolic activity._

7. (a) What problem does rice have when growing in a flooded environment? _____

   (b) Describe two adaptations of rice to low oxygen environments: _____

10 Investigating Fermentation in Yeast

Key Idea: Brewer's yeast preferentially uses alcoholic fermentation when there is excess sugar, releasing CO_2, which can be collected as a measure of fermentation rate. Brewer's yeast is a facultative anaerobe (meaning it can respire aerobically or use fermentation). It will preferentially use alcoholic fermentation when sugars are in excess. One would expect glucose to be the preferred substrate, as it is the starting molecule in cellular respiration, but brewer's yeast is capable of utilising a variety of sugars, including disaccharides, which can be broken down into single units.

The aim

To investigate the suitability of different mono- and disaccharide sugars as substrates for alcoholic fermentation in yeast.

The hypothesis

If glucose is the preferred substrate for fermentation in yeast, then the rate of fermentation will be highest when the yeast is grown on glucose rather than on other sugars.

Background

The rate at which brewer's or baker's yeast (*Saccharomyces cerevisiae*) metabolises carbohydrate substrates is influenced by factors such as temperature, solution pH, and type of carbohydrate available.

The literature describes yeast metabolism as optimal in warm, acid (pH 4-6) environments.

High levels of sugars suppress aerobic respiration in yeast, so yeast will preferentially use the fermentation pathway in the presence of excess substrate.

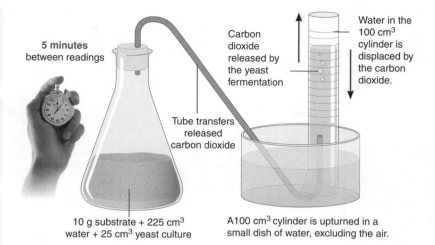

5 minutes between readings

Carbon dioxide released by the yeast fermentation

Water in the 100 cm^3 cylinder is displaced by the carbon dioxide.

Tube transfers released carbon dioxide

10 g substrate + 225 cm^3 water + 25 cm^3 yeast culture

A 100 cm^3 cylinder is upturned in a small dish of water, excluding the air.

The apparatus

In this experiment, all substrates tested used the same source culture of 30 g active yeast dissolved in 150 cm^3 of room temperature (24°C) tap water. 25 g of each substrate to be tested was added to 225 cm^3 room temperature (24°C) tap water buffered to pH 4.5. Then 25 cm^3 of source culture was added to the test solution. The control contained yeast solution but no substrate.

The substrates

Glucose is a monosaccharide, maltose (glucose-glucose), sucrose (glucose-fructose), and lactose (glucose-galactose) are disaccharides.

Substrate Time / min	Volume of carbon dioxide collected / cm^3				
	None	**Glucose**	**Maltose**	**Sucrose**	**Lactose**
0	0	0	0	0	0
5	0	0	0.8	0	0
10	0	0	0.8	0	0
15	0	0	0.8	0.1	0
20	0	0.5	2.0	0.8	0
25	0	1.2	3.0	1.8	0
30	0	2.8	3.6	3.0	0
35	0	4.2	5.4	4.8	0
40	0	4.6	5.6	4.8	0
45	0	7.4	8.0	7.2	0
50	0	10.8	8.9	7.6	0
55	0	13.6	9.6	7.7	0
60	0	16.1	10.4	9.6	0
65	0	22.0	12.1	10.2	0
70	0	23.8	14.4	12.0	0
75	0	26.7	15.2	12.6	0
80	0	32.5	17.3	14.3	0
85	0	37.0	18.7	14.9	0
90	0	39.9	21.6	17.2	0

Experimental design and results adapted from Tom Schuster, Rosalie Van Zyl, & Harold Coller, California State University Northridge 2005

1. Write the equation for the fermentation of glucose by yeast:

_____

2. The results are presented on the table left. Using the final values, calculate the rate of CO_2 production per minute for each substrate:

(a) None: _____

(b) Glucose: _____

(c) Maltose: _____

(d) Sucrose: _____

(e) Lactose: _____

3. What assumptions are being made in this experimental design and do you think they were reasonable?

_____

_____

_____

_____

_____

_____

4. Use the tabulated data to plot an appropriate graph of the results on the grid provided:

5. (a) Identify the **independent variable**: _____

   (b) State the range of values for the independent variable: _____

   (c) Name the unit for the independent variable: _____

6. (a) Identify the **dependent variable**: _____

   (b) Name the unit for the dependent variable: _____

7. (a) Summarise the results of the fermentation experiment: _____

   _____

   _____

   _____

   (b) Why do you think CO_2 production was highest when glucose was the substrate? _____

   _____

   _____

   (c) Suggest why fermentation rates were lower on maltose and sucrose than on glucose:

   _____

   _____

   (d) Suggest why there was no fermentation on the lactose substrate: _____

   _____

8. Predict what would happen to CO2 production rates if the yeast cells were respiring aerobically:

   _____

   _____

© 2016 **BIOZONE** International
ISBN: 978-1-927309-32-2
Photocopying Prohibited

11 Investigating Aerobic Respiration in Yeast

Key Idea: Respiration rate can be investigated using the redox indicator triphenyl tetrazolium chloride.

In simple organisms such as yeast, respiration rate can be affected by different factors, including temperature and availability of respiratory substrates. Yeast is a facultative anaerobe and will respire aerobically when glucose levels are low and oxygen is available. The effect of temperature on yeast respiration rate can be determined using the redox indicator triphenyl tetrazolium chloride (TTC). TTC is a colourless hydrogen acceptor and intercepts the hydrogen ions produced during respiration. It turns red when oxidised and the rate of colour change indicates the rate of respiration.

Background

During respiration, dehydrogenase enzymes remove hydrogens from glucose and pass them to hydrogen acceptors. TTC intercepts these hydrogens and turns red. The rate of colour change indicates the rate of enzyme activity and thus the rate of respiration.

Aim and hypothesis

To investigate the effect of temperature on the rate of aerobic respiration in yeast.
If respiration is occurring, the rate can be indicated by the amount of colour change in the indicator TTC.

The method

A set of three test tubes (tubes 1-3) were set up containing 10 mL of dilute yeast suspension (10 g yeast, 1.5 g glucose per litre) and 1 mL of TTC. At this concentration of glucose and in the presence of oxygen, yeast will respire aerobically.

The test tubes were placed into a water bath at 25 °C. Two more sets of three test tubes were prepared in the same way. The second set was placed into a water bath at 40 °C (tubes 4-6), and the third set was placed into a water bath at 55°C (tubes 7-9). The rate of colour change was measured over 4.5 hours by measuring the absorbance of each tube with a colorimeter (0 being clear or low absorbance and 10 being fully opaque or high absorbance). A control tube containing only yeast and glucose was included in the experiment (tube 10).

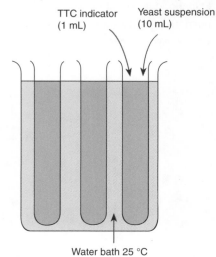

TTC indicator (1 mL)   Yeast suspension (10 mL)

Water bath 25 °C

Caution needs to be taken with TTC use as it can cause skin irritation. Gloves should be used.

	Tube number/ absorbance									
	25 °C			40 °C			55°C			Control
Time / hr	1	2	3	4	5	6	7	8	9	10
1.5	1.13	1.02	1.20	2.34	2.33	2.29	4.11	4.05	4.17	0.40
3.0	1.96	1.88	2.04	5.85	5.89	5.80	8.86	8.90	8.82	0.51
4.5	2.76	2.69	2.81	7.84	7.88	7.80	9.77	9. 87	9.74	0.62

1. Calculate the mean absorbance for each of the times and temperatures above and enter the values in the table below:

	Mean absorbance		
Time / hr	25 °C	40 °C	55 °C
1.5			
3.0			
4.5			

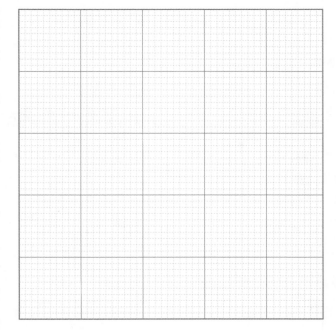

2. Use the table in (1) to plot a graph of absorbance over time for the three temperatures measured:

3. Why did the absorbance of the control tube change?

_____

_____

_____

4. How does temperature affect the respiration rate of yeast?

_____

_____

LINK 8   LINK 7   KNOW

12 Chapter Review

Summarise what you know about this topic under the headings and sub-headings provided. You can draw diagrams or mind maps, or write short notes to organise your thoughts. Use the images and hints to help you and refer back to the introduction to check the points covered:

Mitochondrial structure

HINT: Use a drawing to describe the structure of the mitochondrion.

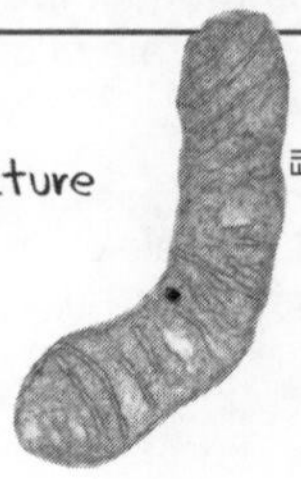

Anaerobic metabolism

HINT: Describe the benefits and disadvantages of ATP generation without oxygen using fermentation.

Respiratory quotient (RQ)

HINT: How can RQ be used to determine which substance is being respired?

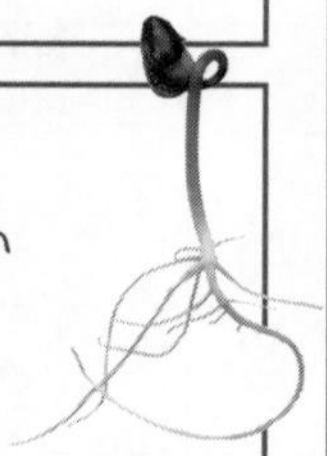

Cellular respiration

HINT: Summarise the stages of cellular respiration and production of ATP.

© 2016 BIOZONE International
ISBN: 978-1-927309-32-2
Photocopying Prohibited

13 KEY TERMS AND IDEAS: Did You Get It?

1. Match each term to its definition, as identified by its preceding letter code.

Term	Answer
aerobic respiration	H
anaerobic metabolism	E
ATP	I
cellular respiration	K
chemiosmosis	~~X~~ B
electron transport chain	~~B~~ N
glycolysis	A
Krebs cycle	J
link reaction	D
matrix	M
mitochondria	C
oxidative phosphorylation	G
pyruvate	L
substrate level phosphorylation	F

A A series of reactions that convert glucose into pyruvate. The energy released is used to produce a small amount of ATP.

B The process in which the synthesis of ATP is coupled to electron transport and the movement of protons.

C Organelles responsible for producing the cell's ATP. They appear oval in shape with an outer double membrane and a convoluted inner membrane.

D The stage in cellular respiration where pyruvate enters the mitochondrion and carbon dioxide is removed.

E A form of respiration that occurs without oxygen.

F A type of metabolic reaction that results in the formation of ATP by direct transfer of a phosphate group to ADP from a phosphorylated reactive intermediate.

G The process in cellular respiration which involves the oxidation of glucose by a series of redox reactions that provide the energy for the formation of ATP.

H Respiration requiring oxygen as the terminal electron acceptor.

I A nucleoside triphosphate used in the transfer of energy in cells.

J Also known as the citric acid cycle. Part of a metabolic pathway involved in the chemical conversion of carbohydrates, fats and proteins to CO_2 and water to generate a form of usable energy (ATP).

K The catabolic process in which the chemical energy in complex organic molecules is coupled to ATP production.

L A product of glycolysis. An important intermediate in many metabolic pathways.

M The inner region of the mitochondrion enclosed by the inner mitochondrial membrane.

N Chain of enzyme based redox reactions which pass electrons from high to low redox potentials. The energy released is used to pump protons across a membrane and produce ATP.

2. The RQs of two species of seeds were calculated at two day intervals after germination. Results are tabulated to the right:

(a) Plot the change in RQ of the two species during early germination:

(b) Explain the values in terms of the possible substrates being respired:

Days after germination	RQ	
	Seedling A	Seedling B
2	0.65	0.70
4	0.35	0.91
6	0.48	0.98
8	0.68	1.00
10	0.70	1.00

3. (a) Name the process described in the equation (right): $C_6H_{12}O_6 + 6O_2 \longrightarrow 6CO_2 + 6H_2O + \text{Energy}$

aerobic respiration

(b) Where does this process occur? mitochondria

(c) Name the type of energy molecule that is produced in this process: ATP

ISBN: 978-1-927309-32-2

Topic 13 Photosynthesis

Key terms

absorption spectrum
accessory pigment
action spectrum
ATP
ATP synthase
C4 plant
Calvin cycle
carotenoid
cellular respiration
chemiosmosis
chloroplast
chlorophyll
chromatography
cyclic photophosphorylation
glycerate 3-phosphate (GP)
grana
light dependent phase
light independent phase
limiting factor
NADP
Non-cyclic photophosphorylation
photolysis
photosynthesis
photosystem
ribulose bisphosphate (RuBP)
RuBisCo
stroma
stroma lamellae
thylakoid discs
triose phosphate

13.1 Photosynthesis as an energy transfer process

Learning outcomes

Activity number

☐ 1 Outline the events in the two stages of photosynthesis and their interdependence.　14 15

☐ 2 Identify the sites of the two stages of photosynthesis.　15

☐ 3 Explain the role of chlorophyll *a* and *b* and accessory pigments in light capture in the grana. Include reference to the photosystems (the protein complexes involved in the absorption of light and the transfer of energy and electrons).　15 16 17

☐ 4 Interpret absorption and action spectra for chloroplast pigments.　17

☐ 5 **PRAC** Use chromatography to separate and identify chloroplast pigments. Investigate differences in chloroplast pigments in different plants.　18

☐ 6 Describe the light dependent reactions, including the absorption of light by the photosystems, transfer of excited electrons between carriers in the thylakoid membranes, the generation of ATP and NADPH, and the photolysis of water.　19

☐ 7 Compare and contrast cyclic and non-cyclic photophosphorylation.　19

☐ 8 Describe the light independent reactions (Calvin cycle), including reference to the role of the enzyme RuBisCo: (1) the carboxylation of ribulose bisphosphate (RuBP) to form glycerate 3-phosphate (GP), (2) reduction of GP to triose phosphate using NADPH and ATP, (3) the regeneration of RuBP using ATP.　20

☐ 9 Describe the fate of the triose phosphate generated in the Calvin cycle.　20 21

Kristian Peters　Dartmouth College

13.2 Investigation of limiting factors

Learning outcomes

Activity number

☐ 10 Explain the term limiting factor in relation to photosynthesis.　22

☐ 11 Explain the effects of changes in carbon dioxide concentration, light intensity, and temperature on the rate of photosynthesis.　22

☐ 12 With reference to limiting factors, explain how controlled environments (e.g. glasshouses) can be used to increase crop yields.　23

☐ 13 **PRAC** Use a redox indicator and a suspension of chloroplasts to investigate the effect of light intensity or light wavelength on the rate of photosynthesis.　24 25

☐ 14 **PRAC** Investigate the effect of light intensity, CO_2 concentration, and temperature on the rate of photosynthesis in whole plants, e.g. *Cabomba*.　26

13.3 Adaptations for photosynthesis

Learning outcomes

Activity number

☐ 15 Describe the relationship between structure and function of the chloroplast using diagrams and electron micrographs　15

☐ 16 Explain how the anatomy and physiology of the leaves of C_4 plants are adapted for high photosynthetic rates at high temperatures. Include reference to the spatial separation of initial carbon fixation from the light dependent stage and the high optimum temperatures of the enzymes involved.　27

14 Energy in Cells

Key Idea: Photosynthesis uses energy from the sun to produce glucose. Glucose breakdown produces ATP, which is used by all cells to provide the energy for metabolism.

A summary of the flow of energy within a plant cell is illustrated below. Heterotrophic cells (animals and fungi) have a similar flow except the glucose is supplied by ingestion or absorption of food molecules rather than by photosynthesis. The energy not immediately stored in chemical bonds is lost as heat. Note that ATP provides the energy for most metabolic reactions, including photosynthesis.

Summary of energy transformations in a photosynthetic plant cell

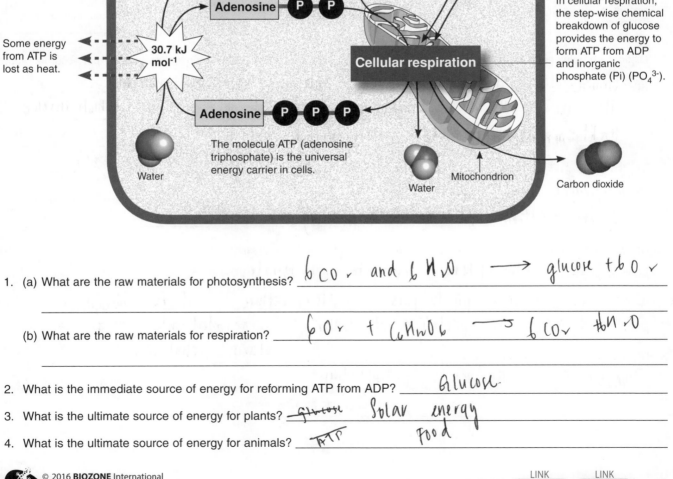

Photosynthesis is a process that captures light energy and stores it in molecules such as glucose as chemical potential energy.

Convert CO$_2$ and H$_2$O to O$_2$ and glucose

Note: Animals and other heterotrophic organisms ultimately get their glucose from plants and other photosynthetic organisms.

Light energy

Water

Carbon dioxide

Chloroplast

Oxygen

Glucose

Other uses of glucose

Oxygen

The energy released by hydrolysis of ATP can be used to power chemical reactions inside the cell.

Hydrolysis of ATP forms ADP (adenosine diphosphate), which has less available energy. It can be recharged by adding a phosphate (PO_4^{3-}).

In cellular respiration, the step-wise chemical breakdown of glucose provides the energy to form ATP from ADP and inorganic phosphate (Pi) (PO_4^{3-}).

Pi   **Pi**

Adenosine **P** **P**

Some energy from ATP is lost as heat.

30.7 kJ mol^{-1}

Cellular respiration

Adenosine **P** **P** **P**

The molecule ATP (adenosine triphosphate) is the universal energy carrier in cells.

Water

Water   Mitochondrion   Carbon dioxide

1. (a) What are the raw materials for photosynthesis? _6 CO$_2$ and 6 H$_2$O ⟶ glucose + 6 O$_2$_

   (b) What are the raw materials for respiration? _6 O$_2$ + C$_6$H$_{12}$O$_6$ ⟶ 6 CO$_2$ + 6 H$_2$O_

2. What is the immediate source of energy for reforming ATP from ADP? _Glucose_

3. What is the ultimate source of energy for plants? ~~Glucose~~ _Solar energy_

4. What is the ultimate source of energy for animals? ~~ATP~~ _Food_

LINK **15**   LINK **2**

KNOW

15 Photosynthesis

Key Idea: Photosynthesis is the process by which light energy is used to convert CO_2 and water into glucose and oxygen.
Photosynthesis is of fundamental importance to living things because it transforms sunlight energy into chemical energy stored in molecules, releases free oxygen gas, and absorbs carbon dioxide (a waste product of cellular metabolism).

Photosynthetic organisms use special pigments, called **chlorophylls**, to absorb light of specific wavelengths and capture the light energy. Photosynthesis involves reduction and oxidation (redox) reactions. In photosynthesis, water is split and electrons are transferred together with hydrogen ions from water to CO_2, reducing it to sugar.

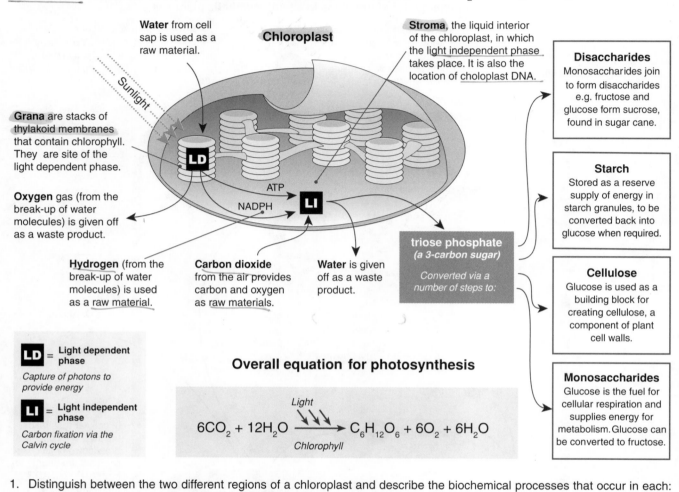

Water from cell sap is used as a raw material.

Chloroplast

Stroma, the liquid interior of the chloroplast, in which the light independent phase takes place. It is also the location of chloroplast DNA.

Sunlight

Grana are stacks of thylakoid membranes that contain chlorophyll. They are site of the light dependent phase.

Oxygen gas (from the break-up of water molecules) is given off as a waste product.

ATP

NADPH

Hydrogen (from the break-up of water molecules) is used as a raw material.

Carbon dioxide from the air provides carbon and oxygen as raw materials.

Water is given off as a waste product.

triose phosphate *(a 3-carbon sugar)*
Converted via a number of steps to:

Disaccharides
Monosaccharides join to form disaccharides e.g. fructose and glucose form sucrose, found in sugar cane.

Starch
Stored as a reserve supply of energy in starch granules, to be converted back into glucose when required.

Cellulose
Glucose is used as a building block for creating cellulose, a component of plant cell walls.

Monosaccharides
Glucose is the fuel for cellular respiration and supplies energy for metabolism. Glucose can be converted to fructose.

LD = **Light dependent phase**
Capture of photons to provide energy

LI = **Light independent phase**
Carbon fixation via the Calvin cycle

Overall equation for photosynthesis

$$6CO_2 + 12H_2O \xrightarrow[\text{Chlorophyll}]{\text{Light}} C_6H_{12}O_6 + 6O_2 + 6H_2O$$

Handwritten annotations at top: thylakoid membrane; use to energise e^- in photosystem

1. Distinguish between the two different regions of a chloroplast and describe the biochemical processes that occur in each:

   (a) *Grana: Stacks of thylakoid membranes containing chlorophyll molecules. They are the site of the light dependent rxns of photosynthesis, which involve light energy capture via photosystems I and II.*

   (b) *Stroma: The liquid interior of the chloroplast in which the light independent phase takes place. The biochemical process involves carbon fixation via the Calvin cycle.*

2. State the origin and fate of the following molecules involved in photosynthesis:

   (a) Carbon dioxide: *atmosphere, fix into carbohydrates*

   (b) Oxygen: *come from photolysis of water, diffuse out of the chloroplast.*

   (c) Hydrogen: *come from photolysis of water, incorporated into glucose.*

3. Discuss the potential uses for the end products of photosynthesis: *starch, cellulose, monosaccharides, disaccharides, respiration*

© 2016 **BIOZONE** International
ISBN: 978-1-927309-32-2
Photocopying Prohibited

16 Chloroplasts

Chlorophylls Carotenoids

Key Idea: Chloroplasts have a complicated internal membrane structure that provides the sites for the light dependent reactions of photosynthesis.

Chloroplasts are the specialised plastids in which photosynthesis occurs. A mesophyll leaf cell contains between 50-100 chloroplasts. The chloroplasts are generally aligned so that their broad surface runs parallel to the cell wall to maximise the surface area available for light absorption. Chloroplasts have an internal structure characterised by a system of membranous structures called **thylakoids** arranged into stacks called **grana**. Special pigments, called **chlorophylls** and **carotenoids**, are bound to the membranes as part of light-capturing photosystems. They absorb light of specific wavelengths and thereby capture the light energy.

The structure of a chloroplast

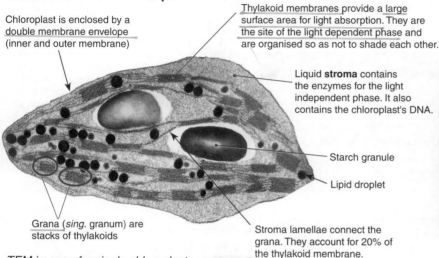

Chloroplast is enclosed by a double membrane envelope (inner and outer membrane)

Thylakoid membranes provide a large surface area for light absorption. They are the site of the light dependent phase and are organised so as not to shade each other.

Liquid **stroma** contains the enzymes for the light independent phase. It also contains the chloroplast's DNA.

Starch granule

Lipid droplet

Grana (*sing.* granum) are stacks of thylakoids

Stroma lamellae connect the grana. They account for 20% of the thylakoid membrane.

TEM image of a single chloroplast

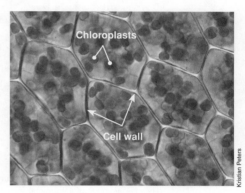

Chloroplasts

Cell wall

Kristian Peters

Chloroplasts visible in plant cells

1. Label the transmission electron microscope image of a chloroplast below:

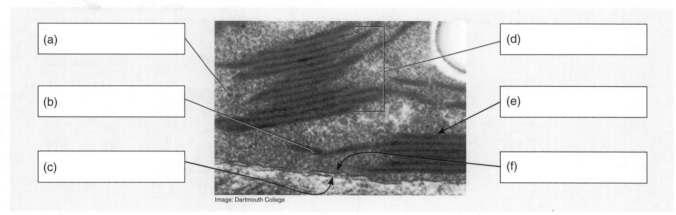

(a)

(b)

(c)

(d)

(e)

(f)

Image: Dartmouth College

2. (a) Where is chlorophyll found in a chloroplast? __thylakoid membrane__

(b) Why is chlorophyll found there? __Chlorophyll is a membrane-bound pigment found in and around the photosystems, embedded in the membranes.__

3. Explain how the internal structure of chloroplasts helps absorb the maximum amount of light: __The internal membranes provide a large surface area for binding chlorophyll molecules and capturing light. Membranes are stacked in such a way that they don't shade each other.__

4. Explain why plant leaves appear green: __Chlorophyll absorbs blue & red light but reflects green light, so leaves look green to human eye.__

LINK 17   LINK 15   **KNOW**

17 Pigments and Light Absorption

Key Idea: Chlorophyll pigments absorb light of specific wavelengths and capture light energy for photosynthesis. Substances that absorb visible light are called **pigments**, and different pigments absorb light of different wavelengths. The ability of a pigment to absorb particular wavelengths of light can be measured with a spectrophotometer. The light absorption vs the wavelength is called the **absorption**

spectrum of that pigment. The absorption spectrum of different photosynthetic pigments provides clues to their role in photosynthesis, since light can only perform work if it is absorbed. An **action spectrum** profiles the effectiveness of different wavelengths of light in fuelling photosynthesis. It is obtained by plotting wavelength against a measure of photosynthetic rate (e.g. O_2 production).

The electromagnetic spectrum

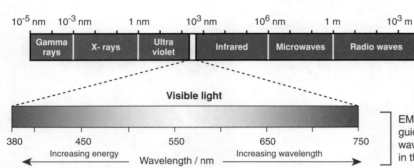

Light is a form of energy known as electromagnetic radiation (EMR). The segment of the electromagnetic spectrum most important to life is the narrow band between about 380 nm and 750 nm. This radiation is known as visible light because it is detected as colours by the human eye. It is visible light that drives photosynthesis.

EMR travels in waves, where wavelength provides a guide to the energy of the photons. The greater the wavelength of EMR, the lower the energy of the photons in that radiation.

Absorption spectra of photosynthetic pigments
(Relative amounts of light absorbed at different wavelengths)

Chlorophyll *b*

Carotenoids

Chlorophyll *a* →

Absorbance / percent (y-axis: 0 to 100)

Action spectrum for photosynthesis
(Effectiveness of different wavelengths in fuelling photosynthesis)

Rate of photosynthesis / as % of rate at 670 nm (y-axis: 0 to 100)

The action spectrum and the absorption spectrum for the photosynthetic pigments (combined) match closely.

Wavelength / nm (x-axis: 400 to 700)

The photosynthetic pigments of plants

The photosynthetic pigments of plants fall into two categories: **chlorophylls** (which absorb red and blue-violet light) and **carotenoids** (which absorb strongly in the blue-violet and appear orange, yellow, or red). The pigments are located on the chloroplast membranes (the thylakoids) and are associated with membrane transport systems.

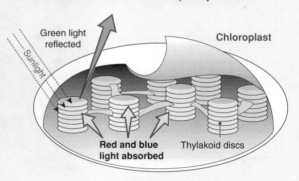

Green light reflected

Chloroplast

Sunlight

Red and blue light absorbed   Thylakoid discs

The pigments of chloroplasts in higher plants (above) absorb blue and red light, and the leaves therefore appear green (which is reflected). Each photosynthetic pigment has its own characteristic absorption spectrum (top left). Only chlorophyll *a* participates directly in the light reactions of photosynthesis, but the accessory pigments (chlorophyll *b* and carotenoids) can absorb wavelengths of light that chlorophyll *a* cannot and pass the energy (photons) to chlorophyll *a*, thus broadening the spectrum that can effectively drive photosynthesis.

Left: Graphs comparing absorption spectra of photosynthetic pigments compared with the action spectrum for photosynthesis.

1. What is meant by the absorption spectrum of a pigment? _Is that wavelength of the light spectrum absorbs by a pigment._

2. Why doesn't the **action spectrum** for photosynthesis exactly match the absorption spectrum of chlorophyll *a*?
Accessory pigments absorbs light wavelengths that chlropyll a cannot absorb, and they pass their energy on to chlrophyll a. This broadens the action spectrum over whic chlrophyll a can fuel photosynthesis.

WEB 17   LINK 18

KNOW

18 Separation of Pigments by Chromatography

Key Idea: Photosynthetic pigments can be separated from a mixture using chromatography.

Chromatography involves passing a mixture dissolved in a mobile phase (a solvent) through a stationary phase, which separates the molecules according to their specific characteristics (e.g. size or charge). In thin layer chromatography, the stationary phase is a thin layer of adsorbent material (e.g. silica gel or cellulose) attached to a solid plate. A sample is placed near the bottom of the plate which is placed in an appropriate solvent (the mobile phase).

Separation of photosynthetic pigments

The four primary pigments of green plants can be easily separated and identified using thin layer chromatography. The pigments from the leaves are first extracted by crushing leaves, together with acetone, using a mortar and pestle. The extract is dotted on to the chromatography plate, which is the stationary phase (a thin layer of coated card). Acetone is used as the mobile phase (solvent). During thin layer chromatography, the pigments separate out according to differences in their relative solubilities. Two major classes of pigments are detected: the two greenish chlorophyll pigments and two yellowish carotenoid pigments.

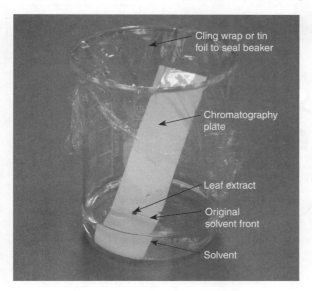

Cling wrap or tin foil to seal beaker

Chromatography plate

Leaf extract

Original solvent front

Solvent

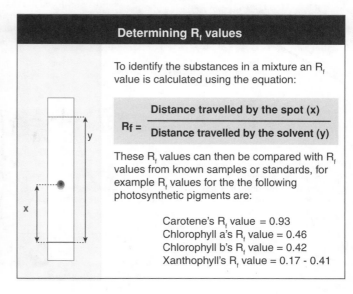

Determining Rf values

To identify the substances in a mixture an R_f value is calculated using the equation:

$$R_f = \frac{\text{Distance travelled by the spot (x)}}{\text{Distance travelled by the solvent (y)}}$$

These R_f values can then be compared with R_f values from known samples or standards, for example R_f values for the the following photosynthetic pigments are:

Carotene's R_f value = 0.93
Chlorophyll a's R_f value = 0.46
Chlorophyll b's R_f value = 0.42
Xanthophyll's R_f value = 0.17 - 0.41

1. Calculate the R_f values for the pigments A-D on the chromatography plate shown right. Then use the R_f values to identify the pigments:

A: R_f value: _____

   Pigment: _____

B: R_f value: _____

   Pigment: _____

C: R_f value: _____

   Pigment: _____

D: R_f value: _____

   Pigment: _____

   Carotenoids.

2. A student carried out a chromatography experiment on a plant adapted for shade and a plant adapted for high levels of sunlight. Use your knowledge of plant photosynthetic pigments and the information on this page to predict the outcome of the two chromatography experiments in terms of the pigments that will appear on the chromatography paper and their relative darkness (indicating the amount of pigment).

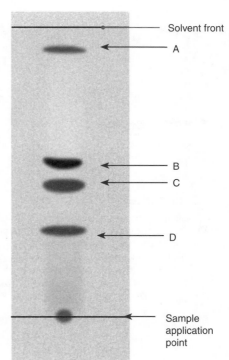

Solvent front

A

B

C

D

Sample application point

_____

_____

_____

_____

19 Light Dependent Reactions — thylakoid membrane

Key Idea: In light dependent reactions of photosynthesis, the energy from photons of light is used to drive the reduction of NADP+ and the production of ATP.

Like cellular respiration, photosynthesis is a redox process, but in photosynthesis, water is split, and electrons and hydrogen ions, are transferred from water to CO_2, reducing it to sugar. The electrons increase in potential energy as they move from water to sugar. The energy to do this is provided by light. Photosynthesis has two phases. In the **light dependent reactions**, light energy is converted to chemical energy (ATP and NADPH). In the **light independent reactions**, the chemical energy is used to synthesise carbohydrate. The light dependent reactions most commonly involve **non-cyclic phosphorylation**, which produces ATP and NADPH in roughly equal quantities. The electrons lost are replaced from water. In **cyclic phosphorylation**, the electrons lost from photosystem II are replaced by those from photosystem I. ATP is generated, but not NADPH.

Non-cyclic phosphorylation

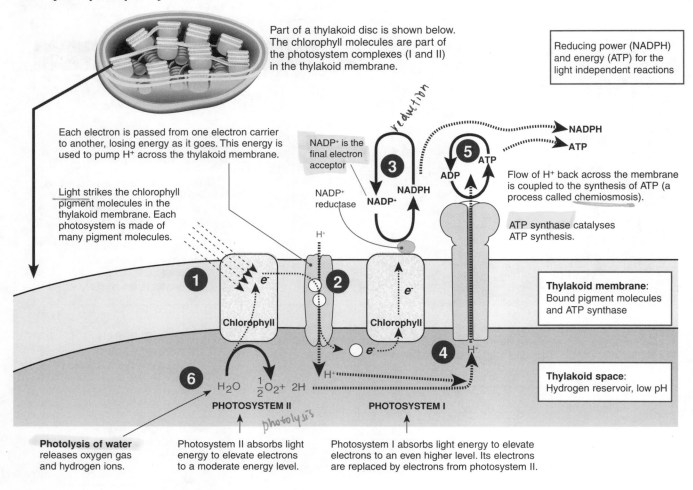

Part of a thylakoid disc is shown below. The chlorophyll molecules are part of the photosystem complexes (I and II) in the thylakoid membrane.

Reducing power (NADPH) and energy (ATP) for the light independent reactions

Each electron is passed from one electron carrier to another, losing energy as it goes. This energy is used to pump H+ across the thylakoid membrane.

Light strikes the chlorophyll pigment molecules in the thylakoid membrane. Each photosystem is made of many pigment molecules.

NADP+ is the final electron acceptor

NADP+ reductase

reduction

NADP+ → NADPH

ADP → ATP → NADPH, ATP

Flow of H+ back across the membrane is coupled to the synthesis of ATP (a process called chemiosmosis).

ATP synthase catalyses ATP synthesis.

Thylakoid membrane: Bound pigment molecules and ATP synthase

Thylakoid space: Hydrogen reservoir, low pH

PHOTOSYSTEM II — photolysis

PHOTOSYSTEM I

H_2O $\frac{1}{2}O_2$ + 2H

Photolysis of water releases oxygen gas and hydrogen ions.

Photosystem II absorbs light energy to elevate electrons to a moderate energy level.

Photosystem I absorbs light energy to elevate electrons to an even higher level. Its electrons are replaced by electrons from photosystem II.

Cyclic phosphorylation

Cyclic phosphorylation involves only photosystem I and NADPH is not generated. Electrons from photosystem I are shunted back to the electron carriers in the membrane. This pathway produces ATP only. The Calvin cycle uses more ATP than NADPH, so cyclic phosphorylation makes up the difference. It is activated when NADPH levels build up, and remains active until enough ATP is made to meet demand.

Electrons are cycled through a pathway that takes them away from NADP+ reductase.

ATP is produced while NADPH production ceases.

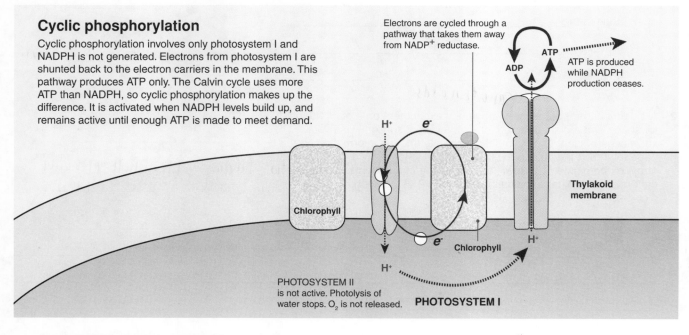

Thylakoid membrane

PHOTOSYSTEM II is not active. Photolysis of water stops. O_2 is not released.

PHOTOSYSTEM I

© 2016 **BIOZONE** International
ISBN: 978-1-927309-32-2
Photocopying Prohibited

1. Describe the role of the carrier molecule (NADP) in photosynthesis: _is a reducing agent in the_ Calvin cycle

2. Explain the role of chlorophyll molecules in photosynthesis: _to absorb light energy,_ and used it to energise electron in photosystem.

3. Summarise the events of the light dependent reactions and identify where they occur: _occur thylakoid_ membrane. Photosystem I II responsible for making NADPH ll ATP .

The light strikes the chlorophyll molecules. in thylakoid membrane

4. Describe how ATP is produced as a result of light striking chlorophyll molecules during the light dependent phase:
Photosystem Electron flow from photosystem ll to electron chain ll then move to photosystem I. Energy released in Electron transport chain ll pumps hydrogen ion H^+ into thylakoid space and diffuses through ATP synthase, making ATP

5. (a) Explain what you understand by the term non-cyclic phosphorylation: _____

_____

_____

(b) Suggest why this process is also known as non-cyclic photophosphorylation: _____

_____

_____

6. (a) Describe how cyclic photophosphorylation differs from non-cyclic photophosphorylation: _____

_____

_____

(b) Both cyclic and non-cyclic pathways operate to varying degrees during photosynthesis. Since the non-cyclic pathway produces both ATP and NAPH, explain the purpose of the cyclic pathway of electron flow:

_____

_____

7. Complete the summary table of the light dependent reactions of photosynthesis

	Non-cyclic phosphorylation	Cyclic phosphorylation
Photosystem involved		
Energy carrier(s) produced		
Photolysis of water (yes / no)		
Production of oxygen (yes / no)		

20 Light Independent Reactions

Key Idea: The light independent reactions of photosynthesis take place in the stroma of the chloroplast and do not require light to proceed.

In the **light independent reactions** (the **Calvin cycle**) hydrogen (H+) is added to CO_2 and a 5C intermediate to make carbohydrate. The H+ and ATP are supplied by the light dependent reactions. The Calvin cycle uses more ATP than NADPH, but the cell uses cyclic phosphorylation (which does not produce NADPH) when it runs low on ATP to make up the difference.

KEY:
- ● Carbon atom
- Ⓟ Phosphate group

The rate of the light independent reaction depends on the availability of carbon dioxide (CO_2) as it is required in the first step of the reaction. Without it, the reaction cannot proceed, showing CO_2 is also a **limiting factor** in photosynthesis.

The Calvin cycle is a series of reactions driven by ATP and NADPH. It generates hexose sugars and reduces the intermediate products to regenerate ribulose 1,5 bisphosphate (RuBP) needed for the first step of the cycle.

The catalysing enzyme **RuBisCo** joins carbon dioxide (CO_2) with RuBP to form glycerate 3-phosphate (**GP**). ATP driven reactions then form 1,3 bisphosphoglycerate before NADPH driven reactions form triose phosphate (**TP**). Some of this then leaves the chloroplast and forms sugars while the rest continues through the cycle to eventually reform RuBP.

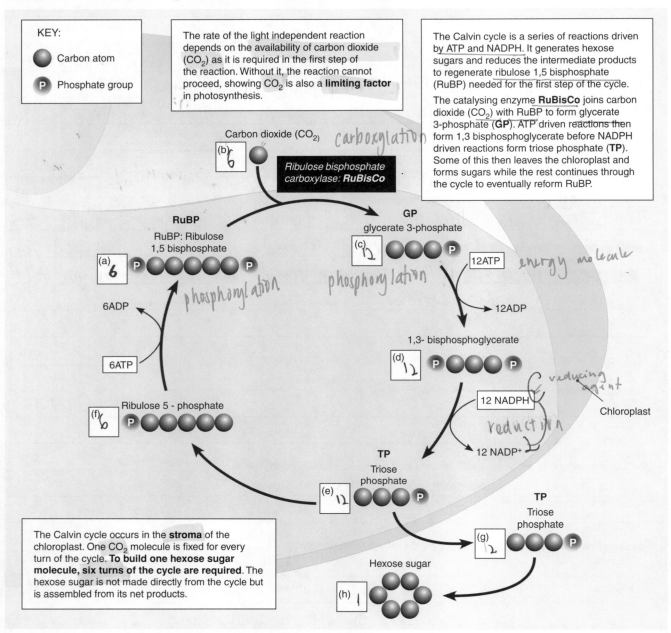

The Calvin cycle occurs in the **stroma** of the chloroplast. One CO_2 molecule is fixed for every turn of the cycle. **To build one hexose sugar molecule, six turns of the cycle are required**. The hexose sugar is not made directly from the cycle but is assembled from its net products.

1. In the boxes on the diagram above, write the number of molecules formed at each step during the formation of **one hexose sugar molecule**. The first one has been done for you: If an enzyme joins co₂ to RuBP.

2. Explain the importance of RuBisCo in the Calvin cycle: Catalyses the reaction that splits CO₂ and joins it with ribulose 1,5-bisphosphate. It fixes carbon from the atmosphere

3. Identify the actual end product on the Calvin cycle: ~~Hexose sugar~~/ Triose phosphate Hexose sugar

4. Write the equation for the production of one hexose sugar molecule from carbon dioxide:
   6 CO₂ + 6H₂O ⟶ C₆H₁₂O₆ + 6O₂

5. Explain why the Calvin cycle is likely to cease in the dark for most plants, even though it is independent of light: because light is needed to make ATP and NADPH which are essential

21 The Fate of Glucose

Key Idea: Glucose is an important precursor molecule used to produce a wide range of other molecules.

Glucose is a versatile biological molecule. It contains the elements carbon, oxygen, and hydrogen, which are used to build many other molecules produced by plants, animals, and other living organisms. Glucose has three main fates: immediate use to produce ATP molecules (available energy

for work), storage for later ATP production, or for use in building other molecules. Plants make their glucose directly through the process of photosynthesis and use it to build all the molecules they require. Animals obtain their glucose (as carbohydrates) by consuming plants or other animals. Other molecules (e.g. amino acids and fatty acids) are also obtained by animals this way.

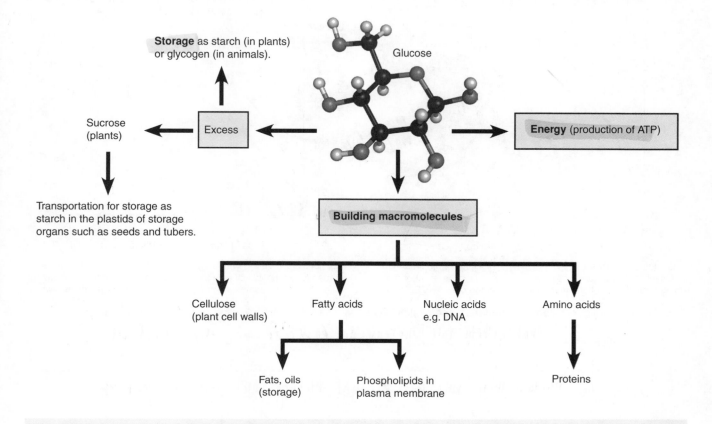

Storage as starch (in plants) or glycogen (in animals).

Glucose

Sucrose (plants)

Excess

Energy (production of ATP)

Transportation for storage as starch in the plastids of storage organs such as seeds and tubers.

Building macromolecules

Cellulose (plant cell walls)

Fatty acids

Nucleic acids e.g. DNA

Amino acids

Fats, oils (storage)

Phospholipids in plasma membrane

Proteins

How do we know how glucose is used?

▶ Labelling the carbon atoms in a glucose molecule with isotopes shows how glucose is incorporated into other molecules.

▶ An isotope is an element (e.g. carbon) whose atoms have a particular number of neutrons in their nucleus. The different number of neutrons allows the isotopes to be identified by their density (e.g. a carbon atom with 13 neutrons is denser than a carbon atom with 12 neutrons).

▶ Some isotopes are radioactive. These radioactive isotopes can be traced using X-ray film or devices that detect the disintegration of the isotopes, such as Geiger counters.

The carbon atom

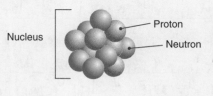

Nucleus

Proton

Neutron

The nucleus of an atom is made up of neutrons and protons. For any element, the number of protons remains the same, but the number of neutrons can vary. Electrons (not shown) are found outside the nucleus.

Naturally occurring C isotopes

^{12}C
6 protons
6 neutrons
Stable. 99.9%
of all C isotopes.

^{13}C
6 protons
7 neutrons
Stable

^{14}C
6 protons
8 neutrons
Radioactive

1. What are the three main fates of glucose? _Storage, building macromolecules, or production of usable energy (ATP)_

2. Identify a use for glucose in a plant that does not occur in animals: _In plant, glucose can be converted to : fructan (energy storage in vacuoles), starch (energy storage in plastids), cellulose (cell wall component)._

3. How can isotopes of carbon be used to find the fate of glucose molecules? _____

_____

© 2016 **BIOZONE** International
ISBN: 978-1-927309-32-2
Photocopying Prohibited

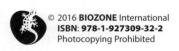

LINK

LINK

20   **4**   **KNOW**

22 Factors Affecting Photosynthesis

Key Idea: Environmental factors, such as CO_2 availability and light intensity, affect the rate of photosynthesis.

The photosynthetic rate is the rate at which plants make carbohydrate. It is dependent on environmental factors, particularly the availability of light and carbon dioxide (CO_2). Temperature is important, but its influence is less clear

because it depends on the availability of the other two limiting factors (CO_2 and light) and the temperature tolerance of the plant. The relative importance of these factors can be tested experimentally by altering one of the factors while holding the others constant. The results for such an experiment are shown below.

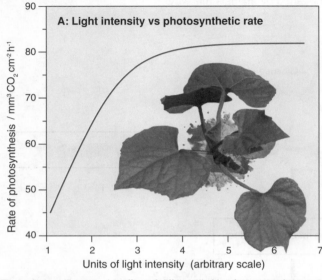

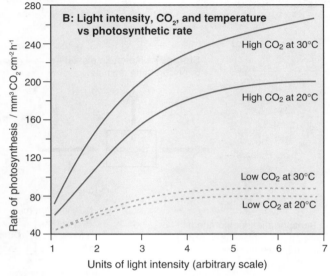

These figures illustrate the effect of different limiting factors on the rate of photosynthesis in cucumber plants. Figure A shows the effect of different light intensities when the temperature and carbon dioxide (CO_2) level are kept constant. Figure B shows the effect of different light intensities at two temperatures and two CO_2 concentrations. In each of these experiments, either CO_2 level or temperature was changed at each light intensity in turn.

1. Based on the figures above, summarise and explain the effect of each of the following factors on photosynthetic rate:

   (a) CO_2 concentration: _Photosynthetic rate increases as CO_2 conc incs then level off._

   (b) Light intensity: _Photosynthetic rate incs as light intensity incs and then level off._

   (c) Temperature: _Increased temp incs the photosynthetic rate, but this effect is not marked at low conc of CO_2._

2. Why does photosynthetic rate decline when the CO_2 level is reduced? _The photosynthetic rate is determined by the rate at which CO_2 enters the leaf. When this declines because of low atmospheric levels, so does photosynthetic rate._

3. (a) In figure B, explain how the effects of CO_2 concentration were distinguished from the effects of temperature: _By changing only one factor at a time (temp or CO_2 level it is possible to acess the effects of each one_

   (b) Which factor (CO_2 or temperature) had the greatest effect on photosynthetic rate: _CO_2_

   (c) How can you tell this from the graph? _At low levels of CO_2, inc in temp has little temp has little effect._

4. How can glasshouses be used to create an environment in which photosynthetic rates are maximised?

5. Design an experiment to demonstrate the effect of temperature on photosynthetic rate. You should include a hypothesis, list of equipment, and methods. Staple your experiment to this page.

© 2016 **BIOZONE** International
ISBN: 978-1-927309-32-2
Photocopying Prohibited

23 Glasshouse Technology

Key Idea: The growth of plants in glasshouses can be increased by manipulating abiotic factors.

Manipulating abiotic (physical) factors can maximise crop yields for economic benefit. For example, covering the soil with black plastic reduces weed growth and increases soil temperature and so boosts production. A more complete control of the abiotic conditions is achieved by growing crops in a controlled-environment system such as a greenhouse.

Temperature, carbon dioxide concentration, and light intensity may be optimised to maximise the rate of photosynthesis and therefore growth. Glasshouses also allow specific abiotic factors to be manipulated to trigger a change in the growing behaviour of some crops (e.g. flowering). Carbon dioxide enrichment dramatically increases the growth of glasshouse crops providing that other important abiotic factors (such as mineral nutrients) are not limiting.

The growing environment can be controlled or modified to varying degrees. Black plastic sheeting can be laid over the soil to control weeds and absorb any excess solar heat. Tunnel enclosures (such as those above) may be used to reduce light intensity and airflow, prevent frost damage, and reduce damage by pests.

Large, commercial glasshouses have elaborate computer-controlled watering systems linked to sensors that measure soil moisture, air temperature, and humidity. Coupled with a timer, they deliver optimal water conditions for plant growth by operating electric solenoid valves attached to the irrigation system.

Air flow through a glasshouse is essential to providing a homogeneous air temperature. Air flow also ensures an even distribution of carbon dioxide gas throughout the enclosure. A general airflow from one end of the enclosure to the other is maintained by a large number of fans all blowing in the same direction.

Carbon dioxide enrichment

Carbon dioxide (CO_2) is a raw material used in photosynthesis. If the supply of carbon dioxide is cut off or reduced, plant growth and development are curtailed. The amount of CO_2 in air is normally 0.03% (250-330 ppm). Most plants will stop growing when the CO_2 level falls below 150 ppm. Even at 220 ppm, a slow-down in plant growth is noticeable (see graph right).

Controlled CO_2 atmospheres, which boost the CO_2 concentration to more than 1000 ppm, significantly increase the rate of formation of dry plant matter and total yield (e.g. of flowers or fruit). Extra carbon dioxide can be generated (at a cost) by burning hydrocarbon fuels, using compressed, bottled CO_2 or dry ice, or by fermentation or decomposition of organic matter.

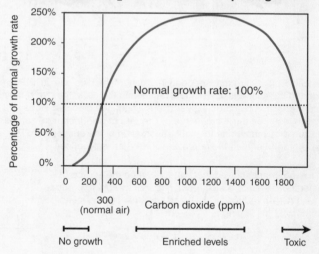

The effect of CO_2 concentration on plant growth

Normal growth rate: 100%

No growth | Enriched levels | Toxic

1. Explain why **CO_2 enrichment** has the capacity to radically increase crop production: _____

_____

_____

2. Explain why air flow needs to be controlled in a glasshouse: _____

_____

_____

3. List the abiotic factors that are controlled in a glasshouse environment: _____

_____

_____

LINK
22

KNOW

24 Experimental Evidence for Photosynthesis

Key Idea: Hill's experiment using isolated chloroplasts and Calvin's "lollipop" experiment provided important information on the process of photosynthesis.

In the 1930s Robert Hill devised a way of measuring

oxygen evolution and the rate of photosynthesis in isolated chloroplasts. During the 1950s Melvin Calvin led a team using radioisotopes of carbon to work out the steps of the light independent reactions (the Calvin cycle).

Robert Hill's experiment

The dye **DCPIP** (2,6-dichlorophenol-indophenol) is blue. It is reduced by H^+ ions and forms $DCPIPH_2$ (colourless). Hill made use of this dye to show that O_2 is produced during photosynthesis even when CO_2 is not present.

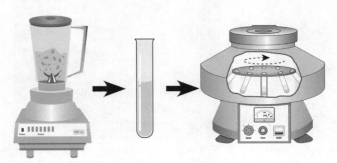

Leaves are homogenised to form a slurry. The slurry is filtered to remove any debris. The filtered extract is then centrifuged at low speed to remove the larger cell debris and then at high speed to separate out the chloroplasts.

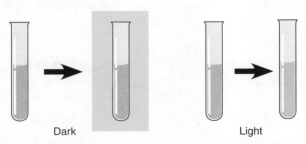

Dark   Light

The chloroplasts are resuspended in a buffer. The blue dye **DCPIP** is added to the suspension. In a test tube left in the dark, the dye remains unchanged. In a test tube exposed to the light, the blue dye fades and the test tube turns green again. The rate of colour change can be measured by measuring the light absorbance of the suspension. The rate is proportional to the rate at which oxygen is produced.

Hill's experiment showed that water must be the source of oxygen (and therefore electrons). It is split by light to produce H^+ ions (which reduce DCPIP) and O^{2-} ions. The equation below summarises his findings:

$$H_2O + A \rightarrow AH_2 + ½ O_2$$

where A is the electron acceptor (*in vivo* this is $NADP^+$)

Calvin's lollipop experiment

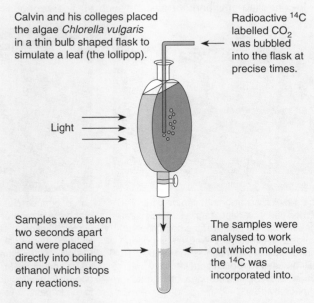

Calvin and his colleges placed the algae *Chlorella vulgaris* in a thin bulb shaped flask to simulate a leaf (the lollipop).

Radioactive ^{14}C labelled CO_2 was bubbled into the flask at precise times.

Light →

Samples were taken two seconds apart and were placed directly into boiling ethanol which stops any reactions.

The samples were analysed to work out which molecules the ^{14}C was incorporated into.

Two-dimensional chromatography was used to separate the molecules in each sample. The sample is run in one direction, then rotated 90 degrees and run again with a different solvent. This separates out molecules that might be close to each other.

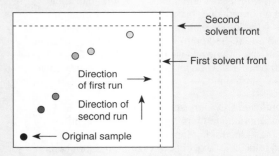

Second solvent front

First solvent front

Direction of first run →

Direction of second run ↑

Original sample

By identifying the order that the molecules incorporating the ^{14}C appeared it was possible to work out the steps of the now called Calvin cycle. This could only be done by taking samples only seconds apart.

---

1. Write an equation for the formation of $DCPIPH_2$ from DCPIP: _____

    _____

2. What important finding about photosynthesis did Hill's experiment show? _____

    _____

3. Why did the samples in Calvin's lollipop experiment need to be taken just seconds apart? _____

    _____

    _____

    _____

© 2016 **BIOZONE** International
ISBN: 978-1-927309-32-2
Photocopying Prohibited

25 Investigating Enzymes in Photosynthesis

Key Idea: Replacing NADP⁺ with DCPIP as the electron acceptor allows the effect of light on the rate of the light dependent reactions to be measured indirectly.

NADP⁺ is the electron acceptor for the light dependent reaction. By substituting the dye DCPIP, which fades from blue to colourless as it accepts electrons, it is possible to indirectly measure the rate of the light dependent reactions and therefore the rate of enzyme activity during the reactions.

Background

Dehydrogenase enzymes play a role in the transport of electrons through the photosystem pathways of the light dependent reactions. The final acceptor of the electron is $NADP^+$, forming NADPH. By substituting DCPIP to accept H^+, the rate of enzyme activity can be measured.

The aim

To investigate the effect of light intensity on the rate of dehydrogenase activity in the light dependent reactions in isolated chloroplasts.

The method

Pieces of spinach leaf were blended using a standard food processor. The pulp was filtered through a muslin cloth into four centrifuge tubes kept in an ice bath. The filtered extract was spun down to produce a pellet and supernatant. The supernatant was discarded and each pellet resuspended with a medium of cold sucrose solution in a boiling tube. In tube 1 and 2 the dye DCPIP was added. In tube 3 DCPIP was added then the tube was covered in foil to exclude light. In tube 4 no DCPIP was added. In a fifth tube DCPIP and sucrose medium were added without any leaf extract. Tubes 1 and 3 were exposed to high intensity light. Tube 2 was exposed to a lower intensity light. The absorbance of all the tubes was measured using a colorimeter at time 0 and every minute for 15 minutes. The absorbance of tube 3 was measured at the beginning and end of the experiment only.

Results

Time / min	Tube number / absorbance				
	1	2	3	4	5
0	5.0	5.0	5.0	0.3	5.0
1	4.8	5.0	-	0.3	5.0
2	4.7	4.9	-	0.3	5.0
3	4.6	4.8	-	0.3	5.0
4	4.3	4.8	-	0.4	5.0
5	4.0	4.7	-	0.3	4.9
6	3.8	4.6	-	0.4	4.9
7	3.4	4.6	-	0.2	4.9
8	3.0	4.5	-	0.3	5.0
9	2.6	4.4	-	0.4	5.1
10	2.2	4.4	-	0.3	5.0
11	1.9	4.3	-	0.2	4.9
12	1.4	4.1	-	0.2	5.0
13	0.9	4.0	-	0.3	4.8
14	0.6	4.0	-	0.3	5.0
15	0.5	3.8	4.7	0.4	5.0

1. Write a brief hypothesis for this experiment:

   _____

   _____

   _____

2. Use the grid below to draw a line graph of the change in absorbance over time of each of the tubes tested.

3. (a) What was the purpose of tube 4? _____

   _____

   _____

   (b) What was the purpose of tube 5? _____

   _____

   _____

4. Why was the absorbance of tube 3 only measured at the start and end of the investigation? _____

   _____

5. Why did the absorbance of tubes 4 and 5 vary? _____

   _____

6. Write a conclusion for the investigation: _____

   _____

26 Investigating Photosynthetic Rate

Key Idea: Measuring the production of oxygen provides a simple means of measuring the rate of photosynthesis.
The rate of photosynthesis can be investigated by measuring the substances involved in photosynthesis. These include measuring the uptake of carbon dioxide, the production of oxygen, or the change in biomass over time. Measuring the rate of oxygen production provides a good approximation of the photosynthetic rate and is relatively easy to carry out.

Cabomba aquatica, a common aquarium plant

The aim

To investigate the effect of light intensity on the rate of photosynthesis in an aquatic plant, *Cabomba aquatica*.

Hypothesis

If photosynthetic rate is dependent on light intensity, more oxygen bubbles will be produced by *Cabomba* per unit time at higher light intensities.

The method

► 0.8-1.0 grams of *Cabomba* stem were weighed. The stem was cut and inverted to ensure a free flow of oxygen bubbles.

► The stem was placed into a beaker filled with a solution containing 0.2 mol L^{-1} sodium hydrogen carbonate (to supply carbon dioxide). The solution was at approximately 20°C. A funnel was inverted over the *Cabomba* and a test tube filled with the sodium hydrogen carbonate solution was inverted on top to collect any gas produced.

► The beaker was placed at distances (20, 25, 30, 35, 40, 45 cm) from a 60W light source and the light intensity measured with a lux meter at each interval. One beaker was not exposed to the light source (5 lx).

► Before recording data, the *Cabomba* stem was left to acclimatise to the new light level for 5 minutes. Because the volumes of oxygen gas produced are very low, bubbles were counted for a period of three minutes at each distance.

The results

Light intensity / lx (distance)	Bubbles counted in three minutes	Bubbles per minute
5	0	
13 (45 cm)	6	
30 (40 cm)	9	
60 (35 cm)	12	
95 (30 cm)	18	
150 (25 cm)	33	
190 (20 cm)	35	

1. Complete the table by calculating the rate of oxygen production (bubbles of oxygen gas per minute):

2. Use the data to draw a graph of the bubble produced per minute vs light intensity:

3. Although the light source was placed set distances from the *Cabomba* stem, light intensity in lux was recorded at each distance rather than distance *per se*. Explain why this would be more accurate:

_____

_____

_____

4. The sample of gas collected during the experiment was tested with a glowing splint. The splint reignited when placed in the gas. What does this confirm about the gas produced?

_____

5. What could be a more accurate way of measuring the gas produced in the experiment? _____

_____

_____

© 2016 **BIOZONE** International
ISBN: 978-1-927309-32-2
Photocopying Prohibited

27 Adaptations for Photosynthesis

Key Idea: Plant adaptations maximise photosynthetic rate.
Plants require a supply of carbon dioxide, light, and water in order to photosynthesise and their leaves have both structural and physiological adaptations to maximise photosynthetic rates under different environmental conditions. The leaves of plants adapted to high light environments have thicker leaves and fix carbon at higher rates than the leaves of shade-adapted plants. However, their thicker leaves take more

energy to maintain. Some plants have further biochemical adaptations in addition to thicker leaves. Most plants are called C_3 plants because the first detectable compound made is a 3-carbon compound called GP (glycerate 3-phosphate). However, some plants first fix carbon in a 4-carbon molecule, which then supplies the Calvin cycle. This C_4 pathway makes these tropical plants capable of fixing a lot of carbon very quickly in conditions of high light and high temperature.

Structure of a leaf from a C_4 plant

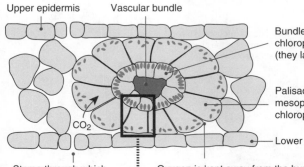

Upper epidermis   Vascular bundle

Bundle sheath cells have chloroplasts without grana (they lack photosystem II).

Palisade cells in the mesophyll have chloroplasts with grana

Lower epidermis

CO_2

Stoma through which CO_2 enters the leaf

Oxygen is kept away from the bundle sheath cells by the tightly packed ring of mesophyll cells. Low oxygen reduces **photorespiration** (the inhibitory effect of oxygen on the Calvin cycle).

A low oxygen environment is essential for the enzyme **ribulose bisphosphate carboxylase** (RuBisCO) to function at maximum efficiency in the Calvin cycle.

Calvin cycle

C3 + CO2
Pyruvate

C4 *Hatch-Slack pathway* **C3**
Malate   PEP

C4
Oxaloacetate

CO2

Bundle sheath
Malate moves from the palisade cells to the inner bundle sheath cells where it is broken down to pyruvate, releasing CO_2. This supplies the Calvin cycle. Photosystem II is lacking and NADP for the Calvin cycle is provided by the NADP-malic enzyme.

Palisade mesophyll cells
Photosynthesis in these cells fixes CO_2 in the cytoplasm and captures light energy in the chloroplasts. The enzyme **PEP carboxylase** has an extremely high affinity for CO_2 even when the latter is in low concentration. This allows the plant to fix large quantities of CO_2 rapidly.

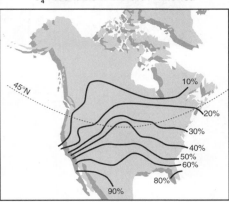

C_4 plants include sugar cane, maize, sorghum, and sun plant (*Portulaca*)

The C_4 pathway effectively fixes carbon twice, so uses more energy (ATP). However, C_4 plants more than compensate for this because losses to photorespiration (which are higher at high temperatures) are minimised.

Distribution of grasses using C_4 mechanism in North America

45°N

10%
20%
30%
40%
50%
60%
80%
90%

The photosynthetic strategy that a plant possesses is an important factor in determining where it is found. Because many of the enzymes of C_4 plants have optimum temperatures well above 25°C, they thrive in hot tropical and sub-tropical climates. Under these conditions, they can out-compete most C_3 plants because they achieve faster rates of photosynthesis. The proportion of grasses using the C_4 mechanism in North America is greatest near the tropics and diminishes northwards.

1. Explain why C_4 plants have a competitive advantage over C_3 plants in the tropics: _____

_____

_____

_____

2. Explain why the bundle sheath cells are arranged in a way that keeps them isolated from air spaces in the leaf:

_____

_____

_____

3. Study the map of North America above showing the distribution of C_4 plants. Explain the distribution pattern in terms of their competitive advantage and the environmental conditions required for this advantage:

_____

_____

The leaf is adapted to maximise light capture and facilitate the entry of CO_2, while minimising water loss. The particular adaptations of the leaf reflect its growth environment, its resistance to water loss, and the importance of the leaf relative to other parts of the plant that may be photosynthetic, such as the stem.

Sun plant

A sun leaf, when exposed to high light intensities, can absorb much of the light available to the cells.

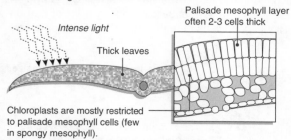

Intense light

Thick leaves

Palisade mesophyll layer often 2-3 cells thick

Chloroplasts are mostly restricted to palisade mesophyll cells (few in spongy mesophyll).

Sun leaves

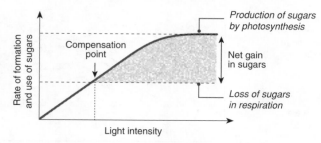

Rate of formation and use of sugars

Compensation point

Production of sugars by photosynthesis

Net gain in sugars

Loss of sugars in respiration

Light intensity

Plants adapted for full sunlight have higher levels of respiration and much higher **compensation points. Sun plants** include many weed species found on open ground. They expend much more energy on the construction and maintenance of thicker leaves than do shade plants. The benefit of this is that they can absorb the higher light intensities available and grow more quickly.

Shade plant

A shade leaf can absorb the light available at lower light intensities. If exposed to high light, most would pass through.

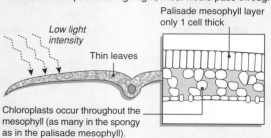

Low light intensity

Thin leaves

Palisade mesophyll layer only 1 cell thick

Chloroplasts occur throughout the mesophyll (as many in the spongy as in the palisade mesophyll).

Shade leaves

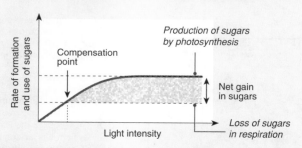

Rate of formation and use of sugars

Compensation point

Production of sugars by photosynthesis

Net gain in sugars

Loss of sugars in respiration

Light intensity

Shade plants typically grow in forested areas, partly shaded by the canopy of larger trees. They have lower rates of respiration than sun plants, mainly because they build thinner leaves. The fewer number of cells requires less energy to produce and maintain. As a result, shade plants reach their compensation point at a low light intensity; much sooner than sun plants do.

4. In C_3 plants, the rate of photosynthesis is enhanced by higher atmospheric CO_2 concentrations. Explain why this is not the case for C_4 plants:

_____

_____

5. (a) From the diagrams above, determine what is meant by the **compensation point** in terms of sugar production:

_____

_____

(b) State which type of plant (sun or shade adapted) has the highest level of respiration: _____

(c) How does the plant compensate for the higher level of respiration? _____

_____

6. Describe some adaptations of leaves in **sun** and **shade plants**: _____

_____

_____

_____

© 2016 **BIOZONE** International
ISBN: 978-1-927309-32-2
Photocopying Prohibited

Summarise what you know about this topic under the
headings and sub-headings provided. You can draw
diagrams or mind maps, or write short notes to organise
your thoughts. Use the images and hints to help you and
refer back to the introduction to check the points covered:

Photosynthesis

HINT: State the general equation for
photosynthesis. Outline the light
dependent and independent reactions.

Factors affecting ph

HINT: Describe and
affecting photosy
products of photo

Adaptations for photosynthesis

HINT: Describe physiological and structural adaptations
for photosynthesis in different environments.

REVISE

matic diagram of photosynthesis below:

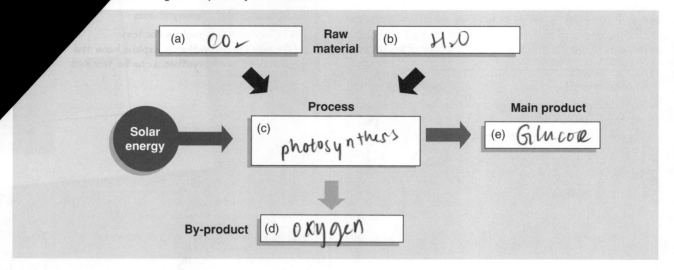

(a) CO₂	**Raw material**
(b) H₂O	

Process

Solar energy → (c) photosynthesis → **Main product** (e) Glucose

By-product (d) oxygen

2. (a) Write the process of photosynthesis as:

A word equation: _Carbon dioxide + water → glucose + oxygen_

A chemical equation: $6CO_2 + 6H_2O \longrightarrow C_6H_{12}O_6 + 6O_2$

(b) Where does photosynthesis occur? _Chloroplast_

3. Test your vocabulary by matching each term to its correct definition, as identified by its preceding letter code.

absorption spectrum _G_

accessory pigments _H_

action spectrum _I_ _G_

Calvin cycle _D_

chlorophyll _~~F~~ J_

grana _K_

light dependent phase _F_

photosynthesis _A_

ribulose bisphosphate _B_

stroma _E_

thylakoid discs _~~F~~ C_

A The biochemical process that uses light energy to convert carbon dioxide and water into glucose molecules and oxygen.

B A 5-carbon molecule which acts as the primary CO_2 acceptor in photosynthesis.

C Membrane-bound compartments in chloroplasts. They are the site of the light dependent reactions of photosynthesis.

D The phase in photosynthesis where chemical energy is used for the synthesis of carbohydrate. Also called the light independent phase.

E The liquid interior of the chloroplast where the light independent phase takes place.

F The phase in photosynthesis when light energy is converted to chemical energy.

G The term to describe the light absorption of a pigment vs the wavelength of light.

H Plant pigments that absorb wavelengths of light that chlorophyll *a* does not absorb.

I A profile of the effectiveness of different wavelengths of light in fuelling photosynthesis.

J The green, membrane-bound pigment involved in the light dependent reactions of photosynthesis.

K The stacks of thylakoids within the chloroplasts of plants.

4. Label the following features of a chloroplast on the diagram below: granum, stroma, thylakoid disc, stroma lamellae

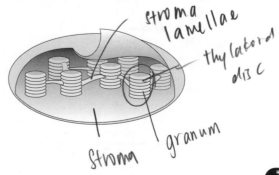

stroma lamellae

thylakoid disc

granum

stroma

© 2016 **BIOZONE** International
ISBN: 978-1-927309-32-2
Photocopying Prohibited

Homeostasis

14.1 Homeostasis in mammals

Learning outcomes

Activity number

☐ 1 Explain what is meant by homeostasis and describe its importance in mammals. Explain the principles of homeostasis in terms of internal and external stimuli, receptors, central control, coordination systems, and effectors. — 30 31

☐ 2 Explain what is meant by negative feedback and outline its role in homeostasis as a stabilising mechanism. Recognise positive feedback as a destabilising mechanism with a specific role in certain physiological processes. — 32 33

☐ 3 Outline the roles of the nervous and endocrine systems in coordinating homeostatic mechanisms. Include reference to thermoregulation, osmoregulation, and the control of blood glucose concentration. — 34 35 40 41

☐ 4 Describe the deamination of amino acids and formation of urea in the urea cycle. — 36

☐ 5 Describe the gross structure and roles of the mammalian kidney to include the renal capsule, medulla, cortex, renal pelvis, ureter, and renal artery and vein. — 37 38

☐ 6 Describe the structure of a nephron and its associated blood vessels using photomicrographs and electron micrographs. — 39

☐ 7 Describe how ultrafiltration and selective reabsorption are involved in the formation of urine in the nephron. — 39

☐ 8 Describe the roles of the hypothalamus, posterior pituitary, ADH, and collecting ducts in osmoregulation (regulation of the water and salt content of the blood). — 39 40

☐ 9 Explain the regulation of blood glucose by negative feedback involving the hormones insulin and glucagon. — 41 42

☐ 10 Describe the role of cyclic AMP as a second messenger in cell signalling with reference to the effect of adrenaline and glucagon on the liver. — 42 43

☐ 11 Describe the stages of cell signalling in the control of blood glucose by adrenaline: (1) hormone-receptor interaction, (2) formation of cAMP and activation of protein kinases, (3) phosphorylation cascade and signal amplification. — 43

☐ 12 With reference to glucose oxidase/peroxidase, explain how enzyme-based dipsticks and biosensors work and how they are used to quantify glucose levels in blood and urine. — 44

☐ 13 Explain the diagnostic use of urine analysis, with reference to glucose, protein, and ketones. — 44

14.2 Homeostasis in plants

Learning outcomes

Activity number

☐ 14 Describe and explain the daily rhtythms of stomatal opening and closing. — 45

☐ 15 Describe the structure and function of guard cells. With reference to the active transport of ions, explain the mechanism by which they open and close stomata. — 45

☐ 16 Describe the role of abscisic acid (ABA) in stomatal closure at times of water stress. Include reference to the role of Ca^{2+} as a second messenger. — 45

30 Homeostasis

Key Idea: Homeostasis refers to the maintenance of a constant physiological state despite fluctuations in the external environment.

Organisms maintain a relatively constant physiological state, called **homeostasis**, despite changes in their environment. Any change in the environment to which an organism responds is called a **stimulus** and, because environmental stimuli are not static, organisms must also adjust their behaviour and physiology constantly to maintain homeostasis. This requires the coordinated activity of the body's organ systems. Homeostatic mechanisms prevent deviations from the steady state and keep the body's internal conditions within strict limits. Deviations from these limits can be harmful.

An example of homeostasis occurs when you exercise (right). Your body must keep your body temperature constant at about 37.0°C despite the increased heat generated by activity. Similarly, you must regulate blood sugar levels and blood pH, water and electrolyte balance, and blood pressure. Your body's organ systems carry out these tasks.

To maintain homeostasis, the body must detect stimuli through receptors, process this sensory information, and respond to it appropriately via effectors. The responses provide new feedback to the receptor. These three components are illustrated below.

How homeostasis is maintained

Muscles and glands

Sense organ (e.g. eye)

Receptor
Detects change and sends a message to the control centre.

Effector
Responds to the output from the control centre.

Brain and spinal cord

Control centre
Receives the message and coordinates a response. Sends an output message to an effector.

The analogy of a thermostat on a heater is a good way to understand how homeostasis is maintained. A heater has sensors (a receptor) to monitor room temperature. It also has a control centre to receive and process the data from the sensors. Depending on the data it receives, the control centre activates the effector (heating unit), switching it on or off. When the room is too cold, the heater switches on. When it is too hot, the heater switches off. This maintains a constant temperature.

1. What is homeostasis? _____

_____

2. What is the role of the following components in maintaining homeostasis:

(a) Receptor: _____

_____

(b) Control centre: _____

_____

(c) Effector: _____

_____

© 2016 **BIOZONE** International
ISBN: **978-1-927309-32-2**
Photocopying Prohibited

31 Maintaining Homeostasis

Key Idea: The body's organ systems work together to maintain homeostasis.

Homeostasis relies on monitoring all the information received from the internal and external environment and coordinating appropriate responses. This often involves many different organ systems working together to ensure proper functioning of the whole organism. Most of the time an organism's body systems are responding to changes at the subconscious level, but sometimes homeostasis is achieved by changing a behaviour (e.g. finding shade if the temperature is too high).

Regulating respiratory gases

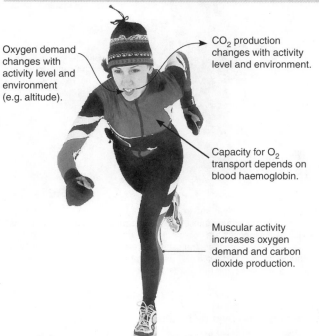

Oxygen demand changes with activity level and environment (e.g. altitude).

CO_2 production changes with activity level and environment.

Capacity for O_2 transport depends on blood haemoglobin.

Muscular activity increases oxygen demand and carbon dioxide production.

Oxygen must be delivered to all cells and carbon dioxide (a waste product of cellular respiration) must be removed. Breathing brings in oxygen and expels CO_2, and the cardiovascular and lymphatic systems circulate these respiratory gases (the oxygen mostly bound to haemoglobin). The rate of breathing is varied according to oxygen demands (as detected by CO_2 levels in the blood).

Coping with pathogens

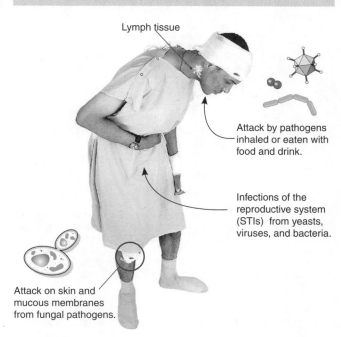

Lymph tissue

Attack by pathogens inhaled or eaten with food and drink.

Infections of the reproductive system (STIs) from yeasts, viruses, and bacteria.

Attack on skin and mucous membranes from fungal pathogens.

All of us are under constant attack from pathogens (disease causing organisms). The body has a number of mechanisms that help to prevent the entry of pathogens and limit the damage they cause if they do enter the body. The skin, the digestive system, and the immune system are all involved in the body's defence, while the cardiovascular and lymphatic systems circulate the cells and antimicrobial substances involved.

Maintaining nutrient supply and removing wastes

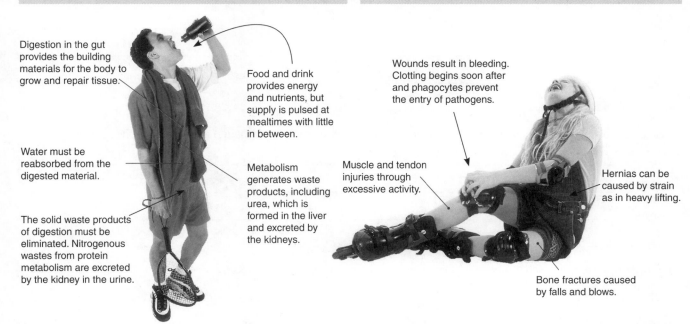

Digestion in the gut provides the building materials for the body to grow and repair tissue.

Food and drink provides energy and nutrients, but supply is pulsed at mealtimes with little in between.

Water must be reabsorbed from the digested material.

Metabolism generates waste products, including urea, which is formed in the liver and excreted by the kidneys.

The solid waste products of digestion must be eliminated. Nitrogenous wastes from protein metabolism are excreted by the kidney in the urine.

Food and drink is taken in to maintain energy supplies. The digestive system makes these nutrients available, and the cardiovascular system distributes them throughout the body. Food intake is regulated largely through nervous mechanisms, while hormones control the cellular uptake of glucose. The liver metabolises proteins to form urea, which is excreted by the kidneys.

Repairing injuries

Wounds result in bleeding. Clotting begins soon after and phagocytes prevent the entry of pathogens.

Muscle and tendon injuries through excessive activity.

Hernias can be caused by strain as in heavy lifting.

Bone fractures caused by falls and blows.

Damage to body tissues triggers the inflammatory response and white blood cells move to the injury site. The inflammatory response is started (and ended) by chemical signals (e.g. from histamine and prostaglandins) released when tissue is damaged. The cardiovascular and lymphatic systems distribute the cells and molecules involved.

LINK **34**   WEB **31**   **KNOW**

Regulating temperature, fluid and electrolytes

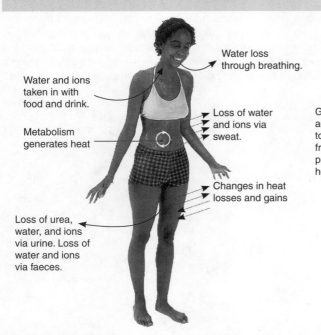

Water loss through breathing.

Water and ions taken in with food and drink.

Metabolism generates heat

Loss of water and ions via sweat.

Changes in heat losses and gains

Loss of urea, water, and ions via urine. Loss of water and ions via faeces.

The balance of fluid and electrolytes (and excretion of wastes) is the job of the kidneys. Osmoreceptors monitor blood volume and bring about the release of the hormones ADH and aldosterone, which regulate reabsorption of water and sodium from blood via the kidneys. The cardiovascular and lymphatic systems distribute fluids around the body. The circulatory system and skin both help to maintain body temperature.

Coordinating responses

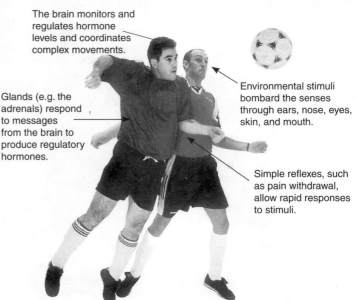

The brain monitors and regulates hormone levels and coordinates complex movements.

Glands (e.g. the adrenals) respond to messages from the brain to produce regulatory hormones.

Environmental stimuli bombard the senses through ears, nose, eyes, skin, and mouth.

Simple reflexes, such as pain withdrawal, allow rapid responses to stimuli.

The body is constantly bombarded by stimuli from the environment. The brain sorts these stimuli into those that require a response and those that do not. Responses are coordinated via nervous or hormonal controls. Simple nervous responses (reflexes) act quickly. Hormones, which are distributed by the cardiovascular and lymphatic systems, take longer to produce a response and the response is more prolonged.

1. Describe two mechanisms that operate to restore homeostasis after infection by a pathogen:

    (a) _____

    _____

    (b) _____

    _____

2. Describe two mechanisms by which responses to stimuli are brought about and coordinated:

    (a) _____

    _____

    (b) _____

    _____

3. Explain two ways in which water and ion balance are maintained. Name the organ(s) and any hormones involved:

    (a) _____

    _____

    (b) _____

    _____

4. Explain two ways in which the body regulates its respiratory gases during exercise:

    (a) _____

    _____

    (b) _____

© 2016 **BIOZONE** International
ISBN: 978-1-927309-32-2
Photocopying Prohibited

32 Negative Feedback

Key Idea: Negative feedback mechanisms detect departures from a set point norm and act to restore the steady state. Most physiological systems achieve homeostasis through negative feedback. In negative feedback systems, movement away from a steady state is detected and triggers a mechanism to counteract that change. **Negative feedback** has a stabilising effect, dampening variations from a set point and returning internal conditions to a steady state.

Negative feedback and control systems

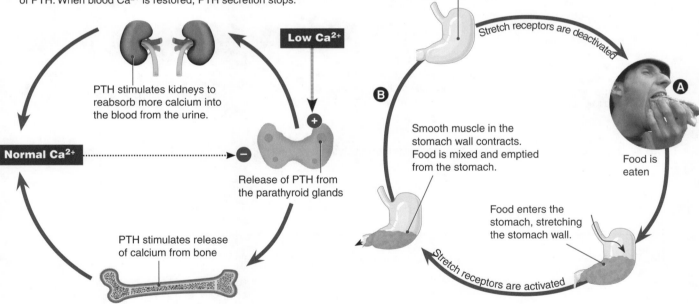

2 Corrective mechanisms activated, e.g. sweating

3 Return to optimum

Stress, e.g. exercise generates excessive body heat

Stress, e.g. cold weather causes excessive heat loss

Corrective mechanisms activated, e.g. shivering

Normal body temperature

1 A **stressor**, e.g. exercise, takes the internal environment away from optimum.

2 Stress is detected by receptors and corrective mechanisms (e.g. sweating or shivering) are activated.

3 Corrective mechanisms act to restore optimum conditions.

Negative feedback acts to counteract departures from steady state. The diagram shows how stress is counteracted in the case of body temperature.

Negative feedback in calcium homeostasis

Blood calcium is regulated by several hormones, including parathyroid hormone (PTH). Low blood Ca^{2+} stimulates release of PTH. When blood Ca^{2+} is restored, PTH secretion stops.

Low Ca²⁺ ... **Low Ca^{2+}**

PTH stimulates kidneys to reabsorb more calcium into the blood from the urine.

Normal Ca^{2+}

+

−

Release of PTH from the parathyroid glands

PTH stimulates release of calcium from bone

Negative feedback in stomach emptying

Empty stomach. Stomach wall is relaxed.

Stretch receptors are deactivated

A Food is eaten

B Smooth muscle in the stomach wall contracts. Food is mixed and emptied from the stomach.

Food enters the stomach, stretching the stomach wall.

Stretch receptors are activated

1. How do negative feedback mechanisms maintain homeostasis in a variable environment? _____

_____

_____

2. On the diagram of stomach emptying:

   (a) State the stimulus at A: _____ State the response at B: _____

   (b) Name the effector in this system: _____

   (c) What is the steady state for this example? _____

33 Feedback Systems Can Interact

Key Idea: Positive feedback results in the escalation of a physiological response and occurs when a particular outcome is required. Positive and negative feedback loops can operate side by side to control a regular sequence of events.

Positive feedback occurs when the response to a stimulus acts to amplify the original response instead of dampen it. Positive feedback is involved in labour, fever, blood clotting, ovulation, and fruit ripening, and its purpose is to achieve a specific physiological outcome. Positive feedback usually stops when the natural resolution is reached (e.g. the baby is born) but it is relatively rare in physiological systems because it creates instability. However, sometimes positive and negative feedback work together to control physiology, as in the control of the female reproductive cycle.

Feedback and ovulation

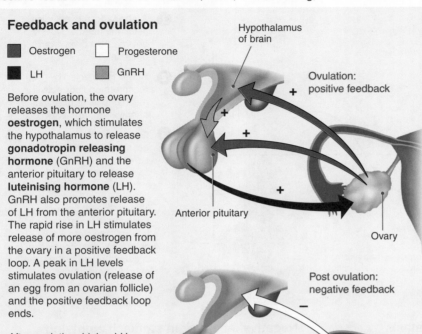

■ Oestrogen   □ Progesterone
■ LH   ■ GnRH

Before ovulation, the ovary releases the hormone **oestrogen**, which stimulates the hypothalamus to release **gonadotropin releasing hormone** (GnRH) and the anterior pituitary to release **luteinising hormone** (LH). GnRH also promotes release of LH from the anterior pituitary. The rapid rise in LH stimulates release of more oestrogen from the ovary in a positive feedback loop. A peak in LH levels stimulates ovulation (release of an egg from an ovarian follicle) and the positive feedback loop ends.

After ovulation, higher LH causes the ruptured follicle to form a corpus luteum. The corpus luteum secretes both oestrogen and **progesterone**. When progesterone is present, the release of GnRH from the hypothalamus and anterior pituitary is inhibited (negative feedback) and the uterine lining is prepared to receive a fertilised egg.

Positive feedback to induce ovulation and negative feedback to regulate hormone levels after ovulation together control the female reproductive cycle.

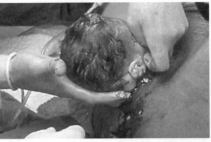

Labour and lactation: During childbirth (above), the release of the hormone oxytocin intensifies the contractions of the uterus so that labour proceeds to its conclusion. The birth itself restores the system by removing the initiating stimulus. After birth, levels of the milk-production hormone prolactin increase. Suckling maintains prolactin secretion and causes the release of oxytocin, resulting in milk release. The more an infant suckles, the more these hormones are produced, so milk production and release are maintained.

Fever is caused by a positive feedback loop. Infection causes macrophages to release interleukins, which stimulate the hypothalamus to increase prostaglandin production. This resets the body's thermostat to a higher 'fever' level by shivering (the chill phase).

1. (a) What is the biological role of positive feedback loops? Describe an example: _____

_____

_____

_____

(b) Why is positive feedback inherently unstable (contrast with negative feedback)? _____

_____

_____

2. Explain how ovulation is controlled by the interaction of positive and negative feed back loops: _____

_____

_____

_____

_____

_____

© 2016 **BIOZONE** International
ISBN: 978-1-927309-32-2
Photocopying Prohibited

34 Nervous and Endocrine Interactions

Key Idea: The nervous and endocrine systems work together to maintain homeostasis.

In mammals, the nervous system and endocrine (hormonal) systems act independently and together to maintain homeostasis. The two systems are quite different in their modes of action, the responses they elicit, and the duration of action. The nervous system stimulates rapid, short-lived responses through electrical signals transmitted directly between adjacent cells. The endocrine system produces a slower, more long-lasting response through blood-borne chemicals called hormones. Hormones control many life processes such as reproduction, growth, and development.

Signalling by neurones (nerve cells)

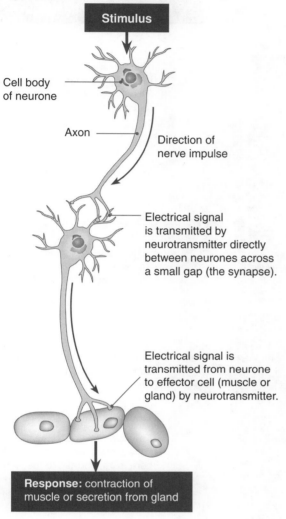

Stimulus

Cell body of neurone

Axon

Direction of nerve impulse

Electrical signal is transmitted by neurotransmitter directly between neurones across a small gap (the synapse).

Electrical signal is transmitted from neurone to effector cell (muscle or gland) by neurotransmitter.

Response: contraction of muscle or secretion from gland

The nervous system transmits electrical impulses directly between cells through electrical junctions or via chemicals called neurotransmitters, which can diffuse across the gap (synapse) between cells. The response of a cell to nervous stimulation is rapid (milliseconds), short lived, and localised. Neural communication is important in rapid responses to stimuli, e.g. reflexes such as pain withdrawal, and may be involved in triggering the release of hormones.

Signalling by hormones

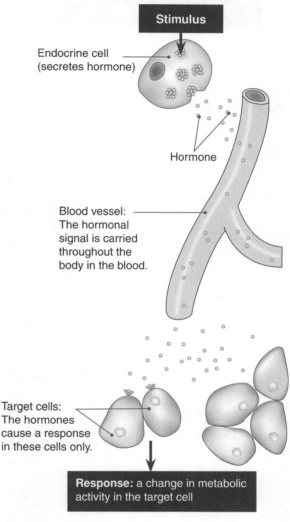

Stimulus

Endocrine cell (secretes hormone)

Hormone

Blood vessel: The hormonal signal is carried throughout the body in the blood.

Target cells: The hormones cause a response in these cells only.

Response: a change in metabolic activity in the target cell

Hormones secreted from endocrine cells are carried in the blood throughout the body, where they interact only with target cells carrying the correct receptor to bring about a response. The speed of hormonal signalling is relatively slow, and it exerts its effects over minutes, hours, or days. Hormonal responses are important in regulating physiological processes such as growth, reproduction, and levels of glucose and electrolytes in the blood.

1. Contrast the mode of action of the nervous and endocrine systems: _____

_____

_____

2. Using examples, explain how the endocrine and nervous systems are involved in maintaining homeostasis:

_____

_____

_____

_____

LINK 48 LINK 41 LINK 40 LINK 35 **KNOW**

35 Thermoregulation in Humans

Key Idea: The temperature regulation centre in humans is in the hypothalamus. Thermoregulation involves negative feedback mechanisms and involves several body systems. The temperature regulation centre of the human body is in the hypothalamus of the brain which has a 'set-point' temperature of 36.7°C. The hypothalamus acts like a thermostat, regulating body temperature through negative feedback. Changes in core body temperature or in skin temperature are registered by the hypothalamus, which then coordinates the nervous and hormonal responses to counteract the changes and restore normal body temperature. When normal temperature is restored, the corrective mechanisms are switched off.

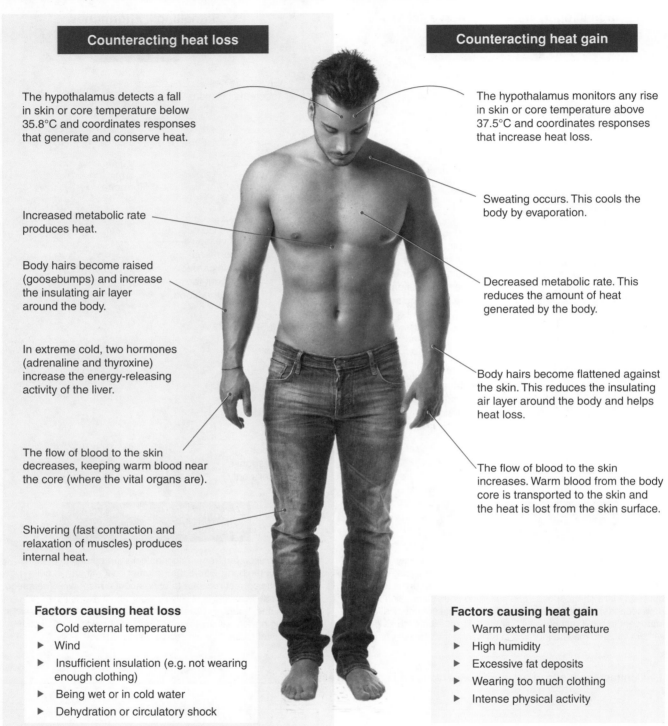

Counteracting heat loss

The hypothalamus detects a fall in skin or core temperature below 35.8°C and coordinates responses that generate and conserve heat.

Increased metabolic rate produces heat.

Body hairs become raised (goosebumps) and increase the insulating air layer around the body.

In extreme cold, two hormones (adrenaline and thyroxine) increase the energy-releasing activity of the liver.

The flow of blood to the skin decreases, keeping warm blood near the core (where the vital organs are).

Shivering (fast contraction and relaxation of muscles) produces internal heat.

Counteracting heat gain

The hypothalamus monitors any rise in skin or core temperature above 37.5°C and coordinates responses that increase heat loss.

Sweating occurs. This cools the body by evaporation.

Decreased metabolic rate. This reduces the amount of heat generated by the body.

Body hairs become flattened against the skin. This reduces the insulating air layer around the body and helps heat loss.

The flow of blood to the skin increases. Warm blood from the body core is transported to the skin and the heat is lost from the skin surface.

Factors causing heat loss
▶ Cold external temperature
▶ Wind
▶ Insufficient insulation (e.g. not wearing enough clothing)
▶ Being wet or in cold water
▶ Dehydration or circulatory shock

Factors causing heat gain
▶ Warm external temperature
▶ High humidity
▶ Excessive fat deposits
▶ Wearing too much clothing
▶ Intense physical activity

1. (a) Where is the temperature regulation centre in humans located? _____

(b) What is its role in thermoregulation: _____

_____

2. State two mechanisms by which body temperature could be reduced after intensive activity: _____

_____

© 2016 **BIOZONE** International
ISBN: **978-1-927309-32-2**
Photocopying Prohibited

Skin section

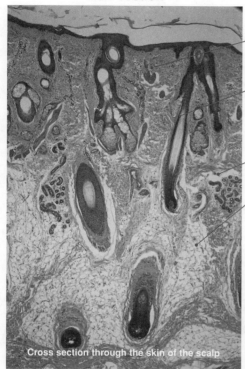

Cross section through the skin of the scalp

Blood vessels in the dermis dilate or constrict to promote or restrict heat loss.

Hairs raised or lowered to increase or decrease the thickness of the insulating air layer between the skin and the environment.

Sweat glands produce sweat, which cools through evaporation.

Fat in the sub-dermal layers insulates the organs against heat loss.

Thermoreceptors in the dermis are free nerve endings, which respond to changes in skin temperature and send that information to the hypothalamus. Hot thermoreceptors detect an increase in skin temperature above 37.5°C and cold thermoreceptors detect a fall below 35.8°C.

Regulating blood flow to the skin

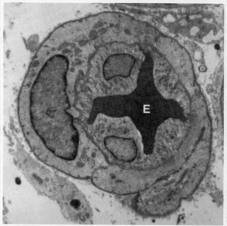

RM Hunt CC 3.0

Constriction of a small blood vessel. An erythrocyte (E) (red blood cell) is in the centre of the vessel.

To regulate heat loss or gain from the skin, the blood vessels beneath the surface constrict (**vasoconstriction**) to reduce blood flow or dilate (**vasodilation**) to increase blood flow. When blood vessels are fully constricted there may be as much as a 10°C temperature gradient from the outer to inner layers of the skin. Extremities such the hands and feet have additional vascular controls which can reduce blood flow to them in times of severe cooling.

The hair erector muscles, sweat glands, and blood vessels are the effectors for mediating a response to information from thermoreceptors. Temperature regulation by the skin involves **negative feedback** because the output is fed back to the skin receptors and becomes part of a new stimulus-response cycle.

Left photograph shows vasodilation and sweating in response high temperature or exertion.
Right photograph shows vasoconstriction and goosebumps in response low temperature or inactivity.

Ildar Sagdejev CC 3.0

3. (a) What is the purpose of sweating and how does it achieve its effect?_____

_____

_____

(b) Why does a dab of methanol or ethanol on the skin feels cold, even if the liquid is at room temperature? _____

_____

4. Describe the feedback system that regulates body temperature: _____

_____

_____

_____

_____

5. How do the blood vessels help to regulate the amount of heat lost from the skin and body? _____

_____

_____

6. (a) What is the role of subcutaneous fat in temperature regulation in humans: _____

_____

(b) Why do excessive deposits of fat tend to lead to overheating during exercise?_____

_____

36 The Liver's Role in Protein Metabolism

Key Idea: The liver has a crucial role in the metabolism of proteins and the storage and detoxification of hormones and ingested or absorbed poisons (including alcohol).

The most critical aspects of protein metabolism occurring in the liver are deamination and transamination of amino acids, removal of ammonia from the body by synthesis of urea, and synthesis of non-essential amino acids. Liver cells are

responsible for synthesis of most of the plasma proteins, including albumins, globulins, and blood clotting proteins. Urea formation via the ornithine cycle occurs primarily in the liver. The urea is formed from ammonia and carbon dioxide by condensation with the amino acid ornithine, which is recycled through a series of enzyme-controlled steps. Urea is transported in the blood to the kidneys and excreted.

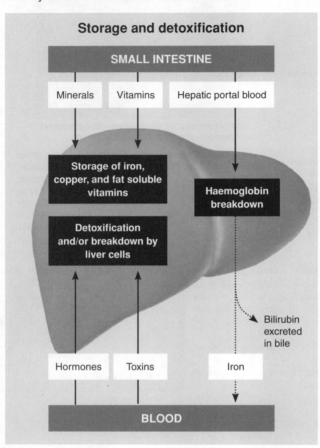

Storage and detoxification

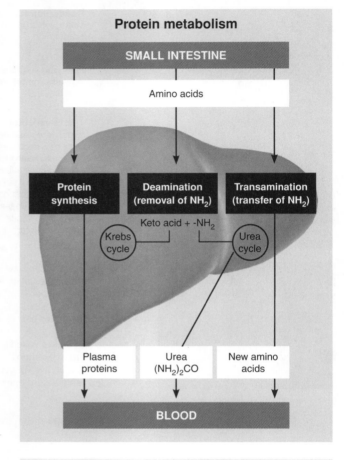

Protein metabolism

1. Describe three aspects of protein metabolism in the liver:

   (a) _____

   _____

   (b) _____

   _____

   (c) _____

   _____

2. Identify the waste products arising from deamination of amino acids and describe their fate:

   _____

   _____

   _____

3. An X-linked disorder of the ornithine cycle results in sufferers lacking the enzyme to convert ornithine to citrulline. Suggest what the symptoms and the prognosis might be:

   _____

   _____

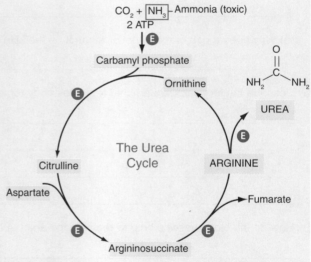

Ammonia (NH_3), the product of protein metabolism, is toxic in even small amounts and must be removed. It is converted to the less toxic urea via the ornithine cycle and is excreted from the body by the kidneys. The liver contains a system of carrier molecules and enzymes (**E**) which quickly convert the ammonia (and CO_2) into urea. One turn of the cycle consumes two molecules of ammonia (one comes from aspartate) and one molecule of CO_2, creates one molecule of urea, and regenerates a molecule of ornithine.

© 2016 **BIOZONE** International
ISBN: 978-1-927309-32-2
Photocopying Prohibited

37 Structure of the Kidney

Key Idea: The urinary system filters the blood and removes wastes, particularly urea, producing urine. The functional unit of the kidney is a selective filter element called the nephron. The urinary system consists of the kidneys and bladder, and their associated blood vessels and ducts. The **kidneys** have a plentiful blood supply from the renal artery. The blood plasma is filtered by the **kidney nephrons** to form **urine**, a waste fluid containing the nitrogenous waste product urea.

Urine is produced continuously, passing via the **ureters** to the **bladder**, a hollow organ lined with stretchable epithelium. Each day the kidneys filter about 180 dm^3 of plasma. Most of this is reabsorbed, leaving a daily urine output of about 1 dm^3. By adjusting the composition of the fluid excreted, the kidneys maintain the body's internal chemical balance. Human kidneys are very efficient, producing a urine that is concentrated to varying degrees depending on requirements.

Urinary system

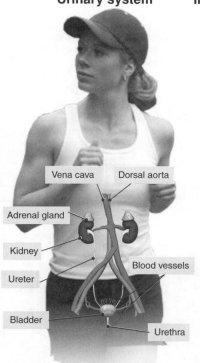

- Vena cava
- Dorsal aorta
- Adrenal gland
- Kidney
- Ureter
- Blood vessels
- Bladder
- Urethra

Internal structure of the human kidney

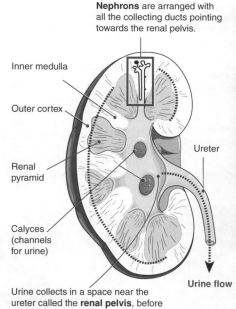

Nephrons are arranged with all the collecting ducts pointing towards the renal pelvis.

- Inner medulla
- Outer cortex
- Renal pyramid
- Ureter
- Calyces (channels for urine)

Urine flow

Urine collects in a space near the ureter called the **renal pelvis**, before leaving the kidney via the ureter.

Sagittal section of kidney (pig)

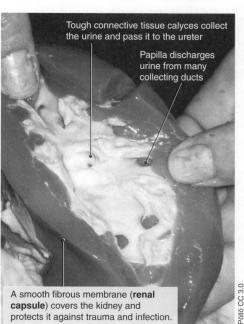

Tough connective tissue calyces collect the urine and pass it to the ureter

Papilla discharges urine from many collecting ducts

A smooth fibrous membrane (**renal capsule**) covers the kidney and protects it against trauma and infection.

Pöllö CC 3.0

The kidneys of most mammals are bean shaped organs that lie at the back of the abdominal cavity to either side of the spine (above). A cut through in a sagittal plane (above right) reveals numerous tough connective tissue calyces. These collect the urine from the papillae where it is discharged. The inner medulla (above centre) is organised into cone-shaped renal pyramids which end in a papilla. The pyramids appear striped because of the precise alignment of the nephrons (the filtering elements of the kidney) and their associated blood vessels. Each kidney contains more than 1 million nephrons. The nephrons filter the blood and modify the filtrate to regulate blood composition and pH, and excrete wastes and toxins.

The kidneys and their blood supply

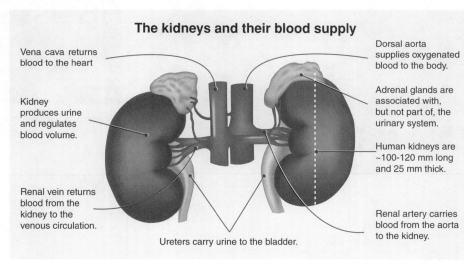

Vena cava returns blood to the heart

Kidney produces urine and regulates blood volume.

Renal vein returns blood from the kidney to the venous circulation.

Ureters carry urine to the bladder.

Dorsal aorta supplies oxygenated blood to the body.

Adrenal glands are associated with, but not part of, the urinary system.

Human kidneys are ~100-120 mm long and 25 mm thick.

Renal artery carries blood from the aorta to the kidney.

1. Calculate the percentage of the plasma reabsorbed by the kidneys: _____

2. Based on the information above, describe the gross structure of the kidney: _____
   _____
   _____
   _____

3. (a) What is a nephron? _____

   (b) What is its role in excretion? _____
   _____

LINK 39   LINK 38   WEB 37   **KNOW**

38 Drawing the Kidney

Key Idea: Drawing from a dissection or histological preparation requires practise and an understanding of structure.

Many observational studies made using microscopes will require you to make accurate representations of what you see. Observations need to be made at both low (X40) and high magnifications to identify the finer structure of the tissue. Tissue sections will usually be provided as longitudinal (LS) or traverse sections (TS). When you have access to both TS and LS images from the same specimen, it is also possible to visualise the three dimensional shape of the structure under view. Observational drawing from a microscope is a skill that must be developed. It requires relaxed viewing in which the image is viewed with one eye, while the other eye attends to the drawing. Attention should be given to the symmetry and proportions of the structure, accurate labelling, statement of magnification and sectioning, and stain used, if this is appropriate. In this activity, you will practise the skills required to translate what is viewed into a good biological drawing.

Biological drawings

► Biological drawings should include as much detail as you need to distinguish different structures and types of tissue, but avoid unnecessary detail.

► Tissue preparations are rarely neat and tidy and there may be areas where it is difficult to distinguish detail. In these cases you will need to infer detail where possible from adjacent cells.

► Avoid shading as this can obscure detail.

► Labelling involves interpretation based on your knowledge. Labels should be away from the drawing with label lines pointing to the structures identified.

► Add a title and details of the image such as magnification.

TASK 1

Complete a biological drawing of the kidney shown below left including the labels on the photo. At this level, the layers of the kidney can be seen while the detail of each layer cannot.

TASK 2

Complete the biological drawing of a TS through the cortical region (cortex) of a kidney nephron (below). The ovoid glomerular cluster of capillaries can be seen in the upper centre of the photograph, separated from the Bowman's capsule by a space. The capsule is lined with squamous epithelium and surrounded by tubules formed by cuboidal epithelial cells. You can infer this from the position and spacing of the cell nuclei. To assist you with the level of detail required, one kidney tubule has been completed for you.

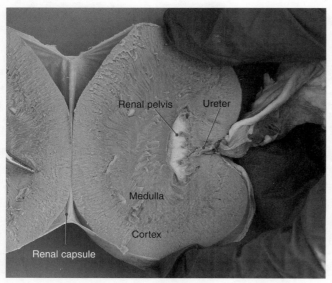

Renal pelvis Ureter
Medulla
Cortex
Renal capsule

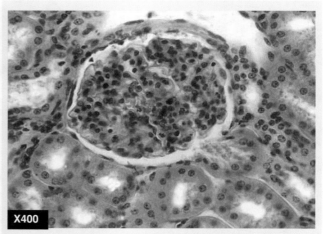

X400

Light micrograph of a transverse section through a kidney nephron to show glomerulus and convoluted tubules.

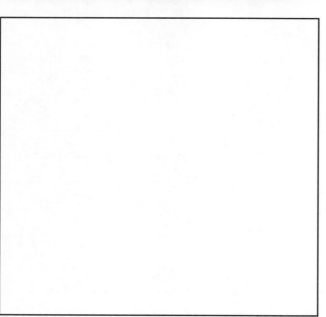

© 2015 **BIOZONE** International
ISBN: 978-1-927309-32-2
Photocopying Prohibited

39 The Physiology of the Kidney

Key Idea: Each nephron comprises a renal corpuscle and its associated tubules and ducts. It produces the urine by ultrafiltration, selective reabsorption, and secretion.

Ultrafiltration, i.e. forcing fluid and dissolved substances through a membrane by pressure, occurs in the first part of the nephron, across the membranes of the capillaries and the glomerular capsule. The passage of water and solutes into the nephron and the formation of the glomerular filtrate depends on the pressure of the blood entering the afferent arteriole (below). If it increases, filtration rate increases. When it falls, glomerular filtration rate also falls. This process is so precisely regulated that, in spite of fluctuations in arteriolar pressure, glomerular filtration rate per day stays constant. After formation of the initial filtrate, the **urine** is modified through secretion and tubular reabsorption according to physiological needs at the time.

Nephron structure and function

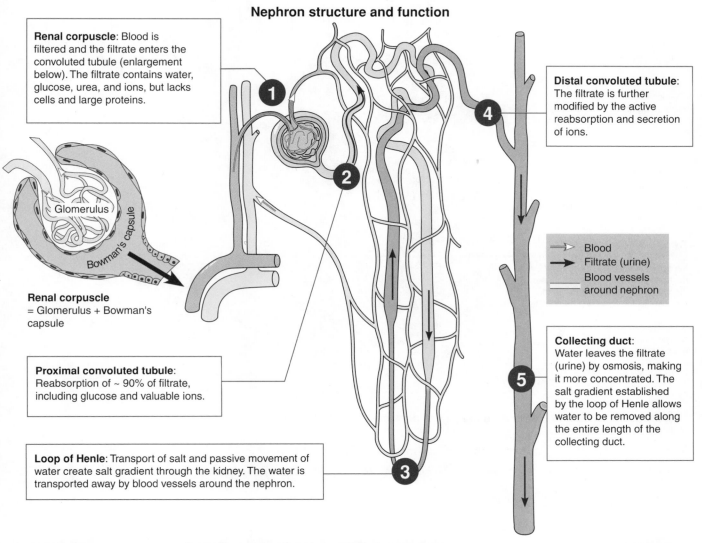

Renal corpuscle: Blood is filtered and the filtrate enters the convoluted tubule (enlargement below). The filtrate contains water, glucose, urea, and ions, but lacks cells and large proteins.

Renal corpuscle
= Glomerulus + Bowman's capsule

Proximal convoluted tubule: Reabsorption of ~ 90% of filtrate, including glucose and valuable ions.

Loop of Henle: Transport of salt and passive movement of water create salt gradient through the kidney. The water is transported away by blood vessels around the nephron.

Distal convoluted tubule: The filtrate is further modified by the active reabsorption and secretion of ions.

Blood
Filtrate (urine)
Blood vessels around nephron

Collecting duct: Water leaves the filtrate (urine) by osmosis, making it more concentrated. The salt gradient established by the loop of Henle allows water to be removed along the entire length of the collecting duct.

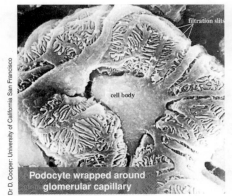

Dr D. Cooper: University of California San Francisco

The epithelium of Bowman's capsule is made up of specialised cells called **podocytes**. The finger-like cellular processes of the podocytes wrap around the capillaries of the glomerulus, and the plasma filtrate passes through the filtration slits between them.

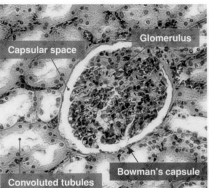

Bowman's capsule is a double walled cup, lying in the cortex of the kidney. It encloses a dense capillary network called the **glomerulus**. The capsule and its enclosed glomerulus form a **renal corpuscle**. In this section, the convoluted tubules can be seen surrounding the renal corpuscle.

Normal, fresh urine is clear and pale to dark yellow or amber in colour. A urine dipstick test is a fast and convenient way to make a qualitative analysis of urine to diagnose a medical problem. The presence of specific molecules in the urine (e.g. glucose) are indicated by a colour change on the dipstick.

LINK **40** LINK **37** WEB **39** **KNOW**

Summary of activities in the kidney nephron

Urine formation begins by **ultrafiltration** of the blood, as fluid is forced through the capillaries of the glomerulus. The filtrate is then modified by **secretion** and **reabsorption** to add or remove substances (e.g. ions). The processes involved in urine formation are summarised below for each region of the nephron.

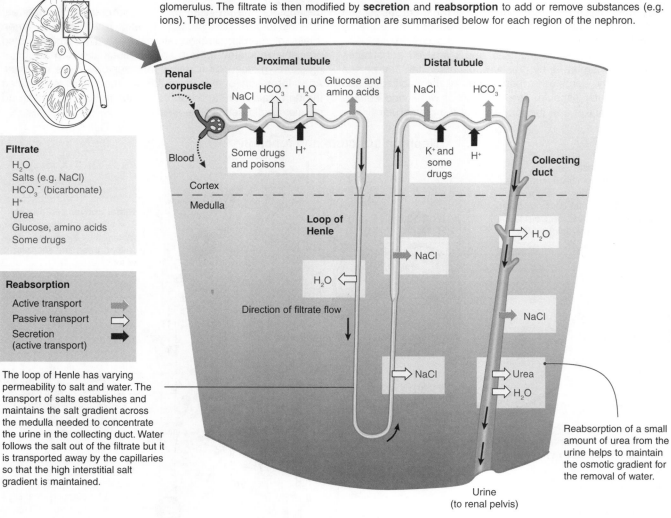

Filtrate

H_2O
Salts (e.g. NaCl)
HCO_3^- (bicarbonate)
H^+
Urea
Glucose, amino acids
Some drugs

Reabsorption

Active transport
Passive transport
Secretion
(active transport)

The loop of Henle has varying permeability to salt and water. The transport of salts establishes and maintains the salt gradient across the medulla needed to concentrate the urine in the collecting duct. Water follows the salt out of the filtrate but it is transported away by the capillaries so that the high interstitial salt gradient is maintained.

Reabsorption of a small amount of urea from the urine helps to maintain the osmotic gradient for the removal of water.

1. Why does the kidney receive blood at a higher pressure than other organs? _____

_____

2. Explain the importance of the following in the production of urine in the kidney nephron:

   (a) Filtration of the blood at the glomerulus: _____

   _____

   (b) Active secretion: _____

   _____

   (c) Reabsorption: _____

   _____

   (d) Osmosis: _____

   _____

3. (a) What is the purpose of the salt gradient in the kidney? _____

   _____

   _____

   (b) How is this salt gradient produced? _____

   _____

40 Control of Urine Output

Key Idea: The body's balance of fluid and electrolytes is regulated by varying the composition and volume of urine. This is achieved through the action of the hormones antidiuretic hormone (ADH) and aldosterone.

The body regulates the composition and volume of the blood to compensate for variations in salt and water intake, and environmental conditions. This is achieved by varying the volume and composition of the urine and is under hormonal control. Antidiuretic hormone (ADH), from the posterior pituitary, regulates water reabsorption from the kidney collecting duct. Aldosterone, from the adrenal cortex, regulates sodium absorption from the kidney tubules.

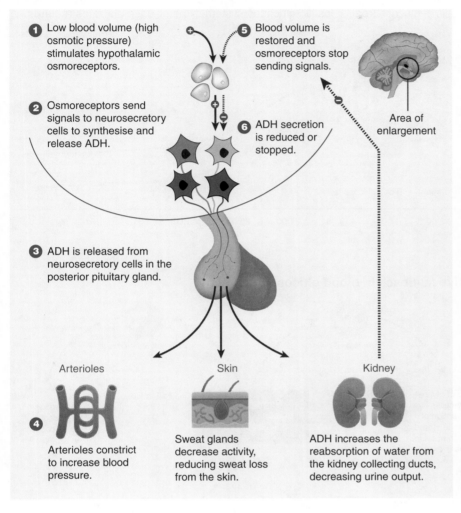

1 Low blood volume (high osmotic pressure) stimulates hypothalamic osmoreceptors.

2 Osmoreceptors send signals to neurosecretory cells to synthesise and release ADH.

3 ADH is released from neurosecretory cells in the posterior pituitary gland.

5 Blood volume is restored and osmoreceptors stop sending signals.

6 ADH secretion is reduced or stopped.

Area of enlargement

Arterioles

4 Arterioles constrict to increase blood pressure.

Skin
Sweat glands decrease activity, reducing sweat loss from the skin.

Kidney
ADH increases the reabsorption of water from the kidney collecting ducts, decreasing urine output.

Osmoreceptors in the **hypothalamus** of the brain respond to changes in blood volume. A blood volume stimulates the synthesis and secretion of the hormone ADH (antidiuretic hormone), which is released from the posterior pituitary into the blood. ADH increases the permeability of the kidney collecting duct to water so that more water is reabsorbed and urine volume decreases. A second hormone, aldosterone, helps by increasing sodium reabsorption.

Factors causing ADH release

▶ Low blood volume
   = More negative water potential
   = High blood sodium levels
   = Low fluid intake
▶ Nicotine and morphine

Factors inhibiting ADH release

▶ High blood volume
   = Less negative water potential
   = Low blood sodium levels
▶ High fluid intake
▶ Alcohol consumption

Factors causing the release of aldosterone

Low blood volumes also stimulate secretion of aldosterone from the adrenal cortex. This is mediated through a complex pathway involving osmoreceptors near the kidney glomeruli and the hormone renin from the kidney.

1. State what happens to urine volume and blood volume when:

   (a) ADH secretion increases: _____

   (b) ADH secretion decreases: _____

2. Diabetes insipidus is caused by a lack of ADH. From what you know about ADH, describe the symptoms of this disease:

   _____

   _____

3. Explain why alcohol consumption (especially to excess) causes dehydration and thirst: _____

   _____

4. (a) State the effect of aldosterone on the kidney nephron: _____

   (b) What would be the net result of this effect: _____

5. Explain the role of negative feedback in the regulation of blood volume and urine output: _____

   _____

   _____

41 Control of Blood Glucose

Key Idea: The endocrine part of the pancreas (the α and β cells of the islets of Langerhans) produces two hormones, glucagon and insulin, which maintain blood glucose homeostasis through negative feedback.
Insulin promotes a decrease in blood glucose by promoting cellular uptake of glucose and synthesis of glycogen. Glucagon promotes an increase in blood glucose through the breakdown of glycogen and the synthesis of glucose from amino acids. Negative feedback stops hormone secretion when normal blood glucose levels are restored. Blood glucose homeostasis allows energy to be available to cells as needed. Extra energy is stored as glycogen or fat. These storage molecules are converted to glucose when energy is needed. The liver has a central role in these carbohydrate conversions. One of the consequences of a disruption to the insulin-glucagon system is the disease **diabetes mellitus**.

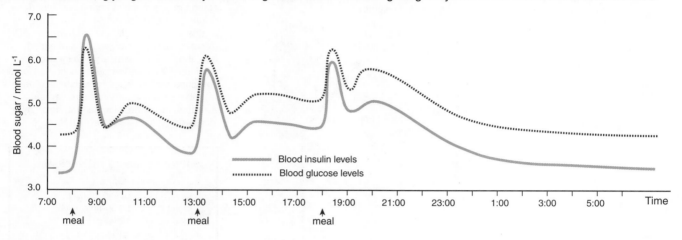

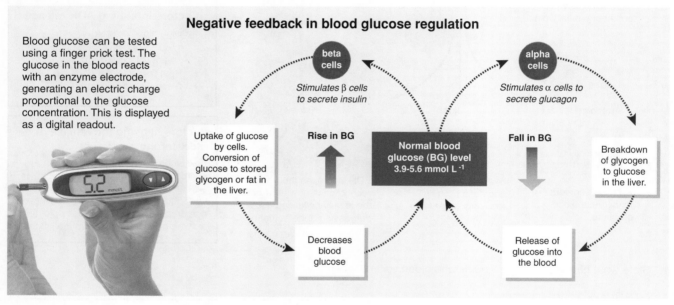

Negative feedback in blood glucose regulation

Blood glucose can be tested using a finger prick test. The glucose in the blood reacts with an enzyme electrode, generating an electric charge proportional to the glucose concentration. This is displayed as a digital readout.

1. (a) Identify the stimulus for the release of insulin: _____

   (b) Identify the stimulus for the release of glucagon: _____

   (c) Explain how glucagon brings about an increase in blood glucose level: _____

   _____

   (d) Explain how insulin brings about a decrease in blood glucose level: _____

   _____

2. Explain the pattern of fluctuations in blood glucose and blood insulin levels in the graph above: _____

   _____

   _____

   _____

   _____

42 The Liver's Role in Carbohydrate Metabolism

Key Idea: Glycogen and glucose interconversions occur in the liver in response to hormones.

The liver has a central role in carbohydrate metabolism, specifically the production of glucose from non-carbohydrate sources (such as lipids and proteins) and the interconversion of glucose and glycogen. These dynamic processes are closely regulated by hormones, principally insulin and glucagon, but also adrenaline and glucocorticoids (e.g. cortisol). They ensure that carbohydrate is stored or made available to cells as required.

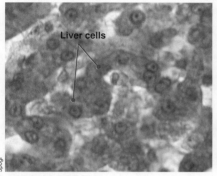

Liver cells

Glycogen is stored within the liver cells. Glucagon stimulates its conversion to glucose.

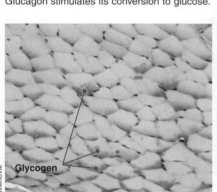

Glycogen

Glycogen is also stored in muscle, where it is squeezed out to the periphery of the cells.

▶ **Glycogenesis**
Excess glucose in the blood is converted to **glycogen** (a glucose polysaccharide). **Insulin** stimulates glycogenesis in response to high blood glucose. Glycogen is stored in the liver and muscle tissue.

▶ **Glycogenolysis**
Conversion of stored glycogen to glucose (glycogen breakdown). The free glucose is released into the blood. The hormones **glucagon** and adrenaline stimulate glycogenolysis in response to low blood glucose.

▶ **Gluconeogenesis**
Production of glucose from non-carbohydrate sources (e.g. glycerol, pyruvate, lactate, and amino acids). Adrenaline and glucocorticoid hormones (e.g. cortisol) stimulate gluconeogenesis in response to fasting, starvation, or prolonged periods of exercise when glycogen stores are exhausted. It is also part of the general adaptation syndrome in response to stress.

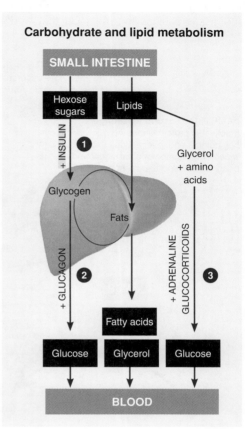

Carbohydrate and lipid metabolism

1. Explain the three important processes of carbohydrate metabolism in the liver, including how these are regulated:

(a) _____

_____

_____

(b) _____

_____

_____

(c) _____

_____

_____

2. Identify the processes occurring at each numbered stage on the diagram above, right:

(a) Process occurring at point 1: _____

(b) Process occurring at point 2: _____

(c) Process occurring at point 3: _____

3. Explain why it is important that the body can readily convert and produce different forms of carbohydrates:

_____

_____

LINK 41   LINK 36   WEB 42

KNOW

43 Cyclic AMP as Second Messenger

Key Idea: Cyclic AMP acts as a second messenger to bring about an amplified response to an extracellular signal.

Cells can regulate metabolic activity by activating or deactivating enzymes as they are needed. When the enzyme is needed by the cell, it can quickly be activated, saving the cell energy and reducing cellular response time. **Cyclic AMP (cAMP)** is a signalling molecule that works in conjunction with protein kinase A to amplify the effect of an extracellular signaling molecule (such as hormone) and bring about the activation of enzymes in a metabolic pathway. In the example below, the cell receives a signal via the hormone adrenaline. cAMP is produced from ATP and activates protein kinase A, beginning a cascade of reactions that ends with the production of glucose from glycogen.

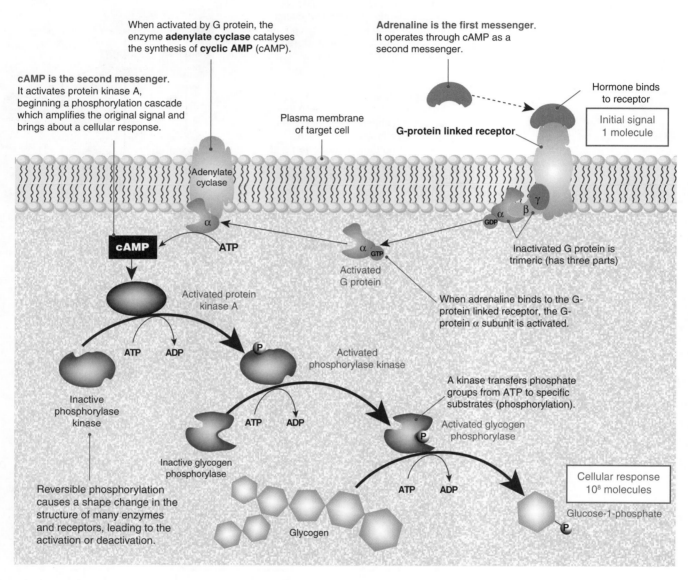

When activated by G protein, the enzyme **adenylate cyclase** catalyses the synthesis of **cyclic AMP** (cAMP).

Adrenaline is the first messenger. It operates through cAMP as a second messenger.

cAMP is the second messenger. It activates protein kinase A, beginning a phosphorylation cascade which amplifies the original signal and brings about a cellular response.

Plasma membrane of target cell

Hormone binds to receptor

Initial signal 1 molecule

G-protein linked receptor

Adenylate cyclase

α

cAMP

ATP

α GTP

Activated G protein

α β γ

GDP

Inactivated G protein is trimeric (has three parts)

Activated protein kinase A

When adrenaline binds to the G-protein linked receptor, the G-protein α subunit is activated.

ATP   ADP

P

Activated phosphorylase kinase

A kinase transfers phosphate groups from ATP to specific substrates (phosphorylation).

Inactive phosphorylase kinase

Inactive glycogen phosphorylase

ATP   ADP

Activated glycogen phosphorylase

P

Reversible phosphorylation causes a shape change in the structure of many enzymes and receptors, leading to the activation or deactivation.

Glycogen

ATP   ADP

Cellular response 10^8 molecules

Glucose-1-phosphate

P

1. (a) What is the role of adrenaline in the example above? _____

_____

(b) What is the role of cAMP in the example above and how does it result in an amplification of the original signal?

_____

_____

2. (a) What is the role of reversible phosphorylation in signal cascades such as the one described above? _____

_____

(b) What are the advantages of this method of regulation? Why are enzymes not just degraded when not required?

_____

_____

© 2016 **BIOZONE** International
ISBN: 978-1-927309-32-2
Photocopying Prohibited

44 Urine Analysis

Key Idea: Urine analysis (urinalysis) can be used to detect metabolic disorders, pregnancy, and the use of illegal drugs. Urine analysis is used as a medical diagnostic tool for a range of metabolic disorders including diabetes mellitus and renal failure. In addition, urine analysis can be used to diagnose pregnancy and to detect illegal substances.

Diagnostic urinalysis

A urinalysis is an array of tests performed on urine. It is one of the most common methods of medical diagnosis, as most tests are quick and easy to perform, and they are non-invasive. Urinalysis can be used to detect for the presence of blood cells in the urine, glucose, proteins, and drugs. Special dipsticks, which use immunological detection of a hormone are used to detect pregnancy.

A urinalysis may include a **macroscopic analysis**, a **dipstick chemical analysis**, in which the test results are read as colour changes, and a **microscopic analysis**, which involves centrifugation of the sample and examination for crystals, blood cells, or microbes.

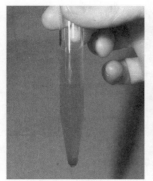

MACROSCOPIC URINALYSIS
The first part of a urinalysis is direct visual observation. Normal, fresh urine is pale to dark yellow or amber in colour and clear. **Turbidity** or cloudiness may be caused by excessive cellular material or protein in the urine. A **red or red-brown** (abnormal) colour may be due to the presence of proteins (haemoglobin or myoglobin). If the sample contained many red blood cells, it would be cloudy as well as red, as in this sample (left) indicating blood in the urine.

DIPSTICK URINALYSIS
A urine dipstick is a narrow band of paper saturated with chemical indicators for specific substances. Dipstick tests include:

Protein: Normal total protein excretion does not exceed 10 mg 100 cm^{-3} in a single specimen. More than 150 mg per day can indicate kidney malfunction.

Glucose: Less than 0.1% of glucose filtered by the glomerulus normally appears in urine. Excess sugar in urine is usually due to untreated diabetes mellitus, which is characterised by high blood glucose levels (the cells cannot take up glucose so it is excreted).

Ketones: Ketones in the urine result from diabetic ketosis or some other form of starvation.

Biosensors

Biosensors are electronic monitoring devices that use biological material to detect the presence or concentration of a particular substance. Enzymes are ideally suited for use in biosensors because of their specificity and sensitivity. This example illustrates how glucose oxidase from the fungus *Aspergillus niger* is used in a biosensor to measure blood glucose level in diabetics.

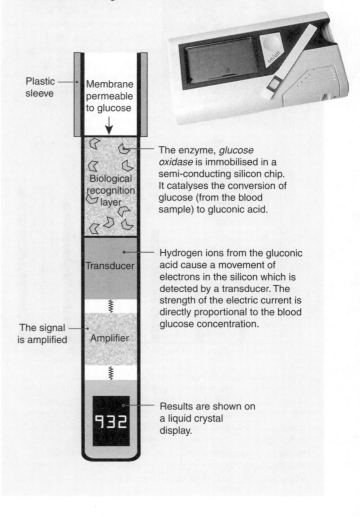

Plastic sleeve — Membrane permeable to glucose

Biological recognition layer

The enzyme, *glucose oxidase* is immobilised in a semi-conducting silicon chip. It catalyses the conversion of glucose (from the blood sample) to gluconic acid.

Transducer

Hydrogen ions from the gluconic acid cause a movement of electrons in the silicon which is detected by a transducer. The strength of the electric current is directly proportional to the blood glucose concentration.

The signal is amplified — Amplifier

932 — Results are shown on a liquid crystal display.

1. Why is **urinalysis** a frequently used diagnostic technique for many common disorders? _____

_____

_____

2. What might the following abnormal results in a urine test suggest to a doctor?

(a) Excess glucose: _____

(b) A red-brown colour: _____

3. Outline the basic principle of enzyme-based biosensors: _____

_____

_____

LINK 41   LINK 39   WEB 44   **KNOW**

45 Homeostasis in Plants

Key Idea: Plant hormones play crucial roles in the timing of activities such as leaf loss, germination, and stomatal closure. Plant hormones (or phytohormones) are chemicals that act as signal molecules to regulate plant growth and responses.

Alone or together, plant hormones target specific cells to cause a specific effect. Many have roles in coordinating timing responses in plants including promoting seed germination, leaf loss, and stomatal closure (below).

Seed germination

In plants, germination refers to when a seed begins to sprout (left) and develop into a seedling. This process is controlled by a group of hormones called **gibberellins** (GA). When conditions are favourable for growth (e.g. moist, warm soil temperature) gibberellins break seed dormancy and promote the growth of the seed. Cell division and cell elongation are stimulated, allowing the root to penetrate the seed coat.

The effect of gibberellic acid on the growth of rhododendron seedlings

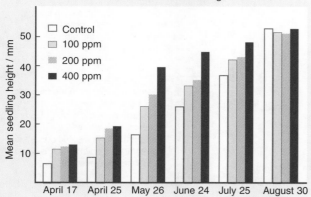

Adapted from Ticknor, R, Journal American Rhododendron Society, Volume 12(2) April 1958

The effect of gibberellic acid (a type of gibberellin) on germination in rhododendron seedlings is shown above. Seeds were initially germinated on sphagnum moss and transferred into soil when two leaves formed. Gibberellic acid of varying concentrations (100, 200, or 400 ppm) was sprayed on the seedlings when they reached 5 mm in height. The controls received no gibberellic acid. The height of the seedlings was measured at varying time intervals (above). Each bar represents the mean height of 15 seedlings.

Leaf loss in deciduous plants

Deciduous plants shed their leaves every autumn in a process called **abscission**. The plant hormones **auxin** and **ethylene** work together to cause leaf loss. As the leaf ages, auxin levels within the leaf drop. The plant becomes more sensitive to the effects of ethylene, and gene expression of enzymes involved in cell wall degradation (e.g. cellulase) increases. These enzymes begin to break down the cell wall in localised regions (the separation layer) at the base of the leaf stalk (petiole). As a result the leaf and its stalk fall away.

Stomatal closure

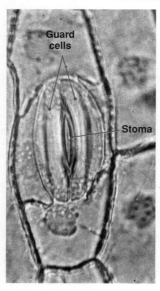

Guard cells

Stoma

Gas exchange and water loss from plants occur via stomata (pores on the leaf surface). Turgor changes in the guard cells flanking the stomata open and close the pore (the pore opens when the guard cells are swollen tight and closes when they are flaccid). This regulates the rate of gas exchange and water loss. The hormone abscisic acid (ABA) is involved in regulating stomatal closure during times of water stress. ABA causes an intracellular increase in the second messenger Ca^{2+} which causes K^+ and Cl^- to leave the guard cells. Water follows by osmosis and the stomata close, reducing water loss via transpiration and conserving water.

1. Describe the results for the graph above and determine if gibberellic acid has any effect on seedling growth: _____

_____

_____

_____

2. Describe the role of auxin and ethylene in leaf loss: _____

_____

_____

3. Why is ABA important in the survival of plants during times of drought? _____

_____

_____

© 2016 **BIOZONE** International
ISBN: 978-1-927309-32-2
Photocopying Prohibited

The guard cells on each side of a stoma control the diameter of the pore by changing shape. When the guard cells take up water and are turgid, the pore is open. When the guard cells lose water and become flaccid, the pore closes. By this mechanism a plant regulates the amount of gas entering, or water leaving, the leaf. The changes in turgor pressure that open and close the pore result mainly from the reversible uptake and loss of potassium ions (and thus water) by the guard cells.

Stomatal pore open

K+ enters the guard cells from the epidermal cells (active transport coupled to a proton pump).

Water follows K+ by osmosis.

Thickened ventral wall

Guard cell swells and becomes turgid.

Pore opens

Nucleus of guard cell

ψguard cell < ψepidermal cell: water enters the guard cells

Stomata open when the guard cells actively take up K+ from the neighbouring epidermal cells. The ion uptake causes the water potential (ψ) to become more negative in the guard cells. As a consequence, water is taken up by the cells and they swell and become turgid. The walls of the guard cells are thickened more on the inside surface (the ventral wall) than the outside wall, so that when the cells swell they buckle outward, opening the pore.

Stomatal pore closed

ABA

Ca^{2+} as second messenger activates K+ channels, so K+ leaves the guard cell and enter the epidermal cells.

Water follows K+ by osmosis.

The guard cells become flaccid.

Pore closes

ψepidermal cell < ψguard cell: water leaves the guard cells

Stomata close when K+ leaves the guard cells. The loss causes the water potential (ψ) to become less negative in the guard cells, and more negative in the epidermal cells. As a result, water is lost by osmosis and the cells sag together and close the pore. The movement of K+ out of the guard cells is brought about by calcium ions acting as a second messenger in response to the hormone ABA. Ca^{2+} triggers the movement of K+ from the guard cell vacuole across the plasma membrane and into the epidermal cells.

The cycle of opening and closing of stomata

The opening and closing of stomata shows a daily cycle that is largely determined by the hours of light and dark.

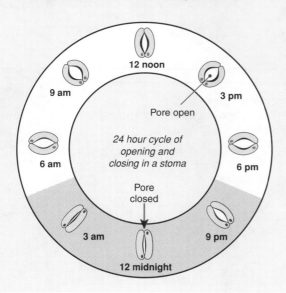

12 noon

9 am

6 am

3 am

12 midnight

3 pm

6 pm

9 pm

Pore open

24 hour cycle of opening and closing in a stoma

Pore closed

The image left shows a scanning electron micrograph (SEM) of a single stoma from the leaf epidermis of a dicot.

Note the guard cells (G), which are swollen tight and open the pore (S) to allow gas exchange between the leaf tissue and the environment.

Factors influencing stomatal opening

Stomata	Guard cells	Daylight	CO_2	Soil water
Open	Turgid	Light	Low	High
Closed	Flaccid	Dark	High	Low

The opening and closing of stomata depends on environmental factors, the most important being light, carbon dioxide concentration in the leaf tissue, and water supply. Stomata tend to open during daylight in response to light, and close at night (left and above). Low CO_2 levels also promote stomatal opening. Conditions that induce water stress cause the stomata to close, regardless of light or CO_2 level.

4. Briefly outline the role of stomata in gas exchange in an angiosperm: _____

_____

5. Summarise the mechanism by which the guard cells bring about the opening and closing of stomata:

_____

_____

_____

_____

46 Chapter Review

Summarise what you know about this topic under the headings and sub-headings provided. You can draw diagrams or mind maps, or write short notes to organise your thoughts. Use the images and hints to help you and refer back to the introduction to check the points covered:

Principles of homeostasis
HINT: Using examples, explain how homeostasis is maintained through feedback mechanisms.

Regulating the internal environment
HINT: Kidneys, urine output, and control of blood glucose.

Thermoregulation in humans
HINT: Include reference to the role of the skin, blood vessels, and hypothalamus.

Homeostasis in plants
HINT: Stomata and guard cell structure and function.

47 KEY TERMS AND IDEAS: Did You Get It?

1. Test your vocabulary by matching each term to its definition, as identified by its preceding letter code.

abscisic acid ....

antidiuretic hormone (ADH) ....

cyclic AMP ....

effector ....

homeostasis ....

insulin ....

kidney ....

negative feedback ....

nephron ....

response ....

second messenger ....

stimulus ....

stomata ....

thermoregulation ....

A Regulation of the internal environment to maintain a stable, constant condition.

B The behaviour occurring as a result of an external or internal stimulus.

C The functional unit of the kidney comprising the glomerulus, Bowman's capsule, convoluted tubules, loop of Henle, and collecting duct.

D A muscle, gland, or organ capable of responding to a stimulus (e.g. nerve impulse).

E A molecule that relays signals from receptors on the cell surface to target molecules inside the cell.

F A mechanism in which the output of a system acts to oppose changes to the input of the system. The net effect is to stabilise the system and dampen fluctuations.

G The regulation of body temperature.

H A hormone, secreted by the pancreas, that lowers blood glucose levels.

I An important intracellular signal transduction molecule, derived from ATP. The second messenger in many signal transduction pathways.

J A plant hormone involved in plant development, including bud dormancy and in the closure of stomata.

K Any change in the environment that is capable of generating a response in an organisms.

L Pores in the leaf surface through which gases can pass.

M Bean shaped organ which removes and concentrates metabolic wastes from the blood.

N The hormone released in response to low blood volumes, high sodium levels, or low fluid intake.

2. Study the graph below, and answer the questions following it. In your answers, use biological terms appropriately to show your understanding.

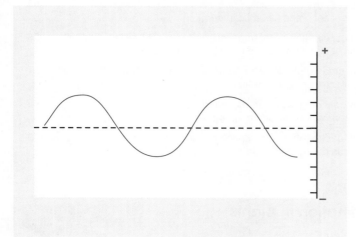

Type of feedback mechanism: _____

_____

_____

Mode of action: _____

_____

_____

_____

Biological examples of this mechanism: _____

_____

3. (a) Name the excretory organ of vertebrates: _____

(b) Name the selective filtering element of the kidney: _____

(c) The length of this is directly related to the ability of an organism to concentrate urine: _____

(d) Name the hormone involved in controlling urine output: _____

TEST

Topic 15

Control and coordination

Key terms

acetylcholine
action potential
auxin
axon
chemoreceptor
cholinergic
contraception
dendrite
depolarisation
FSH
gibberellin
hyperpolarisation
Le/le gene
LH
mechanoreceptor
menstrual cycle
motor neurone
myelin
nastic response
nerve impulse
neuromuscular junction
neurone
node of Ranvier
oestrogen
Pacinian corpuscle
photoreceptor
progesterone
refractory period
relay neurone
resting potential
saltatory conduction
sarcomere
sensory neurone
sensory receptor
sliding filament model
stimulus (pl. stimuli)
striated muscle
synapse
synaptic integration
thermoreceptor
threshold
transducer

15.1 Control and coordination in mammals

Learning outcomes

Activity number

☐ 1 Compare the nervous and endocrine systems as communication systems for the coordination of responses to internal and external stimuli. — 48

☐ 2 Describe the structure and function of sensory and motor neurones. — 49

☐ 3 Outline the role of sensory receptors as biological transducers, converting different types of stimuli into nerve impulses in sensory neurones. — 50 51

☐ 4 Describe the function of sensory, relay, and motor neurones in a reflex arc. — 52

☐ 5 Describe and explain the generation and transmission of an action potential in a myelinated neurone and its initiation from a resting potential. Include reference to the role of Na^+ and K^+ in impulse transmission. — 53

☐ 6 Explain the importance of the myelin sheath and saltatory conduction in determining the speed of impulses and the refractory period in determining their frequency (and direction). — 53

☐ 7 Describe the structure of a cholinergic synapse (one that releases acetylcholine) and explain how it functions, including reference the role of voltage gated calcium channels in the pre-synaptic membrane, diffusion of acetylcholine, and generation of an action potential in the post synaptic cell. — 54

☐ 8 Describe the roles of synapses in the transmission of nerve impulses in one direction and in neuronal connections and synaptic integration. — 55

☐ 9 Describe the roles of neuromuscular junctions, transverse system (T) tubules, and sarcoplasmic reticulum in stimulating muscle contraction in striated muscle. — 56

☐ 10 Describe the ultrastructure of striated muscle with reference to the structure of the basic contractile unit of muscle, the sarcomere. — 57

☐ 11 Explain the sliding filament model of muscle contraction to include the roles of the proteins troponin and tropomyosin, calcium ions, and ATP. — 58

☐ 12 Explain the roles of LH, FSH, oestrogen, and progesterone in controlling changes in the ovary and uterus during the human menstrual cycle. — 33 59

☐ 13 Outline the biological basis of contraceptive pills containing the hormones oestrogen and/or progesterone. — 60

15.2 Control and coordination in plants

Learning outcomes

Activity number

☐ 14 Recognise that plants, like animals, make coordinated responses to stimuli. — 61 63

☐ 15 Describe and explain the rapid response of the Venus fly trap to stimulation. — 62

☐ 16 Explain the role of auxin in the elongation of stems and roots with reference to its action in stimulating proton pumping to acidify cell walls. — 63 64 65

☐ 17 Describe the role of gibberellin in the germination of wheat or barley. — 64

☐ 18 Explain the of gibberellin in stem elongation including the role of the *Le/le* dominant/recessive alleles. — 67

48 Nervous Regulatory Systems

Key Idea: The nervous system coordinates rapid responses to stimuli through a system of sensory receptors, central nervous system processing, and muscles and glands. In mammals, the **nervous** and **endocrine** (hormonal) systems work together to maintain homeostasis. The nervous system is a signalling network with branches carrying information directly to and from specific target tissues. It is made up largely of cells called neurones (nerve cells) which are specialised to transmit information in the form of electrochemical impulses (action potentials). Impulses can be transmitted over considerable distances and the response is very precise and rapid.

Coordination by the nervous system

The mammalian nervous system consists of the central nervous system (brain and spinal cord), and the nerves and receptors outside it (peripheral nervous system). Sensory input to receptors comes via stimuli. Information about the effect of a response is provided by feedback mechanisms so that the system can be readjusted. The basic organisation of the nervous system can be simplified into a few key components: the sensory receptors, a central nervous system processing point, and the effectors which bring about the response (below).

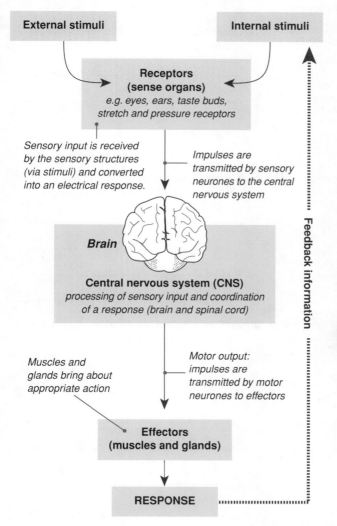

External stimuli

Internal stimuli

Receptors (sense organs)
e.g. eyes, ears, taste buds, stretch and pressure receptors

Sensory input is received by the sensory structures (via stimuli) and converted into an electrical response.

Impulses are transmitted by sensory neurones to the central nervous system

Brain

Central nervous system (CNS)
processing of sensory input and coordination of a response (brain and spinal cord)

Muscles and glands bring about appropriate action

Motor output: impulses are transmitted by motor neurones to effectors

Effectors (muscles and glands)

RESPONSE

Feedback information

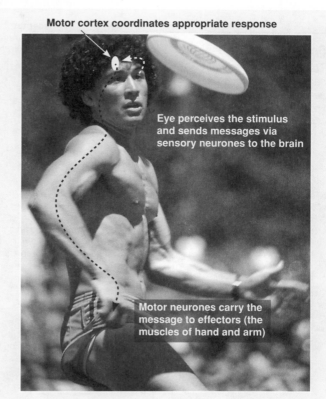

Motor cortex coordinates appropriate response

Eye perceives the stimulus and sends messages via sensory neurones to the brain

Motor neurones carry the message to effectors (the muscles of hand and arm)

In the example above, the approach of the frisbee is perceived by the eye. The motor cortex of the brain integrates the sensory message. Coordination of hand and body orientation is brought about through motor neurones to the muscles.

Comparison of nervous and hormonal control

	Nervous control	Hormonal control
Mode of action	Impulses across synapses	Hormones in the blood
Speed	Very rapid (within a few milliseconds)	Relatively slow (over minutes, hours, or longer)
Duration	Short term and reversible	Longer lasting effects
Target pathway	Specific (through nerves) to specific cells	Hormones broadcast to target cells everywhere
Action	Causes glands to secrete or muscles to contract	Causes changes in metabolic activity

1. Identify the three basic components of a nervous system and describe their role in maintaining homeostasis:

   (a) _____

   (b) _____

   (c) _____

2. Describe three differences between nervous control and endocrine (hormonal) control of body systems:

   (a) _____

   (b) _____

   (c) _____

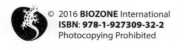

LINK **52** LINK **50** LINK **49** WEB **48** KNOW

49 Neurone Structure

Key Idea: Neurones conduct electrical impulses from sensory receptors along axons to other neurones or to effector cells.
Neurones (nerve cells) transmit nerve impulses. Neurones have a recognisable structure with a cell body (soma) and long processes (dendrites and axons). Most neurones in the peripheral nervous system (nerves outside the brain and spinal cord) are also supported by a fatty insulating sheath of myelin. Information, in the form of electrochemical impulses, is transmitted along neurones from receptors to a coordination centre and then to effectors. The speed of impulse conduction depends primarily on the axon diameter and whether or not the axon is myelinated.

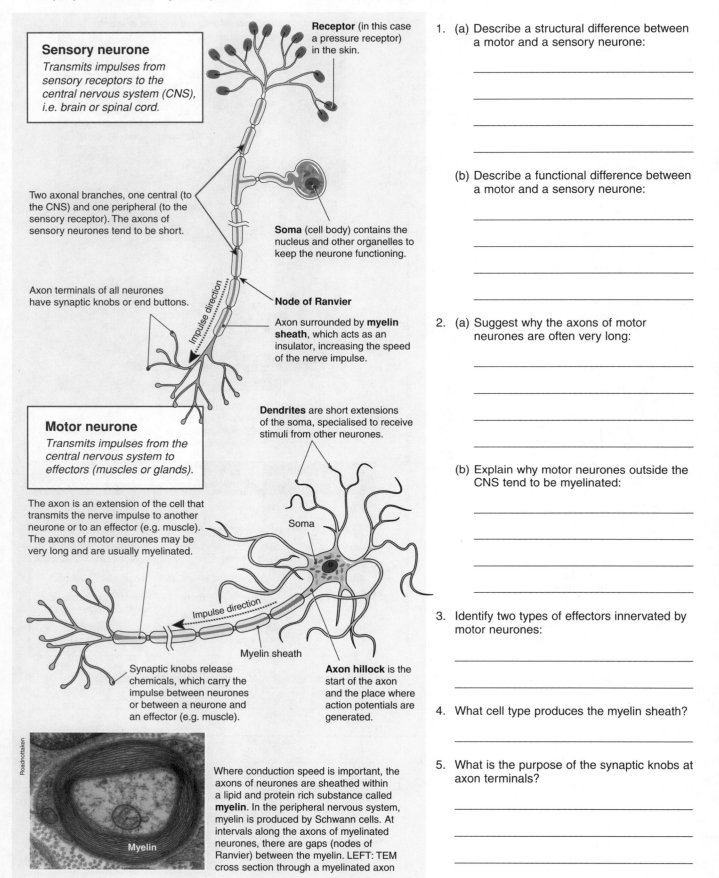

Sensory neurone
Transmits impulses from sensory receptors to the central nervous system (CNS), i.e. brain or spinal cord.

Receptor (in this case a pressure receptor) in the skin.

Two axonal branches, one central (to the CNS) and one peripheral (to the sensory receptor). The axons of sensory neurones tend to be short.

Soma (cell body) contains the nucleus and other organelles to keep the neurone functioning.

Axon terminals of all neurones have synaptic knobs or end buttons.

Impulse direction

Node of Ranvier

Axon surrounded by **myelin sheath**, which acts as an insulator, increasing the speed of the nerve impulse.

Dendrites are short extensions of the soma, specialised to receive stimuli from other neurones.

Motor neurone
Transmits impulses from the central nervous system to effectors (muscles or glands).

The axon is an extension of the cell that transmits the nerve impulse to another neurone or to an effector (e.g. muscle). The axons of motor neurones may be very long and are usually myelinated.

Soma

Impulse direction

Myelin sheath

Synaptic knobs release chemicals, which carry the impulse between neurones or between a neurone and an effector (e.g. muscle).

Axon hillock is the start of the axon and the place where action potentials are generated.

Roadnottaken

Myelin

Where conduction speed is important, the axons of neurones are sheathed within a lipid and protein rich substance called **myelin**. In the peripheral nervous system, myelin is produced by Schwann cells. At intervals along the axons of myelinated neurones, there are gaps (nodes of Ranvier) between the myelin. LEFT: TEM cross section through a myelinated axon

1. (a) Describe a structural difference between a motor and a sensory neurone:

_____

_____

_____

_____

(b) Describe a functional difference between a motor and a sensory neurone:

_____

_____

_____

_____

2. (a) Suggest why the axons of motor neurones are often very long:

_____

_____

_____

_____

(b) Explain why motor neurones outside the CNS tend to be myelinated:

_____

_____

_____

_____

3. Identify two types of effectors innervated by motor neurones:

_____

_____

4. What cell type produces the myelin sheath?

_____

5. What is the purpose of the synaptic knobs at axon terminals?

_____

_____

_____

© 2016 **BIOZONE** International
ISBN: 978-1-927309-32-2
Photocopying Prohibited

50 The Basis of Sensory Reception

Key Idea: Sensory receptors act as transducers, detecting stimuli and converting them to an electrochemical signal.

Sensory receptors are specialised to detect stimuli and respond by producing an electrical (or chemical) discharge. In this way they act as **biological transducers**, converting the energy from a stimulus into an electrochemical signal. They can do this because the stimulus opens (or closes) ion channels and leads to localised changes in membrane potential called **receptor potentials**. Receptor potentials are graded and not self-propagating, but sense cells can amplify them, generating action potentials directly or inducing the release of a neurotransmitter. Whether or not the sensory cell itself fires action potentials, ultimately the stimulus is transduced into action potentials whose frequency is dependent on stimulus strength. The simplest sensory receptors consist of a single sensory neurone (e.g. nerve endings). More complex sense cells form synapses with their sensory neurones (e.g. taste buds). Sensory receptors are classified according to the stimuli to which they respond (e.g. photoreceptors respond to light).

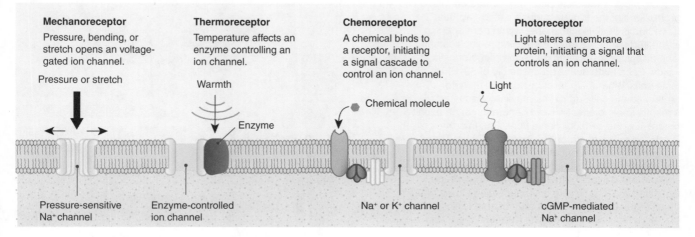

Mechanoreceptor
Pressure, bending, or stretch opens an voltage-gated ion channel.

Pressure or stretch

Pressure-sensitive Na⁺ channel

Thermoreceptor
Temperature affects an enzyme controlling an ion channel.

Warmth

Enzyme

Enzyme-controlled ion channel

Chemoreceptor
A chemical binds to a receptor, initiating a signal cascade to control an ion channel.

Chemical molecule

Na⁺ or K⁺ channel

Photoreceptor
Light alters a membrane protein, initiating a signal that controls an ion channel.

Light

cGMP-mediated Na⁺ channel

Signal transduction

Sensory cells convert one type of stimulus energy (e.g. pressure) into an electrical signal by altering the flow of ions across the plasma membrane and generating receptor potentials. In many cases (as in the Pacinian corpuscle), this leads directly to action potentials which are generated in the voltage-gated region of the sensory cell.

In some receptor cells, the receptor potential leads to neurotransmitter release, which then directly or indirectly leads to action potentials in a post-synaptic cell.

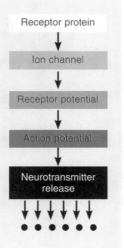

Receptor protein

↓

Ion channel

↓

Receptor potential

↓

Action potential

↓

Neurotransmitter release

↓ ↓ ↓ ↓ ↓
● ● ● ● ● ●

The Pacinian corpuscle

Pacinian corpuscles are pressure receptors in deep tissues of the body. They are relatively large but structurally simple, consisting of a sensory nerve ending (dendrite) surrounded by a capsule of connective tissue layers. Pressure deforms the capsule, stretching the nerve ending and leading to a localised depolarisation called a **receptor potential**. Receptor potentials are graded and do not spread far, although they may sum together and increase in amplitude.

The sense cell converts the receptor potentials to action potentials at the start of the axon (where there are voltage-gated channels). The action potential is then propagated along the axon.

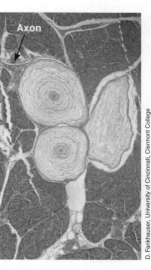

Axon

D. Fankhauser, University of Cincinnati, Clermont College

1. Explain why sensory receptors are termed 'biological transducers': _____

_____

_____

2. Identify one feature that all sensory receptors have in common: _____

_____

3. Explain how a stimulus received by a sensory receptor is converted into an electrical response: _____

_____

_____

4. Describe the properties of receptor potentials: _____

_____

_____

LINK
51

LINK
49

WEB
50

KNOW

51 A Sensory Receptor

Key Idea: Chemosensory receptors detect chemicals in the air or in fluid and are responsible for the sense of smell and taste. The sense organs of taste are the taste buds.

Chemosensory receptors are responsible for our sense of smell (**olfaction**) and taste (**gustation**). The receptors for smell and taste both respond to chemicals, either carried in the air (smell) or dissolved in a fluid (taste). In humans and other mammals, these are located in the nose and tongue respectively. Each receptor type is basically similar: they are collections of receptor cells equipped with chemosensory microvilli or cilia. When chemicals stimulate their membranes, the cells respond by producing nerve impulses that are transmitted to the olfactory and gustatory regions of the cerebral cortex of the brain for interpretation.

Taste

The organs of taste are the **taste buds** of the tongue. Most of the taste buds are located on raised protrusions of the tongue surface called **papillae**. Each bud is flask-like in shape, with a pore opening to the surface of the tongue enabling molecules and ions dissolved in saliva to reach the receptor cells inside. Each taste bud is an assembly of 50-150 taste cells. When a chemical binds to a receptor protein on the cell surface membrane of a taste cell, it results in depolarisation and generation of an action potential in the sensory nerve fibre. This information is relayed to the gustatory region of the brain. There are five basic taste sensations. **Salty** and **sour** operate through ion channels, whereas **sweet**, **bitter**, and **umami** (savoury) operate through membrane signalling proteins. These taste sensations are found on all areas of the tongue although some regions are more sensitive than others. Note that taste also relies heavily on smell because odours from food also stimulate olfactory receptors.

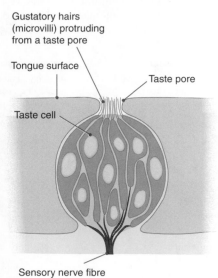

Gustatory hairs (microvilli) protruding from a taste pore

Tongue surface

Taste pore

Taste cell

Taste cell

Sensory nerve fibre

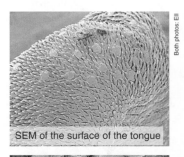

SEM of the surface of the tongue

SEM of one of the papillae

Your senses can be fooled

Taste is not experienced in isolation. In fact, by itself, taste only provides rather crude information about a particular food or drink. A large amount of information comes for the olfactory receptors in the nose. Even visual input has a large impact on how we taste food.

A 2001 study of 54 wine tasters found that when the tasters were presented with a white wine artificially coloured red with an odourless and tasteless food dye, they identified its taste as that of a red wine. The information from the visual receptors over-rode the input from the taste receptors. This may be explained by the fact primates developed colour vision as an ability to identify good foods to eat (e.g. ripe fruit). Another study in 2015 found that taste is affected by noise and air pressure, such as when in a plane, which may explain why airline food always tastes strange.

Airline food not so bad?

1. Describe the basic mechanism by which chemical sense operates: _____

   _____

   _____

   _____

2. Explain why the taste of food changes when you have a blocked nose: _____

   _____

   _____

3. Describe the evidence that smell and sight (and even hearing) play a big part in how something tastes:

   _____

   _____

   _____

   _____

LINK
50

© 2016 **BIOZONE** International
ISBN: 978-1-927309-32-2
Photocopying Prohibited

52 Reflexes

Key Idea: A reflex is an automatic response to a stimulus and involves only a few neurones and a central processing point. A **reflex** is an automatic response to a stimulus. Reflexes require no conscious thought and so act quickly to protect the body from harmful stimuli. Reflexes are controlled by a neural pathway called a reflex arc. A reflex arc involves a small number of neurones and a central nervous system processing point, which is usually the spinal cord, but sometimes the brain stem. Reflexes are classified according to the number of CNS synapses involved. **Monosynaptic reflexes** involve only one CNS synapse (e.g. knee jerk reflex), whereas **polysynaptic reflexes** involve two or more (e.g. pain withdrawal reflex). Both are spinal reflexes. The pupil reflex and the corneal (blink) reflex are cranial reflexes.

Pain withdrawal: a polysynaptic reflex arc

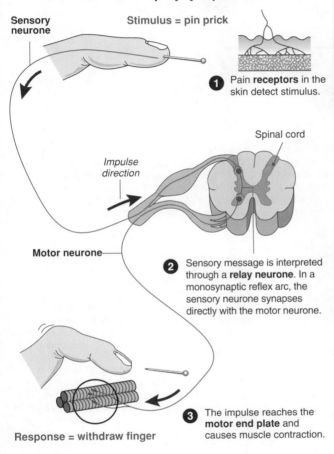

Sensory neurone

Stimulus = pin prick

1 Pain **receptors** in the skin detect stimulus.

Impulse direction

Spinal cord

Motor neurone

2 Sensory message is interpreted through a **relay neurone**. In a monosynaptic reflex arc, the sensory neurone synapses directly with the motor neurone.

3 The impulse reaches the **motor end plate** and causes muscle contraction.

Response = withdraw finger

The patellar (knee jerk) reflex is a simple deep tendon reflex that is used to test the function of the femoral nerve and spinal cord segments L2-L4. It helps to maintain posture and balance when walking.

The corneal (blink) reflex is a rapid involuntary blinking of both eyelids occurring when the cornea is stimulated, e.g. by touching. It is mediated by the brainstem and can be used to evaluate coma.

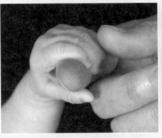

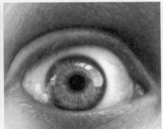

Normal newborns exhibit a number of primitive reflexes in response to particular stimuli. These include the grasp reflex (above) and the startle reflex in which a sudden noise will cause the infant to extend its arms, legs, and head, and cry.

The pupillary light reflex refers to the rapid expansion or contraction of the pupils in response to the intensity of light falling on the retina. It is a polysynaptic cranial reflex and can be used to test for brain death.

1. Identify the function of each of the components of a polysynaptic reflex arc:

   (a) Sensory neurone: _____

   (b) Relay neurone: _____

   (c) Motor neurone: _____

2. Giving an example, explain why higher reasoning or conscious thought are not desirable features of reflex behaviours:

   _____

   _____

   _____

3. Describe the survival value of the following reflexes:

   (a) Knee-jerk reflex: _____

   (b) Corneal blink reflex: _____

   (c) Grasp reflex: _____

   (d) Pupillary light reflex: _____

LINK 49 WEB 52 **KNOW**

53 The Nerve Impulse

Key Idea: A nerve impulse involves the movement of an action potential along a neurone as a series of electrical depolarisation events in response to a stimulus.

The plasma membranes of cells, including neurones, contain **sodium-potassium ion pumps** which actively pump sodium ions (Na^+) out of the cell and potassium ions (K^+) into the cell. The action of these ion pumps in neurones creates a separation of charge (a potential difference or voltage) either side of the membrane and makes the cells **electrically**

excitable. It is this property that enables neurones to transmit electrical impulses. The **resting state** of a neurone, with a net negative charge inside, is maintained by the sodium-potassium pumps, which actively move two K^+ into the neurone for every three Na^+ moved out (below left). When a nerve is stimulated, a brief increase in membrane permeability to Na^+ temporarily reverses the membrane polarity (a **depolarisation**). After the nerve impulse passes, the sodium-potassium pump restores the resting potential.

The resting neurone

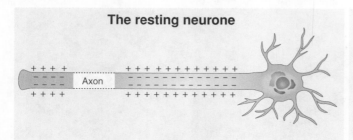

When a neurone is not transmitting an impulse, the inside of the cell is negatively charged relative to the outside and the cell is said to be electrically polarised. The potential difference (voltage) across the membrane is called the **resting potential**. For most nerve cells this is about -70 mV. Nerve transmission is possible because this membrane potential exists.

The nerve impulse

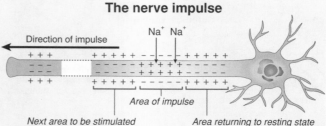

When a neurone is stimulated, the distribution of charges on each side of the membrane briefly reverses. This process of **depolarisation** causes a burst of electrical activity to pass along the axon of the neurone as an **action potential**. As the charge reversal reaches one region, local currents depolarise the next region and the impulse spreads along the axon.

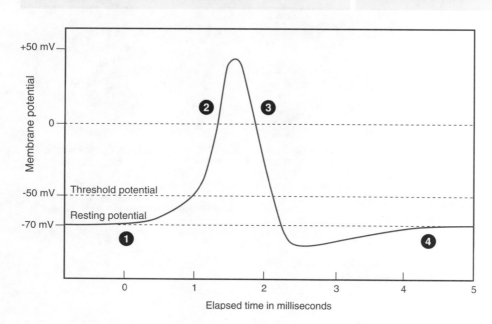

The depolarisation in an axon can be shown as a change in membrane potential (in millivolts). A stimulus must be strong enough to reach the **threshold potential** before an action potential is generated. This is the voltage at which the depolarisation of the membrane becomes unstoppable.

The action potential is **all or nothing** in its generation and because of this, impulses (once generated) always reach threshold and move along the axon without attenuation. The resting potential is restored by the movement of potassium ions (K^+) out of the cell. During this **refractory period**, the nerve cannot respond, so nerve impulses are discrete.

Voltage-gated ion channels and the course of an action potential

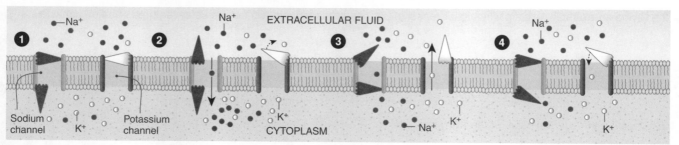

Resting state:

Voltage activated Na^+ and K^+ channels are closed.

Depolarisation:

Voltage activated Na^+ channels open and there is a rapid influx of Na^+ ions. The interior of the neurone becomes positive relative to the outside.

Repolarisation:

Voltage activated Na^+ channels close and the K^+ channels open; K^+ moves out of the cell, restoring the negative charge to the cell interior.

Returning to resting state:

Voltage activated Na^+ and K^+ channels close to return the neurone to the resting state.

© 2016 **BIOZONE** International
ISBN: 978-1-927309-32-2
Photocopying Prohibited

Axon myelination is a feature of vertebrate nervous systems and it enables them to achieve very rapid speeds of nerve conduction. Myelinated neurones conduct impulses by **saltatory conduction**, a term that describes how the impulse jumps along the fibre. In a myelinated neurone, action potentials are generated only at the nodes, which is where the voltage gated channels occur. The axon is insulated so the action potential at one node is sufficient to trigger an action potential in the next node and the impulse jumps along the fibre. This differs from impulse transmission in a non-myelinated neurone in which voltage-gated channels occur along the entire length of the axon.

As well as increasing the speed of conduction, the myelin sheath reduces energy expenditure because the area over which depolarisation occurs is less (and therefore the number of sodium and potassium ions that need to be pumped to restore the resting potential is fewer).

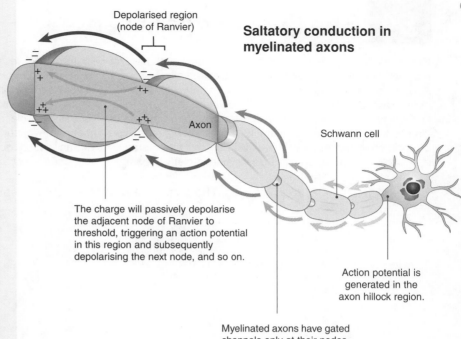

Saltatory conduction in myelinated axons

Depolarised region (node of Ranvier)

Axon

Schwann cell

The charge will passively depolarise the adjacent node of Ranvier to threshold, triggering an action potential in this region and subsequently depolarising the next node, and so on.

Action potential is generated in the axon hillock region.

Myelinated axons have gated channels only at their nodes.

1. In your own words, define what an **action potential** is: _____

   _____

2. (a) Identify the defining **functional feature** of neurones: _____

   _____

   (b) How does this differ from the supporting tissue (e.g. Schwann cells) of the nervous system? _____

   _____

3. Describe the movement of voltage-gated channels and ions associated with:

   (a) Depolarisation of the neurone: _____

   (b) Repolarisation of the neurone: _____

4. Summarise the sequence of events in a neurone when it receives a stimulus sufficient to reach threshold: _____

   _____

   _____

   _____

   _____

5. How is the resting potential restored in a neurone after an action potential has passed? _____

   _____

6. (a) Explain how an action potential travels in a **myelinated neuron**: _____

   _____

   (b) How does this differ from its travel in a **non-myelinated neuron**? _____

   _____

7. (a) Explain how the **refractory period** influences the direction in which an impulse will travel: _____

   _____

   _____

   (b) On the diagram of the action potential opposite, draw an arrow indicating direction of impulse travel.

54 The Cholinergic Synapse

Key Idea: Synapses are junctions between neurones or between neurones and effector (e.g. muscle) cells.

Action potentials are transmitted across junctions called **synapses**. Synapses can occur between two neurones, or between a neurone and an effector cell (e.g. muscle or gland). Chemical synapses are the most widespread type of synapse in nervous systems. In these, the axon terminal is a swollen knob, and a gap (the synaptic cleft) separates

it from the receiving cell. The synaptic knobs are filled with tiny packets of a chemical called **neurotransmitter**. The neurotransmitter diffuses across the gap, where it interacts with the receiving (post-synaptic) membrane and causes an electrical response. In the example below, the neurotransmitter causes a depolarisation and the generation of an action potential. Some neurotransmitters have the opposite effect and cause inhibition (e.g. slowing heart rate).

The structure of a chemical synapse

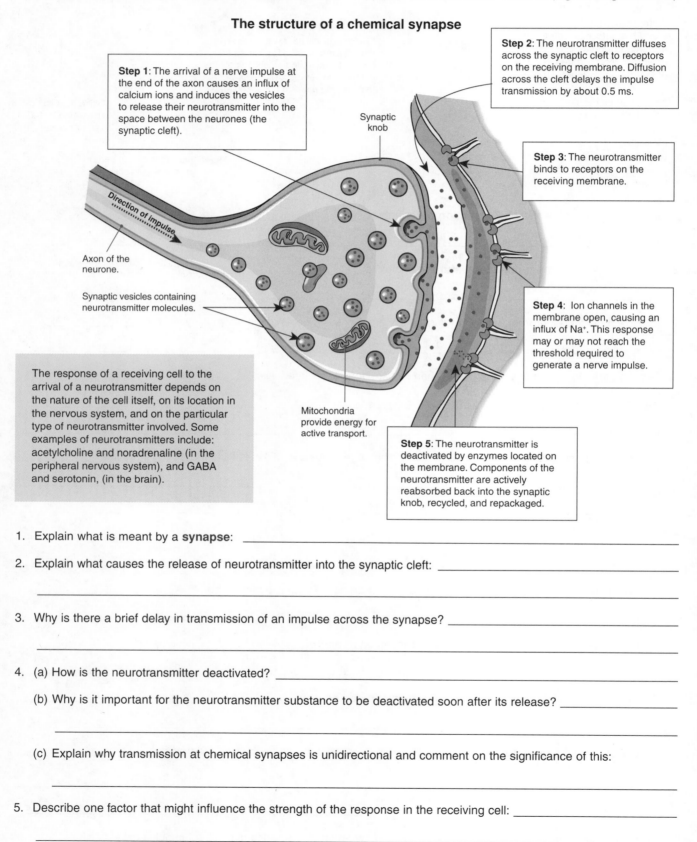

Step 1: The arrival of a nerve impulse at the end of the axon causes an influx of calcium ions and induces the vesicles to release their neurotransmitter into the space between the neurones (the synaptic cleft).

Step 2: The neurotransmitter diffuses across the synaptic cleft to receptors on the receiving membrane. Diffusion across the cleft delays the impulse transmission by about 0.5 ms.

Step 3: The neurotransmitter binds to receptors on the receiving membrane.

Step 4: Ion channels in the membrane open, causing an influx of Na^+. This response may or may not reach the threshold required to generate a nerve impulse.

Step 5: The neurotransmitter is deactivated by enzymes located on the membrane. Components of the neurotransmitter are actively reabsorbed back into the synaptic knob, recycled, and repackaged.

Synaptic knob

Direction of impulse

Axon of the neurone.

Synaptic vesicles containing neurotransmitter molecules.

Mitochondria provide energy for active transport.

The response of a receiving cell to the arrival of a neurotransmitter depends on the nature of the cell itself, on its location in the nervous system, and on the particular type of neurotransmitter involved. Some examples of neurotransmitters include: acetylcholine and noradrenaline (in the peripheral nervous system), and GABA and serotonin, (in the brain).

1. Explain what is meant by a **synapse**: _____

2. Explain what causes the release of neurotransmitter into the synaptic cleft: _____

_____

3. Why is there a brief delay in transmission of an impulse across the synapse? _____

_____

4. (a) How is the neurotransmitter deactivated? _____

   (b) Why is it important for the neurotransmitter substance to be deactivated soon after its release? _____

   _____

   (c) Explain why transmission at chemical synapses is unidirectional and comment on the significance of this:

   _____

5. Describe one factor that might influence the strength of the response in the receiving cell: _____

_____

© 2016 **BIOZONE** International
ISBN: 978-1-927309-32-2
Photocopying Prohibited

55 Integration at Synapses

Key Idea: Synapses play a pivotal role in the ability of the nervous system to respond appropriately to stimulation and to adapt to change by integrating all inputs.

The nature of synaptic transmission in the nervous system allows the **integration** (interpretation and coordination) of inputs from many sources. These inputs can be excitatory (causing depolarisation) or inhibitory (making an action potential less likely). It is the sum of all excitatory and inhibitory inputs that leads to the final response in a post-synaptic cell. Synaptic integration is behind all the various responses we have to stimuli. It is also the most probable mechanism by which learning and memory are achieved.

Summation at synapses

Graded postsynaptic responses (potentials) may sum together to generate an action potential.

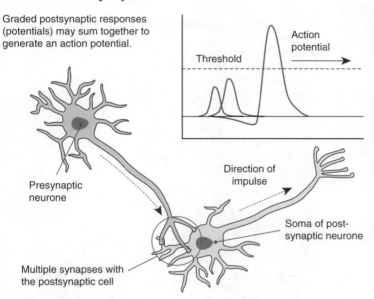

Threshold

Action potential

Direction of impulse

Presynaptic neurone

Soma of post-synaptic neurone

Multiple synapses with the postsynaptic cell

Nerve transmission across chemical synapses has several advantages, despite the delay caused by neurotransmitter diffusion. Chemical synapses transmit impulses in one direction to a precise location and, because they rely on a limited supply of neurotransmitter, they are subject to fatigue (inability to respond to repeated stimulation). This protects the system against overstimulation.

Synapses also act as centres for the **integration** of inputs from many sources. The response of a postsynaptic cell is often not strong enough on its own to generate an action potential. However, because the strength of the response is related to the amount of neurotransmitter released, subthreshold responses can sum together to produce a response in the post-synaptic cell. This additive effect is termed **summation**. Summation can be **temporal** or **spatial** (right).

❶ Temporal summation

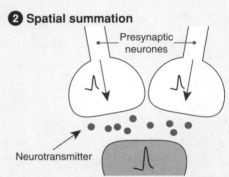

Presynaptic neurone

Action potential

Postsynaptic cell

Several impulses may arrive at the synapse in quick succession from a single axon. The individual responses are so close in time that they sum to reach threshold and produce an action potential in the postsynaptic neurone.

❷ Spatial summation

Presynaptic neurones

Neurotransmitter

Individual impulses from spatially separated axon terminals may arrive simultaneously at different regions of the same postsynaptic neurone. The responses from the different places sum to produce an action potential.

---

1. Explain the purpose of nervous system integration: _____

_____

_____

2. Describe two advantages of chemical synapses:

    (a) _____

    _____

    (b) _____

    _____

3. (a) Explain what is meant by **summation**: _____

    _____

    _____

    (b) In simple terms, distinguish between temporal and spatial summation: _____

    _____

LINK 56   LINK 54   **KNOW**

56 Neuromuscular Junction

Key Idea: The neuromuscular junction is the specialised synapse between a motor neurone and a muscle fibre. Arrival of an action potential at the neuromuscular junction results in contraction of the muscle fibre.

For a muscle fibre to contract, it must receive a threshold stimulus in the form of an action potential. Action potentials are carried by motor neurones from the central nervous system to the muscle fibres they supply. A motor neurone communicates with a muscle fibre across a specialised synapse called the neuromuscular junction. The arrival of an action potential at the neuromuscular junction results in release of the neurotransmitter acetylcholine and contraction of the fibre. The response of a single muscle fibre is **all-or-none**, meaning it contracts maximally or not at all.

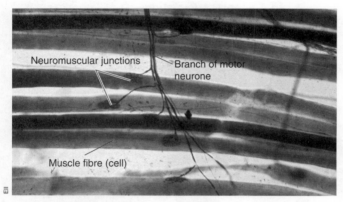

Axon terminals of a motor neurone supplying a muscle. Axon branches end on the sarcolemma (plasma membrane) of a muscle fibre at regions called neuromuscular junctions. Each fibre receives a branch of an axon, but one axon may supply many muscle fibres.

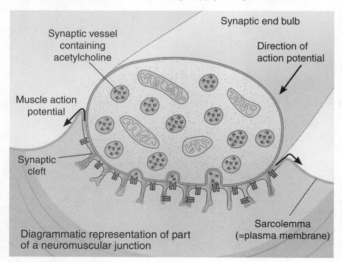

Diagrammatic representation of part of a neuromuscular junction

When an action potential arrives at the neuromuscular junction, it causes release of acetylcholine, which diffuses across the synaptic cleft to stimulate an action potential in the sarcolemma. The action potential is propagated throughout the muscle fibre via the system of T tubules and causes a release of stored calcium ions from the sarcoplasmic reticulum (endoplasmic reticulum of the muscle fibre).

Muscles have graded responses

Muscle fibres respond to an action potential by contracting maximally or not all. This response is called the **all or none law** of muscle contraction. However, skeletal muscles as a whole can produce contractions of varying force. This is achieved by changing the frequency of stimulation (more rapid arrival of action potentials) and by changing the number of fibres active at any one time. A stronger muscle contraction is produced when a large number of muscle fibres are recruited (below left), whereas less strenuous movements, such as picking up a pen, require fewer active fibres (below right).

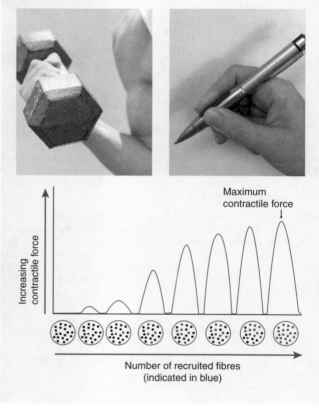

1. (a) Describe the structure of the neuromuscular junction: _____

_____

   (b) What neurotransmitter transmits the signal to the muscle fibre? _____

   (c) What events happen as a result of this? _____

_____

2. (a) What is meant by the all-or-none response of a muscle fibre? _____

_____

   (b) How does a muscle as a whole can produce contractions of varying force? _____

_____

© 2016 **BIOZONE** International
ISBN: 978-1-927309-32-2
Photocopying Prohibited

57 Skeletal Muscle Structure and Function

Key Idea: Skeletal muscle is organised into bundles of muscle cells or fibres. The muscle fibres are made up of repeating contractile units called sarcomeres.

Skeletal muscle is organised into bundles of muscle cells or fibres. Each **fibre** is a single cell with many nuclei and each fibre is itself a bundle of smaller **myofibrils** arranged lengthwise. Each myofibril is in turn composed of two kinds of **myofilaments** (thick and thin), which overlap to form light and dark bands. It is the orderly alternation of these light and dark bands which gives skeletal muscle its striated or striped appearance. The **sarcomere**, bounded by dark Z lines, forms one complete contractile unit.

When viewed under a microscope (above), skeletal muscle has a banded appearance. The cells are large with many nuclei (multinucleate).

Skeletal muscles require a conscious action to control them. Physical actions, such as running, writing, and speaking require the contraction of skeletal muscles to occur.

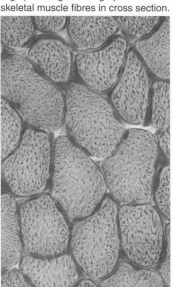

Structure of muscle

Skeletal muscle enclosed in connective tissue

Bundles of muscle fibres (**fascicles**)

Single muscle fibre

The relationship between muscle, fascicles, and muscle fibres (cells)

Structure of a muscle fibre (cell)

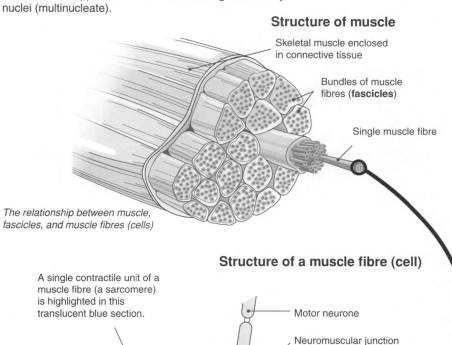

A single contractile unit of a muscle fibre (a sarcomere) is highlighted in this translucent blue section.

Motor neurone

Neuromuscular junction (a chemical synapse between a motor neurone and a muscle fibre).

High power light micrograph of skeletal muscle fibres in cross section.

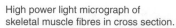

Nucleus

T tubules

The **sarcoplasmic reticulum** is a specialised type of smooth endoplasmic reticulum. It is associated with the T tubules and forms a network containing a store of calcium ions.

The **sarcolemma** is the plasma membrane of the muscle cell and encloses the sarcoplasm (cytoplasm).

A myofibril (blue outline) with myofilaments in cross section.

LINK
58
WEB
57
KNOW

The banding pattern of myofibrils

Within a myofibril, the thin filaments, held together by the **Z lines**, project in both directions. The arrival of an action potential sets in motion a series of events that cause the thick and thin filaments to slide past each other. This is called **contraction** and it results in shortening of the muscle fibre and is accompanied by a visible change in the appearance of the myofibril: the I band and the sarcomere shorten and H zone shortens or disappears (below).

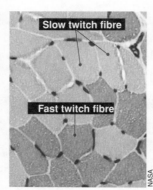

Relaxed

Z line   H zone

I band   A band   I band   A band   I band

Maximally contracted

Longitudinal section of a sarcomere

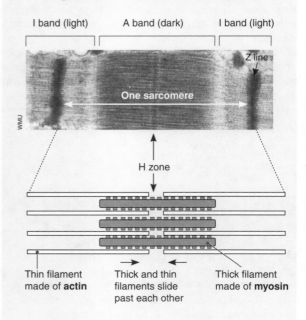

I band (light)   A band (dark)   I band (light)

Z line

One sarcomere

WMU

H zone

Thin filament made of **actin**

Thick and thin filaments slide past each other

Thick filament made of **myosin**

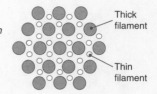

Cross section through a region of overlap between thick and thin filaments.

Thick filament

Thin filament

The photograph of a sarcomere (above) shows the banding pattern arising as a result of the highly organised arrangement of thin and thick filaments. It is represented schematically in longitudinal section and cross section.

Fast vs slow twitch muscle

There are two basic types of muscle fibres: **slow twitch** (type I) and **fast twitch** (type II) fibres. Slow twitch fibres contract slowly and produce ATP slowly over a long period of time. This allows them to keep working for a long time. In contrast, fast twitch muscles contract quickly, but also fatigue rapidly because they only produce ATP for a short period of time. Most muscles contain an even mixture of fibre types.

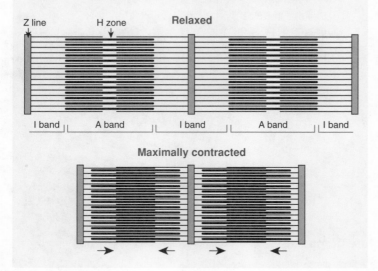

Slow twitch fibre

Fast twitch fibre

NASA

1. (a) Explain the cause of the banding pattern visible in striated muscle: _____

_____

_____

   (b) Explain the change in appearance of a myofibril during contraction with reference to the following:

   The I band: _____

   The H zone: _____

   The sarcomere: _____

2. Study the electron micrograph of the sarcomere (top, right).

   (a) Is it in a contracted or relaxed state (use the diagram, top left to help you decide): _____

   (b) Explain your answer: _____

   _____

   _____

3. What type of fibre (fast or slow) would be in use during a sprint race? Explain your answer: _____

_____

_____

58 The Sliding Filament Theory

Key Idea: The sliding filament theory describes how muscle contraction occurs when the thick and thin myofibrils of a muscle fibre slide past one another. Calcium ions and ATP are required for muscle contraction.

The structure and arrangement of the thick and thin filaments in a muscle fibre make it possible for them to slide past each other and cause shortening (contraction) of the muscle. The ends of the thick myosin filaments have cross bridges that can link to adjacent thin actin filaments. When the cross bridges of the thick filaments connect to the thin filaments, a shape change moves one filament past the other. Two things are necessary for cross bridge formation: calcium ions, which are released from the sarcoplasmic reticulum when the muscle receives an action potential, and ATP, which is present in the muscle fibre and is hydrolysed by ATPase enzymes on the myosin. When cross bridges attach and detach in sarcomeres throughout the muscle cell, the cell shortens.

The sliding filament theory

Muscle contraction requires calcium ions (Ca^{2+}) and energy (in the form of ATP) in order for the thick and thin filaments to slide past each other. The steps are:

1. The binding sites on the **actin** molecule (to which myosin 'heads' will locate) are blocked by a complex of two protein molecules (**tropomyosin** and **troponin**).

2. Prior to muscle contraction, ATP binds to the heads of the myosin molecules, priming them in an erect high energy state. Arrival of an action potential is transmitted along the T tubules and causes a release of Ca^{2+} from the sarcoplasmic reticulum into the sarcoplasm. The Ca^{2+} binds to the troponin and causes the blocking complex to move so that the myosin binding sites on the actin filament become exposed.

3. The heads of the cross-bridging myosin molecules attach to the binding sites on the actin filament. Release of energy from the hydrolysis of ATP accompanies the cross bridge formation.

4. The energy released from ATP hydrolysis causes a change in shape of the myosin **cross bridge**, resulting in a bending action (*the power stroke*). This causes the actin filaments to slide past the myosin filaments towards the centre of the sarcomere.

5. (Not illustrated). Fresh ATP attaches to the myosin molecules, releasing them from the binding sites and repriming them for a repeat movement. They become attached further along the actin chain as long as ATP and Ca^{2+} are available.

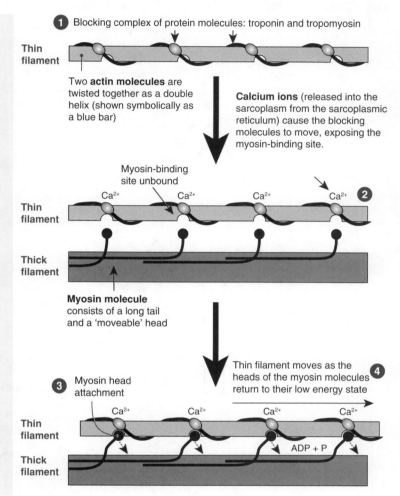

1 Blocking complex of protein molecules: troponin and tropomyosin

Thin filament

Two **actin molecules** are twisted together as a double helix (shown symbolically as a blue bar)

Calcium ions (released into the sarcoplasm from the sarcoplasmic reticulum) cause the blocking molecules to move, exposing the myosin-binding site.

Myosin-binding site unbound

Ca^{2+} Ca^{2+} Ca^{2+} Ca^{2+} **2**

Thin filament

Thick filament

Myosin molecule consists of a long tail and a 'moveable' head

3 Myosin head attachment

Thin filament moves as the heads of the myosin molecules return to their low energy state   **4**

Ca^{2+} Ca^{2+} Ca^{2+} Ca^{2+}

Thin filament

Thick filament

ADP + P

---

1. Match the following chemicals with their functional role in muscle movement (draw a line between matching pairs):

   (a) Myosin   • Bind to the actin molecule in a way that prevents myosin head from forming a cross bridge

   (b) Actin   • Supplies energy for the flexing of the myosin 'head' (power stroke)

   (c) Calcium ions   • Has a moveable head that provides a power stroke when activated

   (d) Troponin-tropomyosin   • Two protein molecules twisted in a helix shape that form the thin filament of a myofibril

   (e) ATP   • Bind to the blocking molecules, causing them to move and expose the myosin binding site

2. (a) Identify the two things necessary for cross bridge formation: _____

   (b) Explain where each of these comes from: _____

   _____

   _____

3. Why are there abundant mitochondria in a muscle fibre?_____

   _____

59 Hormonal Control of the Menstrual Cycle

Key Idea: Hormones from the hypothalamus, anterior pituitary, and ovary regulate the menstrual cycle.

The female menstrual cycle is regulated by the interplay of several reproductive hormones. The main control centres for this regulation are the **hypothalamus** and the **anterior pituitary gland**. The hypothalamus secretes GnRH (gonadotropin releasing hormone), a hormone essential for gonad function in males and females. GnRH is transported in blood vessels to the anterior pituitary where it causes the release of follicle stimulating hormone (FSH) and luteinising hormone (LH). It is these two hormones that induce the cyclical changes in the ovary and uterus. Regulation of blood hormone levels during the menstrual cycle is achieved through **negative feedback**. The exception to this is the mid cycle surge in LH, which is induced by the rapid increase in oestrogen secreted by the developing follicle.

Hormones work together to control the menstrual cycle

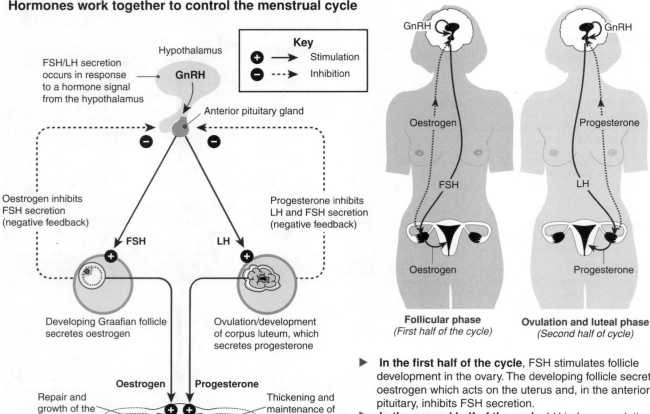

Key
+ → Stimulation
− ⇢ Inhibition

FSH/LH secretion occurs in response to a hormone signal from the hypothalamus

Hypothalamus
GnRH
Anterior pituitary gland

Oestrogen inhibits FSH secretion (negative feedback)

Progesterone inhibits LH and FSH secretion (negative feedback)

FSH
LH

Developing Graafian follicle secretes oestrogen

Ovulation/development of corpus luteum, which secretes progesterone

Oestrogen   **Progesterone**

Repair and growth of the uterine lining

Thickening and maintenance of the uterine lining

Follicular phase
(First half of the cycle)

Ovulation and luteal phase
(Second half of cycle)

▶ **In the first half of the cycle**, FSH stimulates follicle development in the ovary. The developing follicle secretes oestrogen which acts on the uterus and, in the anterior pituitary, inhibits FSH secretion.

▶ **In the second half of the cycle**, LH induces ovulation and development of the corpus luteum. The corpus luteum secretes progesterone which acts on the uterus and also inhibits further secretion of LH (and also FSH).

1. Using the information above and on the previous page, complete the table below summarising the role of hormones in the control of the menstrual cycle. To help you, some of the table has been completed:

Hormone	Site of secretion	Main effects and site of action during the menstrual cycle
GnRH		
		Stimulates the growth of ovarian follicles
LH		
		At high levels, stimulates LH surge. Promotes growth and repair of the uterine lining.
Progesterone		

2. Briefly explain the role of negative feedback in the control of hormone levels in the menstrual cycle:

_____

_____

_____

Events in the menstrual cycle

In humans, fertilisation of the ovum is most likely to occur during a relatively restricted period around the time of **ovulation**. The uterine lining thickens in preparation for pregnancy but is shed as a bloody discharge through the vagina if fertilisation does not occur. This event, called **menstruation**, characterises the human reproductive or **menstrual cycle**. The menstrual cycle starts from the first day of bleeding and lasts for about 28 days. It involves a predictable series of changes that occur in response to hormones from the pituitary and ovaries. The cycle is divided into three phases (follicular, ovulatory, and luteal) defined by the events in each phase.

Luteinising hormone (LH) and follicle stimulating hormone (FSH) from the anterior pituitary: FSH stimulates the development of the ovarian follicles resulting in the release of oestrogen. Oestrogen levels peak, stimulating a surge in LH and triggering ovulation.

Hormone levels: Usually only one of developing follicles (the Graafian follicle) becomes dominant. In the first half of the cycle, oestrogen is secreted by the Graafian follicle. The Graafian follicle develops into the corpus luteum (below right) which secretes large amounts of progesterone (and smaller amounts of oestrogen).

The corpus luteum: Around day 14, the Graafian follicle ruptures to release the egg (ovulation). LH causes the ruptured follicle to develop into a corpus luteum (yellow body). The corpus luteum secretes progesterone which promotes full development of the uterine lining, maintains the embryo in the first 12 weeks of pregnancy, and inhibits the development of more follicles.

Menstruation: If fertilisation does not occur, the corpus luteum breaks down. Progesterone secretion drops, causing the uterine lining to be shed (menstruation). If fertilisation occurs, high progesterone levels maintain the thickened uterine lining. The placenta develops and nourishes the embryo completely by 12 weeks.

Pituitary LH and FSH

FSH stimulates follicle development

LH surge in response to peak in oestrogen triggers ovulation

...FSH...

LH

2 4 6 8 10 12 14 16 18 20 22 24 26 28

Reproductive hormones from the ovary

Progesterone maintains the thickened uterine lining in preparation for the implantation of a fertilised egg

Oestrogen promotes repair and growth of the uterine lining

2 4 6 8 10 12 14 16 18 20 22 24 26 28

Ovarian cycle

Follicle surrounding the egg grows in response to FSH

Ovulation; the follicle ruptures to release the egg The egg may be fertilised.

Corpus luteum degenerates, progesterone secretion stops, and the uterine lining breaks down

Corpus luteum

2 4 6 8 10 12 14 16 18 20 22 24 26 28

Menstrual cycle

The uterine lining breaks down because fertilisation did not occur

| Menstruation | Growth of uterine lining | | Lining vascular and glandular |

Day of the cycle:

2 4 6 8 10 12 14 16 18 20 22 24 26 28

Follicular phase
Menstruation, follicle development

Ovulatory phase
Ovulation

Luteal phase
Formation of corpus luteum

3. Identify the hormone responsible for:

(a) Follicle growth: _____   (b) Ovulation: _____

4. Each month, several ovarian follicles begin development, but only one (the Graafian follicle) develops fully:

(a) What hormone is secreted by the developing follicle? _____

(b) What is the role of this hormone during the follicular phase? _____

(c) What happens to the follicles that do not continue developing? _____

5. (a) What is the principal hormone secreted by the corpus luteum? _____

(b) What is the purpose of this hormone? _____

6. What is the hormonal trigger for menstruation? _____

60 Control of Reproduction

Key Idea: The hormones controlling the menstrual cycle can be manipulated to control fertility.

Contraception refers to the use of methods or devices that prevent conception (fertilisation of an egg by a sperm). There are many contraceptive methods available including physical barriers (such as condoms) that prevent egg and sperm ever meeting. The most effective methods (excluding sterilisation) involve chemical interference in the normal female cycle so that egg production is inhibited. This is done by way of **oral contraceptives** (below, left) or hormonal implants. If taken properly, oral contraceptives are almost 100% effective at preventing pregnancy. The placement of their action in the normal cycle of reproduction (from gametogenesis to pregnancy) is illustrated below. Other contraceptive methods are included for comparison.

Hormonal contraception

The most common method by which to prevent **conception** using hormones is by using an oral contraceptive pill (OCP). These may be **combined OCPs**, or low dose mini pills.

Combined oral contraceptive pills (OCPs)

These pills exploit the feedback controls over hormone secretion normally operating during a menstrual cycle. They contain combinations of synthetic **oestrogens** and **progesterone**. They are taken daily for 21 days, and raise the levels of these hormones in the blood so that FSH secretion is inhibited and no ova develop. Sugar pills are taken for 7 days; long enough to allow menstruation to occur but not long enough for ova to develop. Combined OCPs can be of two types:

Monophasic pills (left): Hormones (**H**) are all at one dosage level. Sugar pills (**S**) are usually larger and differently colored.

Triphasic pills (right): The hormone dosage increases in stages (**1,2,3**), mimicking the natural changes in a menstrual cycle.

Mini-pill (progesterone only)

The mini-pill contains 28 days of low dose progesterone; generally too low to prevent ovulation. The pill works by thickening the cervical mucus and preventing endometrial thickening. The mini-pill is less reliable than combined pills and must be taken at a regular time each day. However, it is safer for older women and those who are breastfeeding.

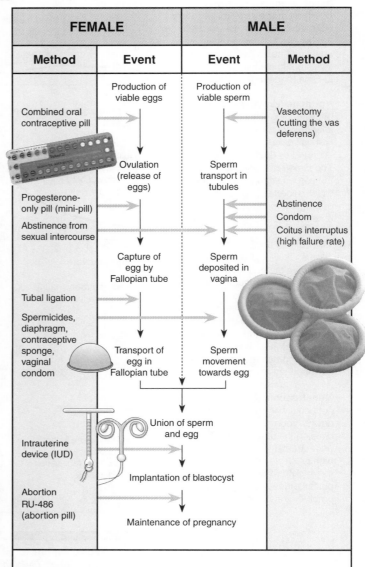

FEMALE		MALE	
Method	**Event**	**Event**	**Method**
	Production of viable eggs	Production of viable sperm	
Combined oral contraceptive pill			Vasectomy (cutting the vas deferens)
	Ovulation (release of eggs)	Sperm transport in tubules	
Progesterone-only pill (mini-pill)			Abstinence
			Condom
Abstinence from sexual intercourse			Coitus interruptus (high failure rate)
	Capture of egg by Fallopian tube	Sperm deposited in vagina	
Tubal ligation			
Spermicides, diaphragm, contraceptive sponge, vaginal condom	Transport of egg in Fallopian tube	Sperm movement towards egg	
	Union of sperm and egg		
Intrauterine device (IUD)			
	Implantation of blastocyst		
Abortion RU-486 (abortion pill)			
	Maintenance of pregnancy		

The flow diagram above illustrates where in the reproductive process, from gametogenesis to pregnancy, various contraceptive methods operate. Note the early action of hormonal contraceptives.

1. Explain briefly how the **combined oral contraceptive pill** acts as a contraceptive: _____

_____

_____

2. Contrast the mode of action of OCPs with that of the mini-pill, giving reasons for the differences: _____

_____

_____

3. Suggest why oral contraceptives offer such effective control over conception: _____

_____

WEB 60   LINK 59

© 2016 **BIOZONE** International
ISBN: 978-1-927309-32-2
Photocopying Prohibited

61 Plant Responses

Key Idea: Plants respond to their environment by either growing to or away from a stimulus or by producing a response that affects some physiological process.

Even though most plants are firmly rooted in the ground, they can still respond to changes in their external environment, mainly through changes in patterns of growth. These responses may involve relatively sudden physiological changes, as in flowering, or a steady growth response, such as a **tropism**. Many of these responses involve annual, seasonal, or circadian (daily) rhythms.

Shoots are positively phototropic and grow toward the light.

Roots are positively gravitropic and grow towards the Earth's gravitational pull.

TROPISMS

Tropisms are growth responses made by plants to directional external stimuli, where the direction of the stimulus determines the direction of the growth response. A tropism may be positive (towards the stimulus), or negative (away from the stimulus). Common stimuli for plants include light, gravity, touch, and chemicals.

LIFE CYCLE RESPONSES

Plants use seasonal changes (such as falling temperatures or decreasing daylength) as cues for starting or ending particular life cycle stages. Such changes are mediated by plant growth factors, such as phytochrome and gibberellin and enable the plant to avoid conditions unfavourable to growth or survival. Examples include flowering, dormancy and germination, and leaf fall.

RAPID RESPONSES TO ENVIRONMENTAL STIMULI

Plants are capable of quite rapid responses. Examples include the closing of stomata in response to water loss, opening and closing of flowers in response to temperature, and nastic responses. These responses may follow a circadian rhythm and are protective in that they reduce the plant's exposure to abiotic stress or grazing pressure.

PLANT COMPETITION AND ALLELOPATHY

Although plants are rooted in the ground, they can still compete with other plants to gain access to resources. Some plants produce chemicals that inhibit the growth of neighbouring plants. Such chemical inhibition is called allelopathy. Plants also compete for light and may grow aggressively to shade out slower growing competitors.

PLANT RESPONSES TO HERBIVORY

Many plant species have responded to grazing or browsing pressure with evolutionary adaptations enabling them to survive constant cropping. Examples include rapid growth to counteract the constant loss of biomass (grasses), sharp spines or thorns to deter browsers (acacias, cacti), or toxins in the leaf tissues (eucalyptus).

1. Identify the stimuli plants typically respond to: _____

_____

2. How do plants benefit by responding appropriately to the environment? _____

_____

_____

3. Describe one adaptive response of plants to each of the following stressors in the environment:

   (a) Low soil water: _____

   (b) Falling autumn air temperatures: _____

   (c) Browsing animals: _____

   (d) Low air temperatures at night: _____

LINK 63   LINK 62   WEB 61   KNOW

62 Nastic Responses

Key Idea: Nastic responses are plant responses in which the direction of the plant response is independent of the stimulus direction. They are often rapid and reversible movements.

Nastic responses in plants are independent of the stimulus direction and may involve quite rapid, reversible movements, often resulting from localised changes in turgor. Nastic responses can occur in response to temperature, light, or touch. The mechanisms involved in the rapid leaf movements of *Mimosa* and the Venus flytrap are result of rapid turgor changes brought about by electrical signals.

Touch responses in *Mimosa*

Mimosa pudica has long leaves composed of small leaflets. When a leaf is touched, it collapses and its leaflets fold together. Strong disturbances cause the entire leaf to droop from its base. This response takes only a few seconds and is caused by a rapid loss of turgor pressure from the cells at the bases of the leaves and leaflets. The message that the plant has been disturbed is passed quickly around the plant by electrical signals (changes in membrane potential), not by plant hormones (as occurs in tropisms). After the disturbance is removed, turgor is restored to the cells, and the leaflets will slowly return to their normal state.

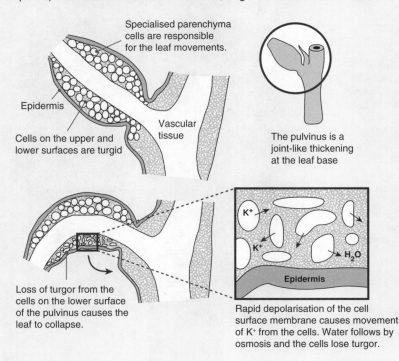

Specialised parenchyma cells are responsible for the leaf movements.

Epidermis

Vascular tissue

Cells on the upper and lower surfaces are turgid

The pulvinus is a joint-like thickening at the leaf base

Loss of turgor from the cells on the lower surface of the pulvinus causes the leaf to collapse.

Rapid depolarisation of the cell surface membrane causes movement of K$^+$ from the cells. Water follows by osmosis and the cells lose turgor.

K$^+$ K$^+$ H$_2$O Epidermis

Leaf

Leaflets

Unstimulated leaf

Disturbed leaf

Touch trigger in Venus flytrap

The leaf blade of the Venus fly trap ends in a pair of hinged lobes. Each lobe has an upper and lower 'hydraulic' layer of cells, which have different turgor. When an insect touches the trigger hairs on the upper epidermis of a lobe (right), the two lobes snap shut, trapping the insect (far right). Once the insect has been digested, the empty lobes reopen.

The mechanism operating is similar to that in *Mimosa*. In the open state, the cells of the upper layer are turgid. Stimulation causes a rapid depolarisation, which spreads to the midrib and causes rapid movement of water from the upper to the lower hydraulic layer. The water moves rapidly through special channels called aquaporins. Trap closure is very rapid (0.1 s) but return to the open state is much slower. The hairs on the leaf must be touched twice in quick succession (within 20 s) for the leaf to close.

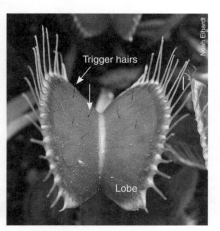

Trigger hairs

Lobe

In the open state, the lobes are bent outwards. When the trap is tripped, the lobes form a cavity. It is the rapid change between two stable states that closes the trap.

1. Describe the basic mechanism behind the sudden leaf movements in the Venus fly-trap and *Mimosa*: _____

_____

_____

_____

2. Suggest the adaptive advantage in the Venus fly trap needing two touches in quick succession before it closes: _____

_____

© 2016 **BIOZONE** International
ISBN: 978-1-927309-32-2
Photocopying Prohibited

63 Tropisms and Growth Responses

Key Idea: Tropisms are directional growth responses to external stimuli. They may be positive (towards a stimulus) or negative (away from a stimulus).

Tropisms are plant growth responses to external stimuli, in which the stimulus direction determines the direction of the growth response. Tropisms are identified according to the stimulus involved, e.g. photo- (light), geo- (gravity), hydro- (water), and are identified as positive (towards the stimulus) or negative (away from the stimulus). Tropisms act to position the plant in the most favourable available environment.

(a) ....
A positive growth response to a chemical stimulus. *Example: Pollen tubes grow towards a chemical, possibly calcium ions, released by the ovule of the flower.*

(b) ....
Stems and coleoptiles (the sheath surrounding the young grass shoot), grow away from the direction of the Earth's gravitational pull.

(c) ....
Growth response to water. Roots are influenced primarily by gravity but will also grow towards water.

(d) ....
Growth responses to light, particularly directional light. Coleoptiles, young stems, and some leaves show a positive response.

(e) ....
Roots respond positively to the Earth's gravitational pull, and curve downward after emerging through the seed coat.

(f) ....
Growth responses to touch or pressure. Tendrils (modified leaves) have a positive coiling response stimulated by touch.

Plant growth responses are adaptive in that they position the plant in a suitable growing environment, within the limits of the position in which it germinated. The responses to stimuli reinforce the appropriate growth behaviour, e.g. roots grow towards gravity and away from the light.

Root mass in a hydroponically grown plant

Sweet pea tendrils

Germinating pollen

Thale cress bending to the light

Kristian Peters

1. Identify each of the plant tropisms described in (a)-(f) above. State whether the response is positive or negative.

2. Describe the adaptive value of the following tropisms:

   (a) Positive geotropism in roots: _____

   (b) Positive phototropism in coleoptiles: _____

   (c) Positive thigmomorphogenesis in weak stemmed plants: _____

   (d) Positive chemotropism in pollen grains: _____

3. Explain the adaptive value of tropisms:_____

   _____

   _____

   _____

© 2016 **BIOZONE** International
ISBN: 978-1-927309-32-2
Photocopying Prohibited

LINK **65**   LINK **64**   WEB **63**   **KNOW**

64 Auxins, Gibberellins, and ABA

Key Idea: Phytohormones, such as auxin, gibberellin, and ABA, play important roles in plant responses to stimuli.

Phytohormones (plant growth regulators) have a wide range of roles in the growth and developmental responses of vascular plants. **Auxin** (indole-acetic acid or IAA) is a naturally occurring phytohormone with a role in suppressing the growth of lateral buds. This inhibitory influence of a shoot tip or apical bud on the lateral buds is called apical dominance. **Gibberellins** are involved in stem and leaf elongation, as well as breaking dormancy in seeds. Specifically, they stimulate cell division and cell elongation. **Abscisic** acid or (ABA) was originally thought to be involved in accelerating abscission in leaves and fruit. Although it now seems that ABA is a growth inhibitor with a variety of roles.

Plant responses and the role of auxins, gibberellins, and abscisic acid

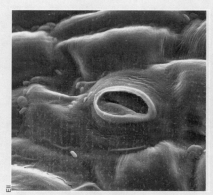

ABA stimulates the closing of stomata in most plant species. Its synthesis is stimulated by water deficiency (water stress). ABA also promotes seed dormancy. It is concentrated in senescent leaves, but it is probably not involved in leaf abscission except in a few species.

Gibberellins are responsible for breaking dormancy in seeds and promote the growth of the embryo and emergence of the seedling. Gibberellins are used to hasten seed germination and ensure germination uniformity in the production of barley malt in brewing.

Differential auxin transport, and therefore differential growth, is responsible for phototropism. Auxins also produce apical dominance in shoots. Auxin is produced in the shoot tip and diffuses down the stem to inhibit the development of the lateral buds.

ABA is produced in ripe fruit and induces fruit fall. The effects of ABA are generally opposite to those of cytokinins.

Gibberellins cause stem and leaf elongation by stimulating cell division and cell elongation. They are responsible for bolting in brassicas.

Auxin is required for fruit growth. The maturing seed releases auxin, inducing the surrounding flower parts to develop into fruit.

1. What is the role of **gibberellins** in stem elongation and in the germination of grasses such as barley?

_____

_____

_____

2. What is the role of **abscisic acid** in closure of stomata? _____

_____

_____

3. Why is abscisic acid often referred to as a growth inhibitor? _____

_____

_____

© 2016 **BIOZONE** International
ISBN: 978-1-927309-32-2
Photocopying Prohibited

65 Transport and Effects of Auxins

Key Idea: Auxin is a plant hormone involved in the differential growth responses of plants to environmental stimuli.

Auxins are plant hormones with a central role in a range of growth and developmental responses in plants. Indole-acetic acid (IAA) is the most potent native auxin in intact plants.

The response of a plant tissue to IAA depends on the tissue itself, the hormone concentration, the timing of its release, and the presence of other hormones. Gradients in auxin concentration during growth prompt differential responses in specific tissues and contribute to directional growth.

Light is an important growth requirement for all plants. Most plants show an adaptive response of growing towards the light. This growth response is called phototropism.

The bending of the plants shown on the right is a phototropism in response to light shining from the left and is caused by the plant hormone **auxin**. Auxin causes the elongation of cells on the shaded side of the stem, causing it to bend (photo right).

Auxin is produced in the shoot tip and is responsible for apical dominance by suppressing growth of the lateral (side) buds.

Auxin movement through the plant is polar. It moves from the shoot tip down the plant.

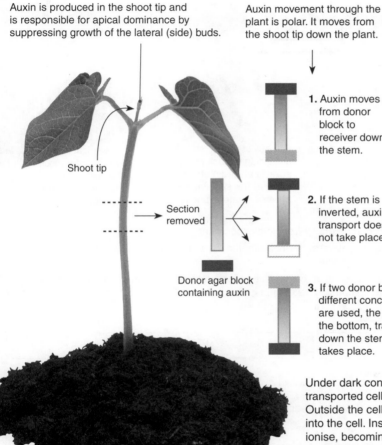

Shoot tip

Section removed

Donor agar block containing auxin

1. Auxin moves from donor block to receiver down the stem.

2. If the stem is inverted, auxin transport does not take place.

3. If two donor blocks of different concentration are used, the higher at the bottom, transport down the stem still takes place.

Plasma membrane

Cell wall

Transport protein

- ● Hydrogen ion (H⁺)
- ● Non-ionised auxin (AH)
- ● Ionised auxin (A⁻)
- ·····▶ Diffusion
- ——▶ Activie transport

Under dark conditions auxin moves evenly down the stem. It is transported cell to cell by diffusion and transport proteins (above right). Outside the cell auxin is a non-ionised molecule (AH) which can diffuse into the cell. Inside the cell the pH of the cytoplasm causes auxin to ionise, becoming A⁻ and H⁺. Transport proteins at the basal end of the cell then transport A⁻ out of the cell where it reacquires an H⁺ ion and reforms AH. In this way auxin is transported in one direction through the plant. When plant cells are illuminated by light from one direction transport proteins in the plasma membrane on the shaded side of the cell are activated and auxin is transported to the shaded side of the plant.

1. What is the term given to the tropism being displayed in the photo (top right)? _____

2. Describe one piece of evidence that demonstrates the transport of auxin is polar: _____

_____

_____

_____

3. What is the effect of auxin on cell growth? _____

_____

© 2016 **BIOZONE** International
ISBN: **978-1-927309-32-2**
Photocopying Prohibited

LINK **66** | LINK **64** | **KNOW**

66 The Role of Auxins in Apical Dominance

Key Idea: Auxin promotes apical growth in plants and inhibits the growth of lateral (side) buds.

Auxins are responsible for apical dominance in shoots. Auxin is produced in the shoot tip and diffuses down to inhibit the development of the lateral (side) buds. The effect of auxin on preventing the development of lateral buds can be demonstrated by removing the source of the auxin and examining the outcome (below).

Auxin was the first substance to be identified as a plant hormone. Charles Darwin and his son Francis were first to recognise its role in stimulating cell elongation. Frits W. Went isolated this growth-regulating substance, which he called auxin, in 1926. Auxin promotes **apical dominance**, where the shoot tip or apical bud inhibits the formation of lateral (side) buds. As a result, plants tend to grow a single main stem upwards, which dominates over lateral branches.

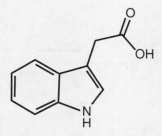

Indole-acetic acid (above) is the only known naturally occurring auxin. It is produced in the apical shoot and young leaves.

No treatment
Apical bud is left intact.

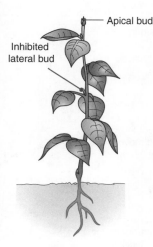

Apical bud

Inhibited lateral bud

In an intact plant, the plant stem elongates and the lateral buds remain inactive. No side growth occurs.

Treatment one
Apical bud is removed; no auxin is applied.

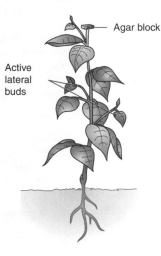

Agar block

Active lateral buds

The apical bud is removed and an agar block without auxin is placed on the cut surface. The seedling begins to develop lateral buds.

Treatment two
Apical bud is removed; auxin is applied.

Agar block

Inhibited lateral bud

The apical bud is removed and an agar block containing auxin is placed on the cut surface. Lateral bud development is inhibited.

Two conclusions can be drawn from this experiment.

(1) The apical bud contains a hormone that inhibits lateral growth because its removal promoted lateral growth.

(2) The presence of auxin in the apical bud inhibits lateral growth because auxin applied to a cut stem tip could inhibit lateral growth and mimic the effect of an intact apical bud.

1. Describe the role of auxins in apical dominance: _____

_____

_____

2. Outline the experimental evidence supporting the role of auxins in apical dominance: _____

_____

_____

_____

_____

3. Study the photo (right) and then answer the following questions:

   (a) Label the apical bud.   (b) Label the lateral bud(s).

   (c) Which buds are the largest? _____

   (d) Why would this be important? _____

   _____

NASA

4. If you were a gardener, how would you make your plants bushier?_____

_____

67 Gibberellins and Stem Elongation

Key Idea: The effect of gibberellins on plant growth can be tested experimentally by comparing the growth of gibberellin treated plants to plants with no hormonal treatment. Gibberellins (GA) are a group of plant hormones that affect stem growth. Gibberellic acid is a type of gibberellin. Dwarf pea plants are a selected variety with a mutation that results in impaired GA synthesis. By applying GA to them, the effect of GA on plant growth can easily be demonstrated. The experiment below was performed by a group of students to determine the effect of GA on dwarf pea stem growth.

The aim and hypothesis

To investigate the effect of gibberellic acid on stem growth in dwarf pea plants.

If gibberellins are responsible for stem elongation, genetically dwarfed pea plants treated with gibberellic acid will grow taller than untreated dwarf pea plants.

Background

Mendel first described the gene for stem length in pea plants in 1865. In 1997, more than 130 years later, the gene controlling this phenotype was isolated. Called *Le*, it encodes an enzyme called gibberellin 3β-hydroxylase, which coverts precursors of gibberellin to an active form. The recessive allele *le* is inactive. Plants that are homozygous for the *le* gene have short stems as they do not produce active gibberellin. This can be verified by giving dwarf peas artificial gibberellins. Instead of remaining short, the plants grow to a normal size.

Method

Students soaked 10 dwarf pea seeds (*Pisum sativum*) overnight in distilled water. The seeds were divided into two groups of five seeds each. The test group received gibberellin treatment and the control group did not. The seeds were planted into two containers filled with potting mix. Once the seeds had germinated, the test group had gibberellic acid paste (500 ppm) painted on them. Both seed groups were watered daily with distilled water.

The heights of the germinating shoots were recorded every few days for 20 days (except for one longer break in recording between days 11 and 18 when the students were away).

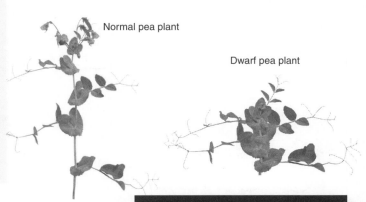

Normal pea plant

Dwarf pea plant

The results from the experiment are described in Table 1.

1. For the control (C) and treatment (T), calculate the mean seedling height and standard deviation for each day and record it in the space provided. Calculate sample standard deviation using a spreadsheet or the equation provided, right. The denominator $n - 1$ is used for small samples.

$$S = \sqrt{\frac{\sum(x - \bar{x})^2}{n-1}}$$

where $\bar{x}$ = mean

Height (in cm) of dwarf pea plants														
Days after germination														
Seed number	2		4		6		9		11		18		20	
	C	T	C	T	C	T	C	T	C	T	C	T	C	T
1	1.2	1.1	3.1	5.5	4.4	12.1	6.1	22.4	8.3	25.9	12.3	37.5	16.1	38.5
2	1.8	0.6	3.6	5.4	5.1	14.6	7.1	24.7	8.8	28.1	15.9	35.8	19.0	30.1
3	1.3	1.1	3.3	6.6	4.6	15.0	6.4	24.5	8.9	26.8	15.4	34.8	18.1	30.0
4	0.4	0.9	2.9	6.7	4.2	14.2	6.3	21.7	9.5	26.5	12.0	30.3	13.4	38.2
5	1.2	0.4	3.7	4.8	5.1	14.1	6.9	23.6	7.2	25.9	10.8	29.0	12.3	39.2
Mean														
SD														

2. (a) Using a spreadsheet or a separate piece of paper, plot a line graph showing the mean plant heights for the two groups of dwarf peas. Plot the standard deviation for each mean as error bars either side of the mean.

(b) Describe the effect of gibberellin on the growth of dwarf pea plants: _____

_____

(c) Do the results support the hypothesis? _____

LINK

64 KNOW

68 Chapter Review

Summarise what you know about this topic under the headings and sub-headings provided. You can draw diagrams or mind maps, or write short notes to organise your thoughts. Use the images and hints to help you and refer back to the introduction to check the points covered.

Plant responses

HINT: Tropisms, plant hormones and growth.

Neurones and action potentials

HINT: Describe the structure and function of neurones. Describe a reflex arc and explain the generation of action potentials.

Muscles

HINT: Skeletal muscle structure and function and the sliding filament hypothesis.

Reproductive hormones

HINT: Role of hormones in the menstrual cycle and contraception.

69 KEY TERMS AND IDEAS: Did You Get?

1. Complete the crossword below:

Across

4. A self propagating nerve impulse is called an action _ _ _ _ _ _ _ _ _ .

6. Extension of the nerve cell body specialised to receive stimuli.

8. A specialised cell that detects stimuli and responds by producing a nerve impulse.

9. Long extension of the nerve cell which transits the nerve impulse to another cell.

10. A cell specialised to transmit electrical impulses.

11. An organ system comprising a network of specialised cells or neurones, which coordinates responses and transmits signals between parts of the body (2 words: 7, 6).

Down

1. A temporary change in membrane potential caused by influx of sodium ions.

2. The gap between neighbouring neurones or between a neurone and an effector.

3. These synapses release acetylcholine.

5. This lipid-rich substance surrounds and insulates the axons of nerves in the peripheral nervous system.

7. Motor nerves carry impulses from the central nervous system to these.

2. (a) What is the name given to a plant growth response to directional light? _____

(b) What is the name given to a plant growth response to gravity? _____

(c) What is the name given to a plant response that is independent of stimulus direction? _____

(d) What plant hormone is principally responsible for the phototropic effect? _____

3. (a) What responses are being shown by the orchid pictured right:

_____

_____

_____

_____

(b) What is the stimulus involved? _____

_____

4. (a) Put these in order from largest to smallest: myofibril, muscle tissue, myofilament, muscle fibre, fascicles.

_____

(b) Identify the structural unit shown below: _____

(c) On the diagram above, label the following: thin filament, thick filament, H zone.

(d) What happens to the H zone when the muscle is fully contracted? _____

5. Name the hormones involved regulating the menstrual cycle and ovulation: _____

_____

6. What are the hormones used in combined oral contraceptive pills? _____

© 2016 **BIOZONE** International
ISBN: 978-1-927309-32-2
Photocopying Prohibited

TEST

Topic 16

Inherited change

16.1 Passage of information from parent to offspring
Learning outcomes

Activity number

☐ 1 Explain what is meant by homologous pairs of chromosomes.   70

☐ 2 Explain the terms haploid and diploid. Explain the need for a reduction division (meiosis) prior to fertilisation in sexually reproducing organisms.   71

☐ 3 Outline the role of meiosis in gametogenesis in humans and sporogenesis in flowering plants. Understand that, in flowering plants, haploid spores develop into the male and female gametophytes (pollen grains and embryo sacs).   71

☐ 4 Describe the behaviour of chromosomes, nuclear envelope, cell surface membrane, and spindle in plant and animal cells during meiosis.   72

☐ 5 Explain how sexual reproduction results in variation in the offspring and can lead to the expression of rare, recessive alleles. Include reference to crossing over and random (independent) assortment of homologous chromosomes during meiosis, and random fusion of gametes at fertilisation.   72 73 74

16.2 The roles of genes in determining phenotype
Learning outcomes

Activity number

☐ 6 Demonstrate understanding and use of the terms used in studying inheritance: gene, allele, locus, trait, dominant, recessive, codominant, heterozygous, homozygous, genotype, phenotype, test cross, linkage, F_1/F_2 generation.   70 75 76 78 82 83

☐ 7 Use genetic diagrams to solve problems involving monohybrid and dihybrid crosses, including those involving autosomal linkage, sex linkage, codominance and multiple alleles, and gene interactions (including epistasis).   76-85 89 90

☐ 8 Use genetic diagrams to solve problems involving test crosses.   75

☐ 9 Use the chi-squared test (for goodness of fit) to test the significance of differences between the observed and expected results of genetic crosses.   86 87

☐ 10 Explain that gene mutations occur by substitution, deletion, or insertion of base pairs in DNA. Describe how gene mutations may affect phenotype.   91 92 93

☐ 11 Outline the effects of mutated alleles on phenotype, for example, in albinism, sickle cell disease (sickle cell anaemia), haemophilia, and Huntington's disease.   92 94 95 96

☐ 12 Explain the relationship between genes, enzymes, and phenotype with reference to the tyrosinase enzyme that converts tyrosine into melanin.   96

16.3 Gene control
Learning outcomes

Activity number

☐ 13 Distinguish between structural and regulatory genes and between repressible and inducible enzymes.   97 98

☐ 14 Explain the control of protein production with reference to the *lac* operon in *E. coli*.   97

☐ 15 Explain the role of transcription factors in gene expression in eukaryotes.   99

☐ 16 Explain how gibberellin activates genes by causing the breakdown of DELLA protein repressors, which are normally involved in inhibiting transcription.   99

70 Describing Alleles

Key Idea: Eukaryotes generally have paired chromosomes. Each chromosome contains many genes and each gene may have a number of versions called alleles. Sexually reproducing organisms usually have paired sets of chromosomes, one set from each parent. The equivalent chromosomes that form a pair are termed **homologues**. They carry equivalent sets of genes, but there is the potential for different versions of a gene (**alleles**) to exist in a population.

but the   *from each parent*   *may differ)*

Homologous chromosomes

In sexually reproducing organisms, most cells have a homologous pair of chromosomes (one coming from each parent). This diagram shows the position of three different genes on the same chromosome that control three different traits (A, B and C).

Chromosomes are formed from DNA and proteins. DNA tightly winds around special proteins to form the chromosome.

Having two different versions (alleles) of gene A is a **heterozygous** condition. Only the dominant allele (A) will be expressed. Alleles differ by only a few bases.

When both chromosomes have identical copies of the dominant allele for gene B the organism is **homozygous dominant** for that gene.

When both chromosomes have identical copies of the recessive allele for gene C the organism is said to be **homozygous recessive** for that gene.

Maternal chromosome originating from the egg of this individual's mother.

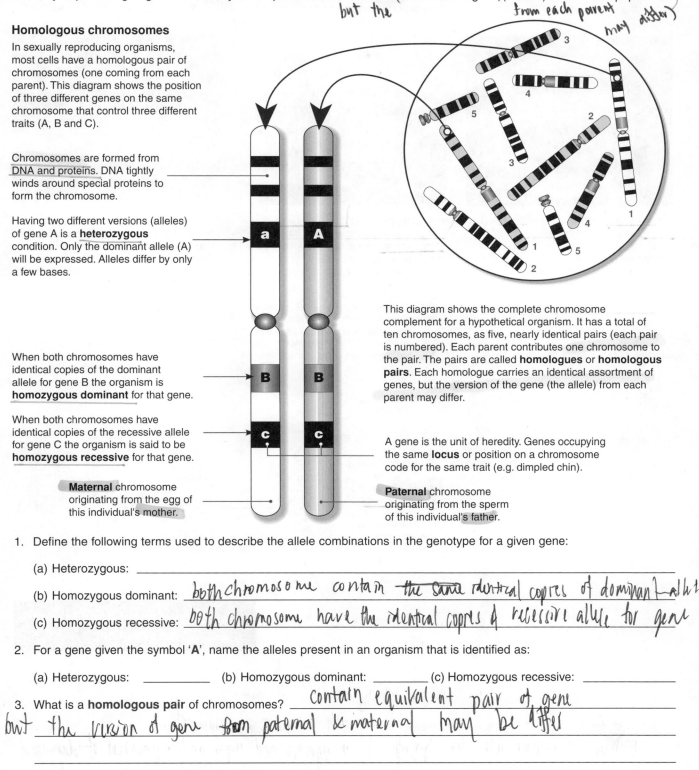

This diagram shows the complete chromosome complement for a hypothetical organism. It has a total of ten chromosomes, as five, nearly identical pairs (each pair is numbered). Each parent contributes one chromosome to the pair. The pairs are called **homologues** or **homologous pairs**. Each homologue carries an identical assortment of genes, but the version of the gene (the allele) from each parent may differ.

A gene is the unit of heredity. Genes occupying the same **locus** or position on a chromosome code for the same trait (e.g. dimpled chin).

Paternal chromosome originating from the sperm of this individual's father.

1. Define the following terms used to describe the allele combinations in the genotype for a given gene:

   (a) Heterozygous: _____

   (b) Homozygous dominant: both chromosome contain ~~the same~~ identical copies of dominan allh to

   (c) Homozygous recessive: both chromosome have the identical copies of recessive allue for gene

2. For a gene given the symbol 'A', name the alleles present in an organism that is identified as:

   (a) Heterozygous: _____   (b) Homozygous dominant: _____   (c) Homozygous recessive: _____

3. What is a **homologous pair** of chromosomes? contain equivalent pair of gene but the version of gene from paternal & maternal may be differ

   _____

4. Discuss the significance of genes existing as **alleles**: _____

   _____

   _____

   _____

   _____

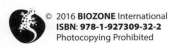

KNOW

71 The Role of Meiosis

Key Idea: There are two types of cell division in eukaryotes, mitosis and meiosis, but only meiosis produces cells that are genetically different to the parent cell.

New cells are formed when existing cells divide. There are two forms of cell division in eukaryotes, mitosis and meiosis.

Mitosis produces two identical daughter cells from a parent cell. **Meiosis** is a special type of cell division, and produces sex cells (gametes or spores) for sexual reproduction. In sexual reproduction, sex cells from two parents combine to form an individual that is genetically different to its parents.

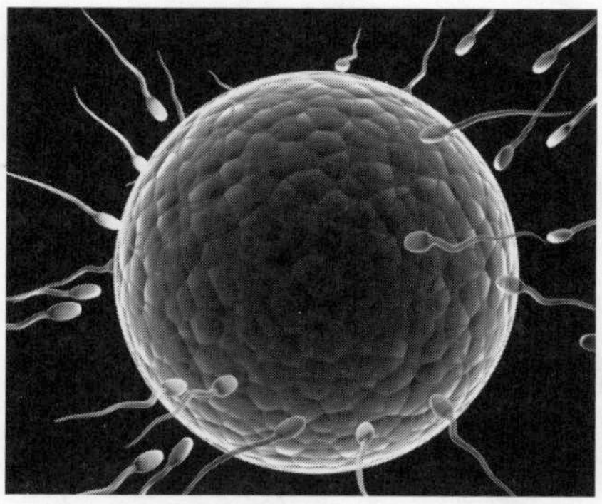

The sex cells in humans, called eggs and sperm, are produced by meiosis. Events occurring during meiosis creates gametes with unique combinations of gene variants and so creates genetic variability.

Sexual reproduction rearranges and reshuffles the genetic material into new combinations. This is why family members may look similar, but they'll never be identical (except for identical twins).

Pollen is formed by meiosis followed by mitosis. In the anther, the microsporocyte undergoes meiosis to form four haploid microspores. These then undergo mitosis to form pollen grains containing the sperm cells.

The **2N (diploid) number** refers to the cells each having two whole sets of chromosomes. For a normal human embryo, all cells will have a 2N number of 46.

Gametes are produced by **meiosis**; a special division which reduces the chromosome number to half that of a somatic cell. The **1N** (haploid) number indicates a single set of chromosomes.

Many mitotic divisions give rise to the adult. Mitosis continues throughout life for cell replacement and repair of tissues. e.g. blood cells are replaced at a rate of two million per second, and a layer of skin cells is constantly lost and replaced about every 28 days.

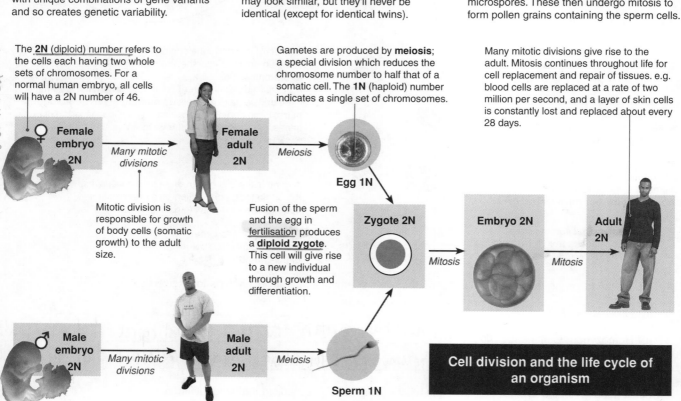

Mitotic division is responsible for growth of body cells (somatic growth) to the adult size.

Fusion of the sperm and the egg in fertilisation produces a **diploid zygote**. This cell will give rise to a new individual through growth and differentiation.

Cell division and the life cycle of an organism

Handwritten left margin: fertilisation → diploid zygote.

1. (a) Where does mitosis take place in animals? _body cell_

   (b) Describe the roles of mitosis in the human body: _growth, repair, replacement, Mitosis is responsible for growth of an organism and repair and replacement of damaged cells._

   (c) In mitosis, the daughter cells are genetically different to the parent cell. True or ~~False~~ (delete one)

2. (a) Where does meiosis take place in animals? _Sex cell occurs in sex organs in animals (ovaries & testes)_

   (b) What is the purpose of meiosis? _It produces sex cells (gametes or eggs and sperm) for the purpose of sexual reproduction_

   (c) In meiosis, the sex cells are genetically different to the parent cell. True or ~~False~~ (delete one)

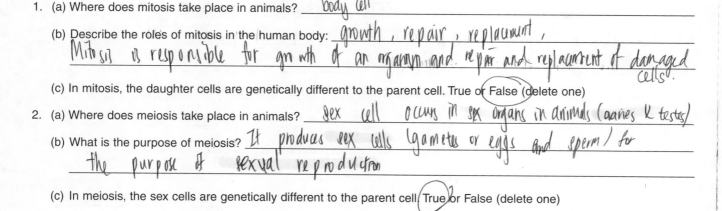

WEB 71   LINK 72   LINK 74

KNOW

© 2016 **BIOZONE** International
ISBN: 978-1-927309-32-2
Photocopying Prohibited

72 Meiosis

[handwritten annotations:] daughter cells non-identical — make cell with variation for / are haploid (n) / 4 daughter cell / — testem (to ovaria) / man women / sexual reproduction

Key Idea: Meiosis is a special type of cell division. It produces sex cells (gametes) for the purpose of sexual reproduction. Meiosis involves a single chromosomal duplication followed by two successive nuclear divisions, and results in a halving of the diploid chromosome number. Meiosis occurs in the sex organs of plants and animals. If genetic mistakes (**gene** and **chromosome mutations**) occur here, they will be passed on to the offspring (they will be inherited).

[handwritten:] fertilisation - two nucleic form together.

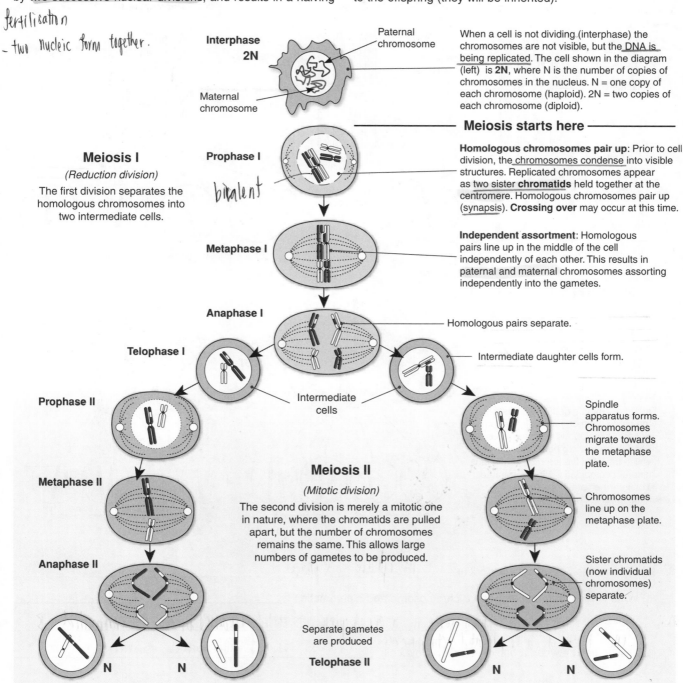

Interphase 2N

Paternal chromosome

Maternal chromosome

When a cell is not dividing (interphase) the chromosomes are not visible, but the DNA is being replicated. The cell shown in the diagram (left) is **2N**, where N is the number of copies of chromosomes in the nucleus. N = one copy of each chromosome (haploid). 2N = two copies of each chromosome (diploid).

— **Meiosis starts here** —

Meiosis I
(Reduction division)

The first division separates the homologous chromosomes into two intermediate cells.

Prophase I *[handwritten:]* bivalent

Homologous chromosomes pair up: Prior to cell division, the chromosomes condense into visible structures. Replicated chromosomes appear as two sister **chromatids** held together at the centromere. Homologous chromosomes pair up (synapsis). **Crossing over** may occur at this time.

Metaphase I

Independent assortment: Homologous pairs line up in the middle of the cell independently of each other. This results in paternal and maternal chromosomes assorting independently into the gametes.

Anaphase I

Homologous pairs separate.

Telophase I

Intermediate daughter cells form.

Intermediate cells

Prophase II

Spindle apparatus forms. Chromosomes migrate towards the metaphase plate.

Meiosis II
(Mitotic division)

The second division is merely a mitotic one in nature, where the chromatids are pulled apart, but the number of chromosomes remains the same. This allows large numbers of gametes to be produced.

Metaphase II

Chromosomes line up on the metaphase plate.

Anaphase II

Sister chromatids (now individual chromosomes) separate.

Separate gametes are produced

Telophase II

N   N   N   N

---

1. Describe the behaviour of the chromosomes in the first division of meiosis: *[handwritten:]* homologous chromosomes are separated into different daughter all In the first division of meiosis, homologous pairs of chromosomes pair to form bivalents. Segments of chromosome may be exchanged in crossing over and the homologues then separate. The division reduces the num of chromosomes in the intermediate cells, so that only one chromosome from each homologous pair is present.

2. Describe the behaviour of the chromosomes in the second division of meiosis: *[handwritten:]* sister chromatids are separated into different daughter cells In the second division of meiosis, chromatids separate (are pulled apart), but the num of chromosomes stays the same. This is more or less a 'mitotic division'.

LINK **74** LINK **73** WEB **72** KNOW

Crossing over and recombination

Chromosomes replicate during interphase, before meiosis, to produce replicated chromosomes with sister chromatids held together at the centromere (see below). When the replicated chromosomes are paired during the first stage of meiosis, non-sister chromatids may become entangled and segments may be exchanged in a process called **crossing over.** Crossing over results in the **recombination** of alleles (variations of the same gene) producing greater variation in the offspring than would otherwise occur.

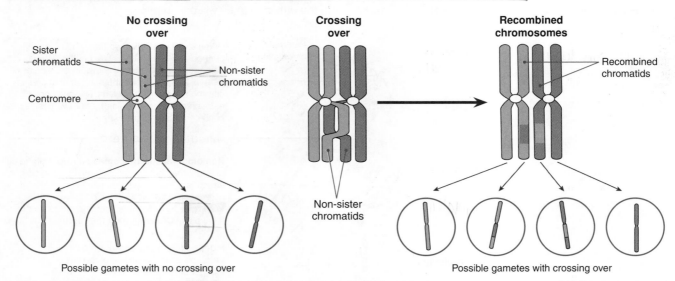

No crossing over

Sister chromatids

Non-sister chromatids

Centromere

Crossing over

Non-sister chromatids

Recombined chromosomes

Recombined chromatids

Possible gametes with no crossing over

Possible gametes with crossing over

Independent assortment

Independent assortment is the random alignment and distribution of chromosomes during meiosis. Independent assortment is an important mechanism for producing variation in gametes. During the first stage of meiosis, replicated homologous chromosomes pair up along the middle of the cell. The way the chromosomes pair up is random. For the homologous chromosomes right, there are two possible ways in which they can line up resulting in four different combinations in the gametes. The intermediate steps of meiosis have been left out for simplicity.

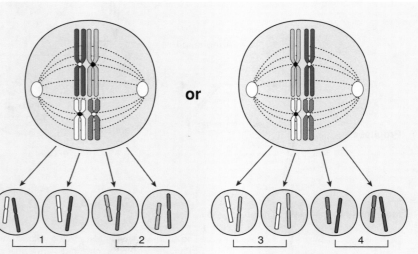

or

1   2   3   4

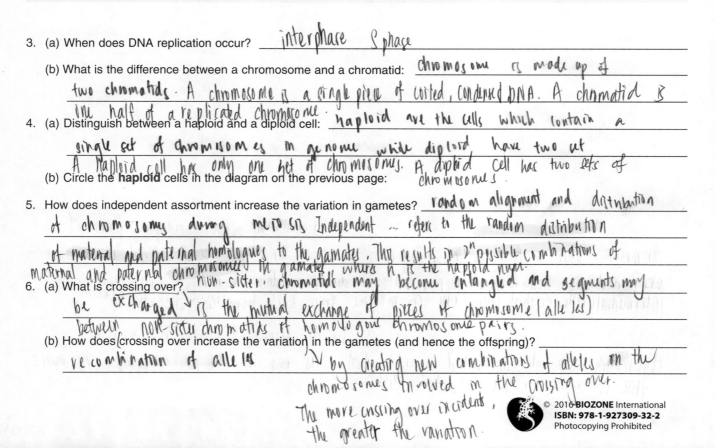

3. (a) When does DNA replication occur? ___interphase S phase___

(b) What is the difference between a chromosome and a chromatid: chromosome is made up of two chromatids. A chromosome is a single piece of coiled, condensed DNA. A chromatid is one half of a replicated chromosome.

4. (a) Distinguish between a haploid and a diploid cell: haploid are the cells which contain a single set of chromosomes in genome while diploid have two set A haploid cell has only one set of chromosomes. A diploid cell has two sets of chromosomes.

(b) Circle the **haploid** cells in the diagram on the previous page:

5. How does independent assortment increase the variation in gametes? random alignment and distribution of chromosomes during meiosis Independent ... refers to the random distribution of maternal and paternal homologues to the gametes. This results in 2^n possible combinations of maternal and paternal chromosomes in gamete, where n is the haploid num.

6. (a) What is crossing over? non-sister chromatids may become entangled and segments may be exchanged is the mutual exchange of pieces of chromosome (alleles) between non-sister chromatids of homologous chromosome pairs.

(b) How does (crossing over increase the variation) in the gametes (and hence the offspring)? recombination of alleles by creating new combinations of alleles on the chromosomes involved in the crossing over. The more crossing over incidents, the greater the variation.

© 2016 **BIOZONE** International
ISBN: 978-1-927309-32-2
Photocopying Prohibited

73 Modelling Meiosis

Key Idea: We can simulate crossing over, gamete production, and the inheritance of alleles during meiosis using ice-block sticks to represent chromosomes.

This practical activity simulates the production of gametes (sperm and eggs) by meiosis and shows you how crossing over increases genetic variability. This is demonstrated by studying how two of your own alleles are inherited by the child produced at the completion of the activity. Completing this activity will help you to visualise and understand meiosis. It will take 25-45 minutes.

Background

Each of your somatic cells contain 46 chromosomes. You received 23 chromosomes from your mother (**maternal chromosomes**), and 23 chromosomes from your father (**paternal chromosomes**). Therefore, you have 23 homologous (same) pairs. For simplicity, the number of chromosomes studied in this exercise has been reduced to four (two homologous pairs). To study the effect of crossing over on genetic variability, you will look at the inheritance of two of your own traits: the ability to **tongue roll** and **handedness**.

Chromosome #	Phenotype	Genotype
10	Tongue roller	TT, Tt
10	Non-tongue roller	tt
2	Right handed	RR, Rr
2	Left handed	rr

Record your phenotype and genotype for each trait in the table (right).
NOTE: If you have a dominant trait, you will not know if you are heterozygous or homozygous for that trait, so you can choose either genotype for this activity.

BEFORE YOU START THE SIMULATION: Partner up with a classmate. Your gametes will combine with theirs (fertilisation) at the end of the activity to produce a child. Decide who will be the female, and who will be the male. You will need to work with this person again at step 6.

1. Collect four ice-blocks sticks. These represent four chromosomes. Colour two sticks blue or mark them with a P. These are the paternal chromosomes. The plain sticks are the maternal chromosomes. Write your initial on each of the four sticks. Label each chromosome with their chromosome number (right).

    Label four sticky dots with the alleles for each of your phenotypic traits, and stick it onto the appropriate chromosome. For example, if you are heterozygous for tongue rolling, the sticky dots with have the alleles **T** and **t**, and they will be placed on chromosome 10. If you are left handed, the alleles will be **r** and **r** and be placed on chromosome 2 (right).

2. Randomly drop the chromosomes onto a table. This represents a cell in either the testes or ovaries. **Duplicate** your chromosomes (to simulate DNA replication) by adding four more identical ice-block sticks to the table (below). This represents **interphase**.

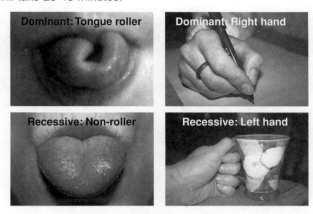

Trait	Phenotype	Genotype
Handedness		
Tongue rolling		

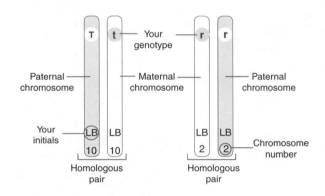

3. Simulate **prophase I** by lining the duplicated chromosome pair with their homologous pair (below). For each chromosome number, you will have four sticks touching side-by-side (A). At this stage **crossing over** occurs. Simulate this by swapping sticky dots from adjoining homologs (B).

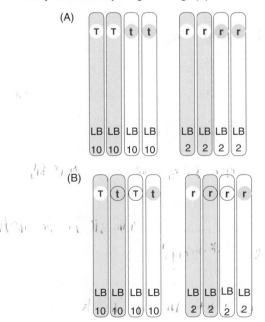

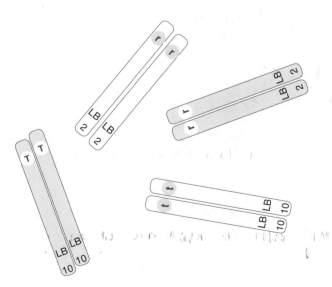

4. Randomly align the homologous chromosome pairs to simulate alignment on the metaphase plate (as occurs in **metaphase I**). Simulate **anaphase I** by separating chromosome pairs. For each group of four sticks, two are pulled to each pole.

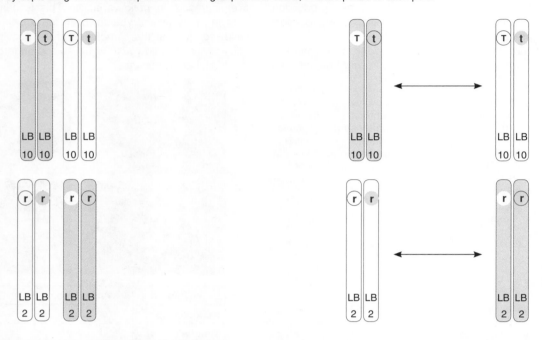

5. **Telophase I:** Two intermediate cells are formed. If you have been random in the previous step, each intermediate cell will contain a mixture of maternal and paternal chromosomes. This is the end of **meiosis 1**.

    Now that meiosis 1 is completed, your cells need to undergo **meiosis 2.** Carry out prophase II, metaphase II, anaphase II, and telophase II. Remember, there is no crossing over in meiosis II. At the end of the process each intermediate cell will have produced two haploid gametes (below).

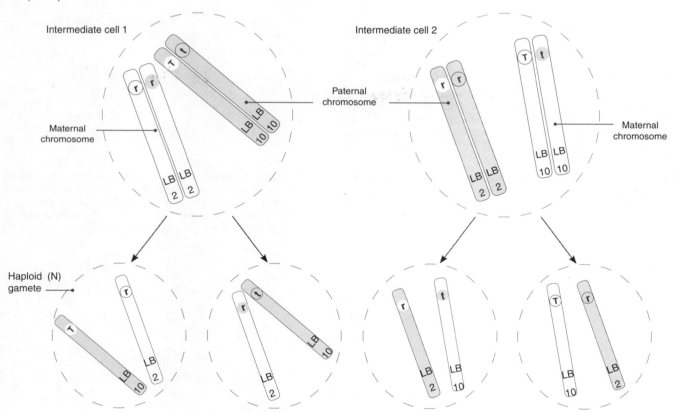

6. Pair up with the partner you chose at the beginning of the exercise to carry out **fertilisation**. Randomly select one sperm and one egg cell. The unsuccessful gametes can be removed from the table. Combine the chromosomes of the successful gametes. You have created a child! Fill in the following chart to describe your child's genotype and phenotype for tongue rolling and handedness.

Trait	Phenotype	Genotype
Handedness		
Tongue rolling		

74 Meiosis and Variation

Key Idea: The genetically variable gametes produced by meiosis pair up randomly, producing variation in the offspring. Variation in offspring can arise because of events during meiosis (crossing over and recombination), but it can also occur because of how the gametes produced from meiosis pair up. The way in which gametes pair up is random. Therefore the offspring will carry a random combination of alleles from the mother and from the father.

Gametes and variation

The example right shows how alleles from two heterozygous individuals can be distributed to the gametes. The heterozygotes display only the dominant phenotype. However the random combination of gametes in fertilisation can produce both homozygous and heterozygous individuals. In this case, there is a 75% chance that the offspring will carry the dominant alleles. They will all therefore display the dominant phenotypes. There is a 25% chance of producing a homozygous recessive individual. This individual will display the recessive phenotype.

There are many human disorders that are related to single recessive alleles. When two carriers (heterozygotes) of a recessive allele for a disorder produce offspring, there is a 25% chance that the offspring may have the disorder.

The vast majority of people with a recessive allele-related disorder will have parents that are carriers, even for rare disorders with a relatively low birth rate such as 1 in 2500. In this case, the frequency of carriers in the population would be 1 in 25. In a randomly breeding population, the chances of two carriers meeting are 1 in 650, which is far greater than the chances of two affected people meeting (more than 1 in 6 million).

Some human disorders caused by recessive alleles include cystic fibrosis (1 in 2000 births), phenylketonuria (1 in 8500 births), and sickle cell disease (1 in 2500 births).

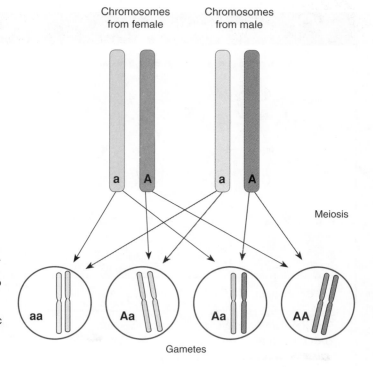

Chromosomes from female   Chromosomes from male

a   A   a   A

Meiosis

aa   Aa   Aa   AA

Gametes

1. Explain how variation is produced when two gametes unite to produce a zygote: Variation in offspring can arise because of events during meiosis Gametes united randomly.

2. For a recessive disorder with the alleles B and b, what is the chance of the offspring being affected in a cross between a carrier (Bb) and an affected person (bb)?

   Bb x bb = Bb or bb

   50% chance of offspring being affected

3. Explain why the parents of a person affected by a disorder caused by a rare recessive allele are more likely to be carriers than affected people:

4. (a) What is the birth rate of people affected with cystic fibrosis? _____

   (b) The frequency of carriers with a rare recessive allele can be approximated by doubling the square root of the frequency of the affected people. What is the approximate frequency of cystic fibrosis carriers?

   (c) Calculate the frequency as a whole number ratio (e.g. 1: 20): _____

   (d) What are the chances of two carriers meeting? _____

LINK   WEB

72 **74**   KNOW

75 The Monohybrid Cross

Key Idea: The outcome of a cross depends on the parental genotypes. A true breeding parent is homozygous for the gene involved.

Examine the diagrams depicting monohybrid (single gene) inheritance. The F_1 generation by definition describes the offspring of a cross between distinctly different, **true-breeding** (homozygous) parents. A **back cross** refers to any cross between an offspring and one of its parents. If the back cross is to a homozygous recessive, it is diagnostic, and is therefore called a test cross.

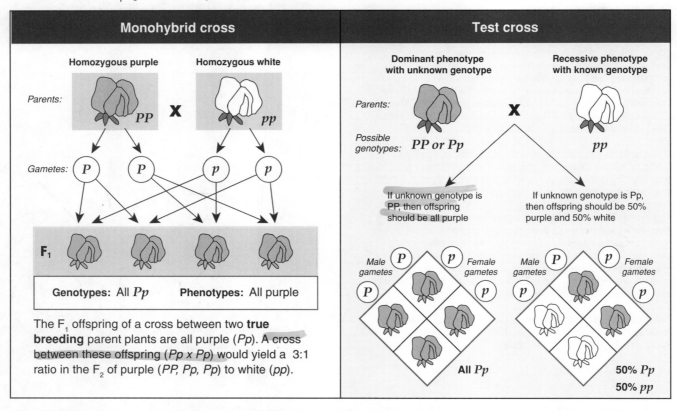

The F_1 offspring of a cross between two **true breeding** parent plants are all purple (Pp). A cross between these offspring (Pp x Pp) would yield a 3:1 ratio in the F_2 of purple (PP, Pp, Pp) to white (pp).

1. Study the diagrams above and explain why white flower colour does not appear in the F_1 generation but reappears in the F_2 generation:

_____

_____

_____

_____

2. Complete the crosses below:

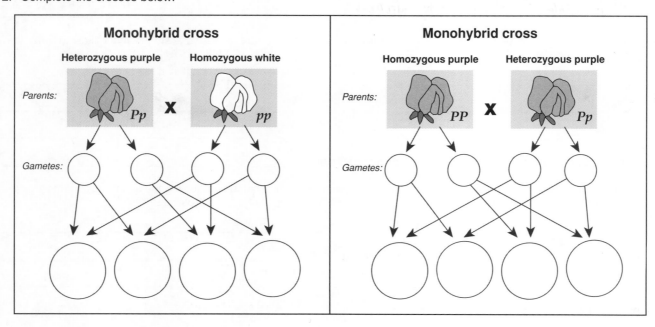

© 2016 **BIOZONE** International
ISBN: **978-1-927309-32-2**
Photocopying Prohibited

76 Monohybrid Crosses

75,76,80,81,82

Key Idea: A monohybrid cross studies the inheritance pattern of one gene. The offspring of these crosses occur in predictable ratios.

In this activity, you will examine six types of matings possible for a pair of alleles governing coat colour in guinea pigs. A dominant allele (**B**) produces black hair and its recessive allele (**b**), produces white. Each parent can produce two types of gamete by meiosis. Determine the **genotype** and **phenotype frequencies** for the crosses below. For crosses 3 to 6, also determine the gametes produced by each parent (write these in the circles) and offspring genotypes and phenotypes (write these inside the offspring shapes).

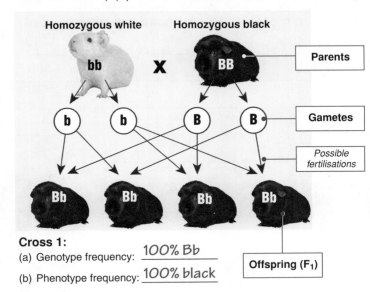

Cross 1:
(a) Genotype frequency: 100% Bb
(b) Phenotype frequency: 100% black

Parents · Gametes · Possible fertilisations · Offspring (F₁)

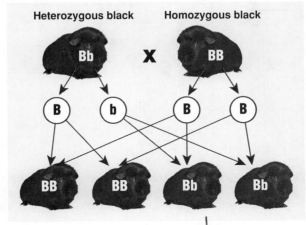

Cross 2:
(a) Genotype frequency: 50% BB 50% Bb
(b) Phenotype frequency: 100% black

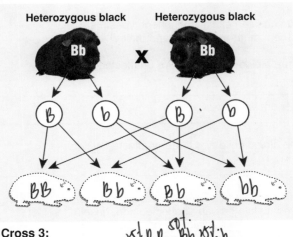
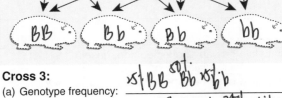

Cross 3:
(a) Genotype frequency: 25% BB 50% Bb 25% bb
(b) Phenotype frequency: 75% Black 25% White

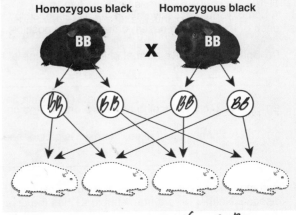

Cross 4:
(a) Genotype frequency: 100% BB
(b) Phenotype frequency: 100% Black.

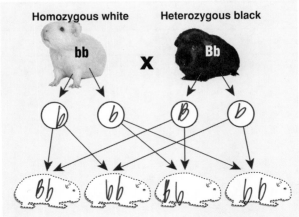
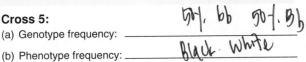

Cross 5:
(a) Genotype frequency: 50% bb 50% Bb
(b) Phenotype frequency: Black White

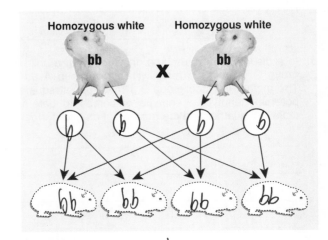
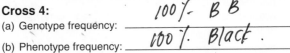

Cross 6:
(a) Genotype frequency: 100% bb
(b) Phenotype frequency: 100% White

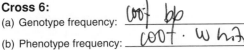

LINK 77 LINK 75 WEB 76 **KNOW**

77 Problems Involving Monohybrid Inheritance

Key Idea: For monohybrid crosses involving autosomal unlinked genes, the offspring appear in predictable ratios. The following problems involve Mendelian crosses. The alleles involved are associated with various phenotypic traits controlled by a single gene. The problems are to give you practise in problem solving using Mendelian genetics.

1. A dominant gene (**W**) produces wire-haired texture in dogs; its recessive allele (**w**) produces smooth hair. A group of heterozygous wire-haired individuals are crossed and their F_1 progeny are then test-crossed. Determine the expected genotypic and phenotypic ratios among the **test cross** progeny:

_____

_____

_____

_____

2. In sheep, black wool is due to a recessive allele (**b**) and white wool to its dominant allele (**B**). A white ram is crossed to a white ewe. Both animals carry the black allele (b). They produce a white ram lamb, which is then back crossed to the female parent. Determine the probability of the **back cross** offspring being black:

_____

_____

_____

3. A homozygous recessive allele, **aa**, is responsible for albinism. Humans can exhibit this phenotype. In each of the following cases, determine the possible genotypes of the mother and father, and their children:

(a) Both parents have normal phenotypes; some of their children are albino and others are unaffected: _____

_____

(b) Both parents are albino and have only albino children: _____

(c) The woman is unaffected, the man is albino, and they have one albino child and three unaffected children:

_____

4. Two mothers give birth to sons at a busy hospital. The son of the first couple has haemophilia, a recessive, X-linked disease. Neither parent from couple #1 has the disease. The second couple has an unaffected son, despite the fact that the father has haemophilia. The two couples challenge the hospital in court, claiming their babies must have been swapped at birth. You must advise as to whether or not the sons could have been swapped. What would you say?

_____

_____

_____

5. In a dispute over parentage, the mother of a child with blood group O identifies a male with blood group A as the father. The mother is blood group B. Draw Punnett squares to show possible genotype/phenotype outcomes to determine if the male is the father and the reasons (if any) for further dispute:

_____

_____

_____

_____

_____

© 2016 **BIOZONE** International
ISBN: 978-1-927309-32-2
Photocopying Prohibited

78 Codominance of Alleles

Key Idea: In inheritance involving codominant alleles, neither allele is recessive and both alleles are equally and independently expressed in the heterozygote.

Codominance is an inheritance pattern in which both alleles in a heterozygote contribute to the phenotype and both alleles are **independently** and **equally expressed**. Examples include the human blood group AB and certain coat colours in horses and cattle. Reddish coat colour is equally dominant with white. Animals that have both alleles have coats that are roan (both red and white hairs are present).

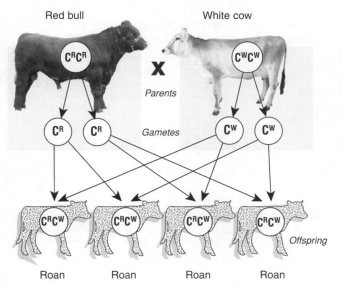

Red bull — $C^R C^R$ — White cow — $C^W C^W$

X

Parents

Gametes — C^R C^R — C^W C^W

Offspring — $C^R C^W$ $C^R C^W$ $C^R C^W$ $C^R C^W$

Roan   Roan   Roan   Roan

A roan shorthorn heifer

In the shorthorn cattle breed, coat colour is inherited. White shorthorn parents always produce calves with white coats. Red parents always produce red calves. However, when a red parent mates with a white one, the calves have a coat colour that is different from either parent; a mixture of red and white hairs, called roan. Use the example (left) to help you to solve the problems below.

1. Explain how codominance of alleles can result in offspring with a phenotype that is different from either parent:

_____

2. A white bull is mated with a roan cow (right):

   (a) Fill in the spaces to show the genotypes and phenotypes for parents and calves:

   (b) What is the phenotype ratio for this cross?

   _____

   (c) How could a cattle farmer control the breeding so that the herd ultimately consisted of only red cattle:

   _____
   _____
   _____
   _____
   _____

White bull   Roan cow

X

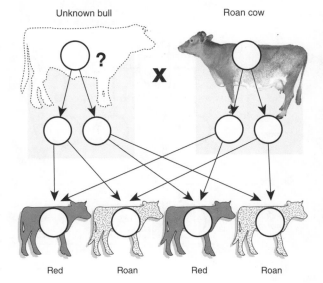

3. A farmer has only roan cattle on his farm. He suspects that one of the neighbours' bulls may have jumped the fence to mate with his cows earlier in the year because half the calves born were red and half were roan. One neighbour has a red bull, the other has a roan.

   (a) Fill in the spaces (right) to show the genotype and phenotype for parents and calves.

   (b) Which bull serviced the cows? **red** or **roan** (*delete one*)

4. Describe the classical phenotypic ratio for a codominant gene resulting from the cross of two heterozygous parents (e.g. a cross between two roan cattle):

   _____
   _____

Unknown bull   Roan cow

?   X

Red   Roan   Red   Roan

LINK 76   LINK 75   WEB 78   **KNOW**

79 Codominance in Multiple Allele Systems

Key Idea: The human ABO blood group system is a multiple allele system involving the codominant alleles *A* and *B* and the recessive allele *O*.

The four common blood groups of the human 'ABO blood group system' are determined by three alleles: *A*, *B*, and *O*. The ABO antigens consist of sugars attached to the surface of red blood cells. The alleles code for enzymes (proteins) that join these sugars together. The allele O produces a non-

functioning enzyme that is unable to make any changes to the basic antigen (sugar) molecule. The other two alleles (*A*, *B*) are **codominant** and are expressed equally. They each produce a different functional enzyme that adds a different, specific sugar to the basic sugar molecule. The blood group A and B antigens are able to react with antibodies present in the blood of other people so blood must always be matched for transfusion.

Recessive allele: **O** produces a non-functioning protein
Dominant allele: **A** produces an enzyme which forms **A antigen**
Dominant allele: **B** produces an enzyme which forms **B antigen**

Blood group (phenotype)	Possible genotypes	Frequency in the UK
O	*OO*	47%
A	*AA, AO*	42%
B		8%
AB		3%

If a person has the **AO** allele combination then their blood group will be group **A**. The presence of the recessive allele has no effect on the blood group in the presence of a dominant allele. Another possible allele combination that can create the same blood group is **AA**.

Source: http://www.transfusionguidelines.org.uk/ Allele terminology follows latest recommended (use of *I* allele terminology has been discontinued as inaccurate)

1. Use the information above to complete the table for the possible genotypes for blood group B and group AB.

2. Below are four crosses possible between couples of various blood group types. The first example has been completed for you. Complete the genotype and phenotype for the other three crosses below:

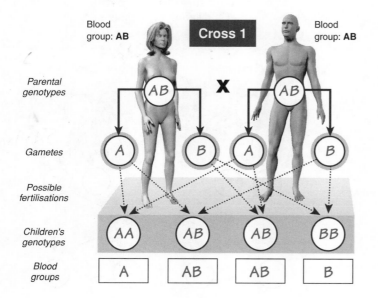

Cross 1 — Blood group: **AB** × Blood group: **AB**

- Parental genotypes: AB × AB
- Gametes: A, B, A, B
- Children's genotypes: AA, AB, AB, BB
- Blood groups: A, AB, AB, B

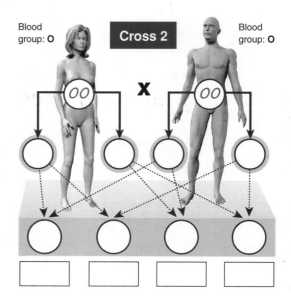

Cross 2 — Blood group: **O** × Blood group: **O**

- Parental genotypes: OO × OO

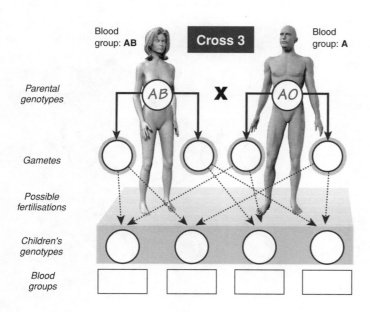

Cross 3 — Blood group: **AB** × Blood group: **A**

- Parental genotypes: AB × AO

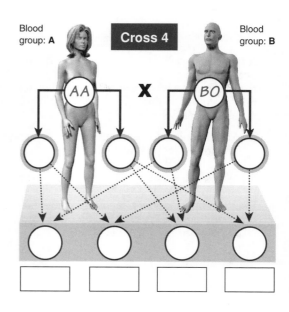

Cross 4 — Blood group: **A** × Blood group: **B**

- Parental genotypes: AA × BO

 © 2016 **BIOZONE** International
ISBN: 978-1-927309-32-2
Photocopying Prohibited

80 Sex Linked Genes

Key Idea: Many genes on the X chromosome do not have a match on the Y chromosome. In males, a recessive allele on the X chromosome cannot therefore be masked by a dominant allele.

Sex linkage occurs when a gene is located on a sex chromosome (usually the X). The result of this is that the character encoded by the gene is usually seen only in one sex (the heterogametic sex). In humans, recessive sex linked genes cause a number of heritable disorders in males, e.g. haemophilia. Women who have a recessive allele are said to be carriers. One of the gene loci controlling coat colour in cats is sex-linked. The two alleles, red and non-red (or black), are found only on the X-chromosome.

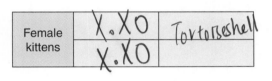

Allele types

X_o = Non-red (=black)
X_O = Red

Genotypes

X_oX_o, X_oY = Black coated female, male
X_OX_O, X_OY = Orange coated female, male
X_OX_o = Tortoiseshell (intermingled black and orange in fur) in female cats only

Phenotypes

1. An owner of a cat is thinking of mating her black female cat with an orange male cat. Before she does this, she would like to know what possible coat colours could result from such a cross. Use the symbols above to fill in the diagram on the right. Summarise the possible genotypes and phenotypes of the kittens in the tables below.

	Genotypes	Phenotypes
Male kittens	X_oY	Black
	X_oY	

Female kittens	X_oX_O	Tortoiseshell
	X_oX_O	

2. A female tortoiseshell cat mated with an unknown male cat in the neighbourhood and has given birth to a litter of six kittens. The owner of this female cat wants to know what the appearance and the genotype of the father was of these kittens. Use the symbols above to fill in the diagram on the right. Also show the possible fertilisations by placing appropriate arrows.

Describe the father cat's:

(a) Genotype: X_OY

(b) Phenotype: Orange

3. The owner of another cat, a black female, also wants to know which cat fathered her two tortoiseshell female and two black male kittens. Use the symbols above to fill in the diagram on the right. Show the possible fertilisations by placing appropriate arrows.

Describe the father cat's:

(a) Genotype: X_OY

(b) Phenotype: Orange

(c) Was it the same male cat that fathered both this litter and the one above?
YES / NO   (delete one)

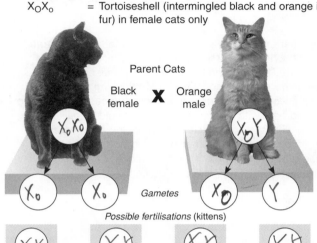

Parent Cats

Black female **X** Orange male
X_oX_o — X_OY

Gametes
X_o X_o — X_O Y

Possible fertilisations (kittens)
X_oX_O X_oY X_oX_O X_oY

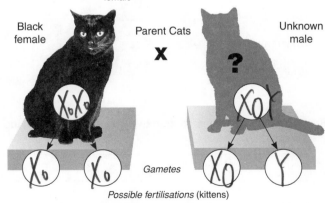

Tortoiseshell female — Parent Cats — Unknown male
X_OX_o — **X** — ? X_OY

Gametes
X_O X_o — X_O Y

Possible fertilisations (kittens)
X_OX_O X_OX_o X_OY X_OY
2 orange females | 1 tortoiseshell female | 1 black male | 2 orange males

Black female — Parent Cats — Unknown male
X_oX_o — **X** — ? X_OY

Gametes
X_o X_o — X_O Y

Possible fertilisations (kittens)
X_OX_o X_OX_o X_oY X_oY
1 tortoiseshell female | 1 tortoiseshell female | 1 black male | 1 black male

LINK **81**   LINK **76**   LINK **75**   WEB **80**   DATA

100 Home ad

Dominant allele in humans

A rare form of rickets in humans is determined by a **dominant** allele of a gene on the **X chromosome** (it is not found on the Y chromosome). This condition is not successfully treated with vitamin D therapy. The allele types, genotypes, and phenotypes are as follows:

Allele types	Genotypes	Phenotypes
X_R = affected by rickets	$X_R X_R, X_R X_Y$ =	Affected female
X = normal	$X_R Y$ =	Affected male
	XX_Y, XY_Y =	Normal female, male

As a genetic counsellor you are presented with a married couple where one of them has a family history of this disease. The husband is affected by this disease and the wife is normal. The couple, who are thinking of starting a family, would like to know what their chances are of having a child born with this condition. They would also like to know what the probabilities are of having an affected boy or affected girl. Use the symbols above to complete the diagram right and determine the probabilities stated below (expressed as a proportion or percentage).

4. Determine the probability of having:

    (a) Affected children: _____ 50%

    (b) An affected girl: _____ 100%

    (c) An affected boy: _____ 0%

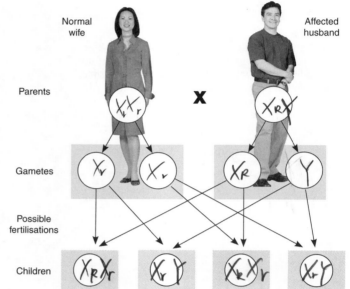

Another couple with a family history of the same disease also come in to see you to obtain genetic counselling. In this case the husband is normal and the wife is affected. The wife's father was not affected by this disease. Determine what their chances are of having a child born with this condition. They would also like to know what the probabilities are of having an affected boy or affected girl. Use the symbols above to complete the diagram right and determine the probabilities stated below (expressed as a proportion or percentage).

5. Determine the probability of having:

    (a) Affected children: _____ 50%

    (b) An affected girl: _____ 50%

    (c) An affected boy: _____ 50%

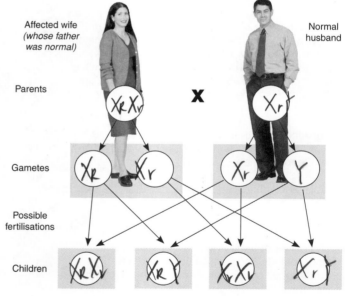

6. Describing examples other than those above, discuss the role of **sex linkage** in the inheritance of genetic disorders:

_____

_____

_____

_____

_____

81 Inheritance Patterns

Key Idea: Sex-linked traits and autosomal traits have different inheritance patterns.
Complete the following monohybrid crosses for different types of inheritance patterns in humans: autosomal recessive, autosomal dominant, sex linked recessive, and sex linked dominant inheritance.

1. Inheritance of autosomal recessive traits
Example: *Albinism*

Albinism (lack of pigment in hair, eyes and skin) is inherited as an autosomal recessive allele (not sex-linked).

Using the codes: **PP** (normal) **Pp** (carrier)
pp (albino)

(a) Enter the parent phenotypes and complete the Punnett square for a cross between two carrier genotypes.

(b) Give the ratios for the phenotypes from this cross.

Phenotype ratios: ___Normal 3 : albino 1___

Female parent phenotype: **Normal, carrier !**

Male parent phenotype: **Normal carrier**

	P (eggs)	p
P (sperm)	PP	Pp
p	Pp	~~PP~~

2. Inheritance of autosomal dominant traits
Example: *Woolly hair*

Woolly hair is inherited as an autosomal dominant allele. Each affected individual will have at least one affected parent.

Using the codes: **WW** (woolly hair)
Ww (woolly hair, heterozygous)
ww (normal hair)

(a) Enter the parent phenotypes and complete the Punnett square for a cross between two heterozygous individuals.

(b) Give the ratios for the phenotypes from this cross.

Phenotype ratios: ___Normal 1 : woodly 3___

Female parent phenotype: **woolly hair**

Male parent phenotype: **woolly hair**

	W (eggs)	w
W (sperm)	WW	Ww
w	Ww	ww

3. Inheritance of sex linked recessive traits
Example: *Haemophilia*

Inheritance of haemophilia is sex linked. Males with the recessive (haemophilia) allele, are affected. Females can be carriers.

Using the codes: **XX** (normal female)
XX_h (carrier female)
X_hX_h (haemophiliac female)
XY (normal male)
X_hY (haemophiliac male)

(a) Enter the parent phenotypes and complete the Punnett square for a cross between a normal male and a carrier female.

(b) Give the ratios for the phenotypes from this cross.

Phenotype ratios: ___Female = Normal 2, Haemophiliac 0___
___Male : 1 : 1___

Female parent phenotype: [ ]

Male parent phenotype: [ ]

	X (eggs)	X_h
X (sperm)	XX_h	X_hX_h
Y	XY	X_hY

4. Inheritance of sex linked dominant traits
Example: *Sex linked form of rickets*

A rare form of rickets is inherited on the X chromosome.

Using the codes: **XX** (normal female); **XY** (normal male)
X_RX (affected heterozygote female)
X_RX_R (affected female)
X_RY (affected male)

(a) Enter the parent phenotypes and complete the Punnett square for a cross between an affected male and heterozygous female.

(b) Give the ratios for the phenotypes from this cross.

Phenotype ratios: ___Female - normal 0, rickets 2___
___Male : 1 : 1___

Female parent phenotype: [ ]

Male parent phenotype: [ ]

	X_R (eggs)	X
X_R (sperm)	X_RX_R	X_RX_r
Y	X_RY	X_rY

TEST

82 Dihybrid Cross

Key Idea: A dihybrid cross studies the inheritance pattern of two genes. In crosses involving unlinked autosomal genes, the offspring occur in predictable ratios.

There are four types of gamete produced in a cross involving two genes, where the genes are carried on separate chromosomes and are sorted independently of each other during meiosis. The two genes in the example below are on separate chromosomes and control two unrelated characteristics, **hair colour** and **coat length**. Black (B) and short (L) are dominant to white and long.

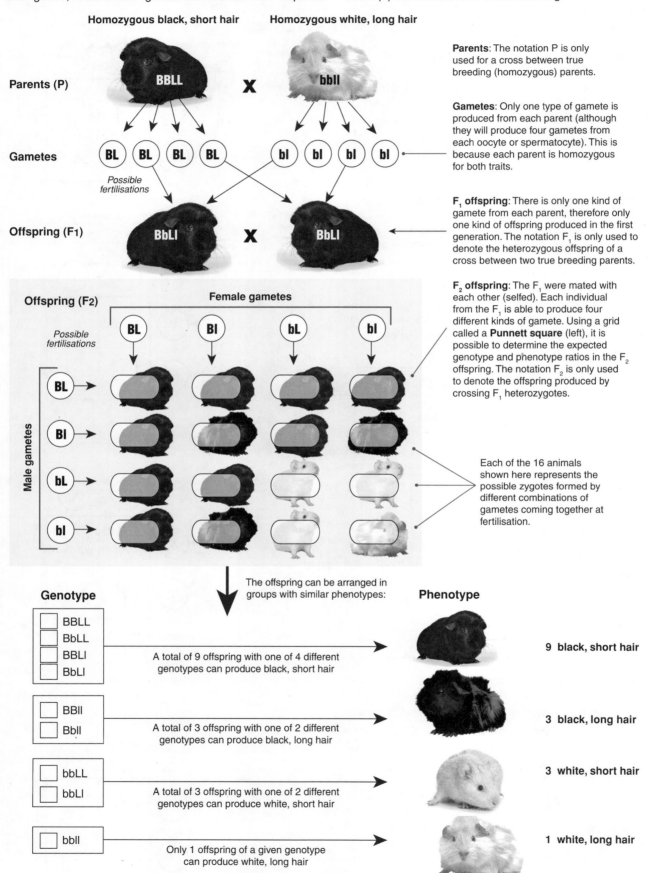

Homozygous black, short hair

Homozygous white, long hair

Parents (P) BBLL **X** bbll

Gametes BL BL BL BL bl bl bl bl

Possible fertilisations

Offspring (F1) BbLl **X** BbLl

Parents: The notation P is only used for a cross between true breeding (homozygous) parents.

Gametes: Only one type of gamete is produced from each parent (although they will produce four gametes from each oocyte or spermatocyte). This is because each parent is homozygous for both traits.

F₁ offspring: There is only one kind of gamete from each parent, therefore only one kind of offspring produced in the first generation. The notation F₁ is only used to denote the heterozygous offspring of a cross between two true breeding parents.

Offspring (F2)

Female gametes

Possible fertilisations

BL Bl bL bl

Male gametes

BL →

Bl →

bL →

bl →

F₂ offspring: The F₁ were mated with each other (selfed). Each individual from the F₁ is able to produce four different kinds of gamete. Using a grid called a **Punnett square** (left), it is possible to determine the expected genotype and phenotype ratios in the F₂ offspring. The notation F₂ is only used to denote the offspring produced by crossing F₁ heterozygotes.

Each of the 16 animals shown here represents the possible zygotes formed by different combinations of gametes coming together at fertilisation.

The offspring can be arranged in groups with similar phenotypes:

Genotype

Phenotype

☐ BBLL
☐ BbLL
☐ BBLl
☐ BbLl

A total of 9 offspring with one of 4 different genotypes can produce black, short hair

9 black, short hair

☐ BBll
☐ Bbll

A total of 3 offspring with one of 2 different genotypes can produce black, long hair

3 black, long hair

☐ bbLL
☐ bbLl

A total of 3 offspring with one of 2 different genotypes can produce white, short hair

3 white, short hair

☐ bbll

Only 1 offspring of a given genotype can produce white, long hair

1 white, long hair

1. Complete the Punnett square above and use it to fill in the number of each genotype in the boxes (above left).

WEB **82** LINK **83** LINK **84**

© 2016 **BIOZONE** International
ISBN: 978-1-927309-32-2
Photocopying Prohibited

83 Inheritance of Linked Genes

Key Idea: Linked genes are genes found on the same chromosome and tend to be inherited together. Linkage reduces the genetic variation in the offspring.

Genes are **linked** when they are on the same chromosome. Linked genes tend to be inherited together and the extent of crossing over depends on how close together they are on the chromosome. In genetic crosses, linkage is indicated when a greater proportion of the offspring from a cross are of the parental type (than would be expected if the alleles were on separate chromosomes and assorting independently). Linkage reduces the genetic variation that can be produced in the offspring.

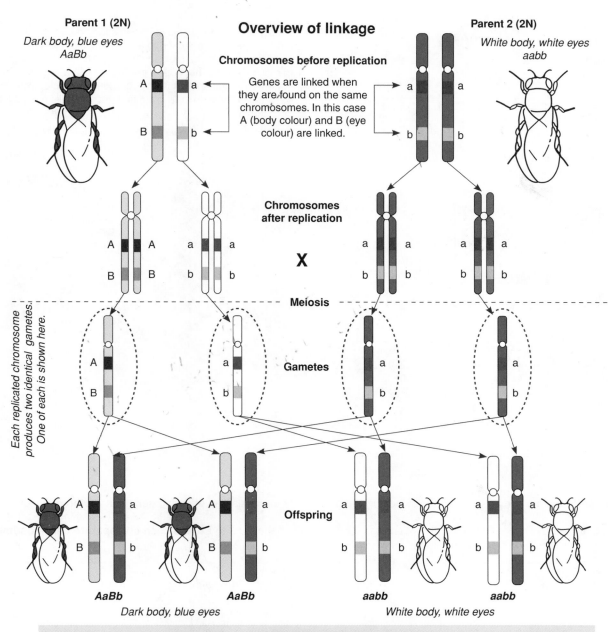

Overview of linkage

Parent 1 (2N)
Dark body, blue eyes
AaBb

Chromosomes before replication

Genes are linked when they are found on the same chromosomes. In this case A (body colour) and B (eye colour) are linked.

Parent 2 (2N)
White body, white eyes
aabb

Chromosomes after replication

X

Each replicated chromosome produces two identical gametes. One of each is shown here.

Meiosis

Gametes

Offspring

AaBb — *Dark body, blue eyes*

aabb — *White body, white eyes*

Possible offspring
Only two kinds of genotype combinations are possible. They are they same as the parent genotype.

1. What is the effect of **linkage** on the inheritance of genes? _____

_____

_____

2. Explain how linkage decreases the amount of genetic variation in the offspring: _____

_____

_____

_____

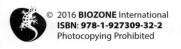
© 2016 **BIOZONE** International
ISBN: 978-1-927309-32-2
Photocopying Prohibited

LINK **86** LINK **85** LINK **84** WEB **83** KNOW

An example of linked genes in *Drosophila*

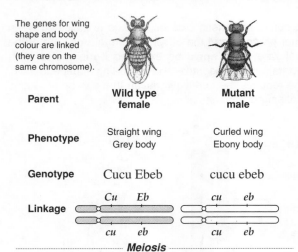

The genes for wing shape and body colour are linked (they are on the same chromosome).

	Wild type female	Mutant male
Parent		
Phenotype	Straight wing Grey body	Curled wing Ebony body
Genotype	Cucu Ebeb	cucu ebeb
Linkage		

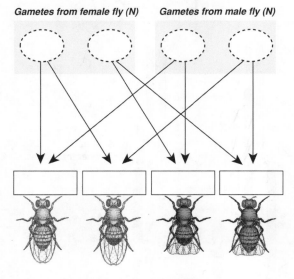

Meiosis

Gametes from female fly (N)　　**Gametes from male fly (N)**

Sex of offspring is irrelevant in this case

Contact **Newbyte Educational Software** for details of their superb *Drosophila Genetics* software package which includes coverage of linkage and recombination. *Drosophila* images © Newbyte Educational Software.

Drosophila and linked genes

In the example shown left, wild type alleles are dominant and are given an upper case symbol of the mutant phenotype (Cu or Eb). This notation used for *Drosophila* departs from the convention of using the dominant gene to provide the symbol. This is necessary because there are many mutant alternative phenotypes to the wild type (e.g. curled and vestigial wings). A lower case symbol of the wild type (e.g. ss for straight wing) would not indicate the mutant phenotype involved.

Drosophila melanogaster is known as a model organism. Model organisms are used to study particular biological phenomena, such as mutation. *Drosophila melanogaster* is particularly useful because it produces such a wide range of heritable mutations. Its short reproduction cycle, high offspring production, and low maintenance make it ideal for studying in the lab.

Drosophila melanogaster examples showing variations in eye and body colour. The wild type is marked with a w in the photo above.

3. Complete the linkage diagram above by adding the gametes in the ovals and offspring genotypes in the rectangles.

4. (a) List the possible genotypes in the offspring (above, left) if genes Cu and Eb had been on **separate chromosomes**:

_____

(b) If the female *Drosophila* had been homozygous for the dominant wild type alleles (CuCu EbEb), state:

The genotype(s) of the F_1: _____　The phenotype(s) of the F_1: _____

5. A second pair of *Drosophila* are mated. The female genotype is Vgvg EbEb (straight wings, grey body), while the male genotype is vgvg ebeb (vestigial wings, ebony body). Assuming the genes are linked, carry out the cross and list the genotypes and phenotypes of the offspring. Note vg = vestigial (no) wings:

_____

_____

_____

The genotype(s) of the F_1: _____　The phenotype(s) of the F_1: _____

6. Explain why *Drosophila* are often used as model organisms in the study of genetics: _____

_____

_____

© 2016 **BIOZONE** International
ISBN: 978-1-927309-32-2
Photocopying Prohibited

84 Recombination and Dihybrid Inheritance

Key Idea: Recombination is the exchange of alleles between homologous chromosomes as a result of crossing over. Recombination increases the genetic variation in the offspring. The alleles of parental linkage groups separate and new associations of alleles are formed in the gametes. Offspring formed from these gametes are called **recombinants** and show combinations of characteristics not seen in the parents.

In contrast to linkage, recombination increases genetic variation in the offspring. Recombination between the alleles of parental linkage groups is indicated by the appearance of non-parental types in the offspring, although not in the numbers that would be expected had the alleles been on separate chromosomes (independent assortment).

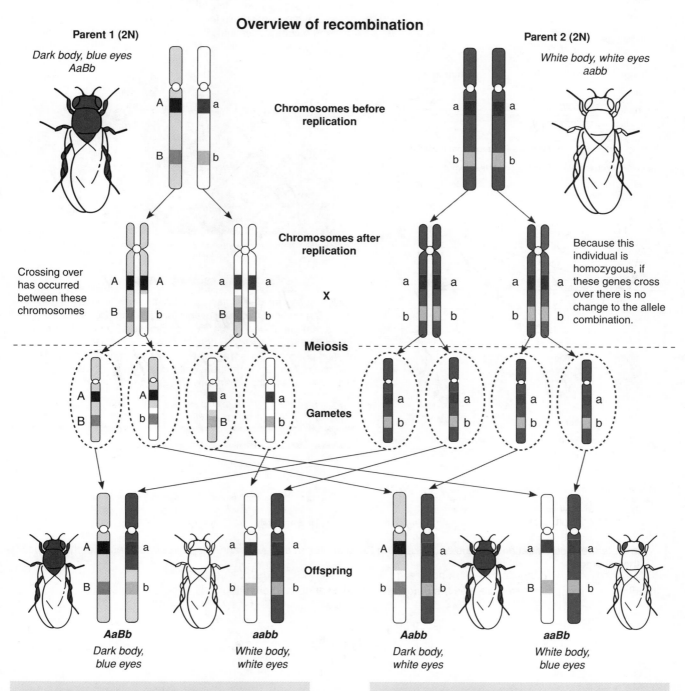

Overview of recombination

Parent 1 (2N)

Dark body, blue eyes
AaBb

Chromosomes before replication

Crossing over has occurred between these chromosomes

Parent 2 (2N)

White body, white eyes
aabb

Chromosomes after replication

X

Because this individual is homozygous, if these genes cross over there is no change to the allele combination.

Meiosis

Gametes

Offspring

AaBb
Dark body, blue eyes

aabb
White body, white eyes

Aabb
Dark body, white eyes

aaBb
White body, blue eyes

Non-recombinant offspring
These two offspring show allele combinations that are expected as a result of independent assortment during meiosis. Also called parental types.

Recombinant offspring
These two offspring show unexpected allele combinations. They can only arise if one of the parent's chromosomes has undergone crossing over.

1. Describe the effect of **recombination** on the inheritance of genes: _____

_____

_____

LINK 86 LINK 85 LINK 83 WEB 84 **KNOW**

An example of recombination

In the female parent, crossing over occurs between the linked genes for wing shape and body colour

Parent	Wild type female	Mutant male
Phenotype	Straight wing Grey body	Curled wing Ebony body
Genotype	Cucu Ebeb	cucu ebeb

Linkage

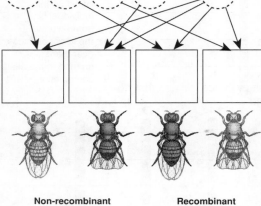

Cu   *Eb*   *cu*   *eb*

cu   *eb*   *cu*   *eb*

---------- Meiosis ----------

Gametes from female fly (N)
Crossing over has occurred, giving four types of gametes

Gametes from male fly (N)
Only one type of gamete is produced in this case

Non-recombinant offspring   **Recombinant offspring**

The sex of the offspring is irrelevant in this case

Contact **Newbyte Educational Software** for details of their superb *Drosophila Genetics* software package which includes coverage of linkage and recombination. *Drosophila* images © Newbyte Educational Software.

The cross (left) uses the same genotypes as the previous activity but, in this case, crossing over occurs between the alleles in a linkage group in one parent. The symbology used is the same.

Recombination produces variation

If crossing over does not occur, the possible combinations in the gametes is limited. **Crossing over and recombination increase the variation in the offspring**. In humans, even without crossing over, there are approximately $(2^{23})^2$ or 70 trillion genetically different zygotes that could form for every couple. Taking crossing over and recombination into account produces at least $(4^{23})^2$ or 5000 trillion trillion genetically different zygotes for every couple.

Family members may resemble each other, but they'll never be identical (except for identical twins).

Using recombination

Analysing recombination gave geneticists a way to map the genes on a chromosome. Crossing over is less likely to occur between genes that are close together on a chromosome than between genes that are far apart. By counting the number of offspring of each phenotype, the **frequency of recombination** can be calculated. The higher the frequency of recombination between two genes, the further apart they must be on the chromosome.

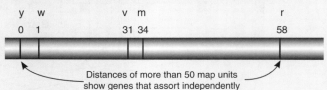

y   w   v m   r
0   1   31 34   58

Distances of more than 50 map units show genes that assort independently

Map of the X chromosome of *Drosophila*, showing the relative distances between five different genes (in map units).

2. Complete the recombination diagram above, adding the gametes in the ovals and offspring genotypes and phenotypes in the rectangles:

3. Explain how recombination increases the amount of genetic variation in offspring: _____

_____

_____

4. Explain why it is not possible to have a recombination frequency of greater than 50% (half recombinant progeny):

_____

_____

5. A second pair of *Drosophila* are mated. The female is Cucu YY (straight wing, grey body), while the male is Cucu yy (straight wing, yellow body). Assuming recombination, perform the cross and list the offspring genotypes and phenotypes:

_____

_____

_____

85 Detecting Linkage in Dihybrid Crosses

Key Idea: Linkage between genes can be detected by observing the phenotypic ratios in the offspring.

Shortly after the rediscovery of Mendel's work early in the 20th century, it became apparent that his ratios of 9:3:3:1 for heterozygous dihybrid crosses did not always hold true.

Experiments on sweet peas by William Bateson and Reginald Punnett, and on *Drosophila* by Thomas Hunt Morgan, showed that there appeared to be some kind of coupling between genes. This coupling, which we now know to be linkage, did not follow any genetic relationship known at the time.

Sweet pea cross

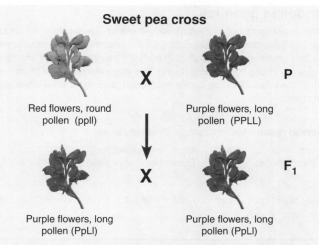

X **P**

Red flowers, round pollen (ppll) | Purple flowers, long pollen (PPLL)

X **F₁**

Purple flowers, long pollen (PpLl) | Purple flowers, long pollen (PpLl)

Bateson and Punnett studied sweet peas in which purple flowers (P) are dominant to red (p), and long pollen grains (L) are dominant to round (l). If these genes were unlinked, the outcome of an cross between two heterozygous sweet peas should have been a 9:3:3:1 ratio.

Table 1: Sweet pea cross results

	Observed	Expected
Purple long (P_L_)	284	
Purple round (P_ll)	21	
Red long (ppL_)	21	
Red round (ppll)	55	
Total	381	381

1. Fill in the missing numbers in the **expected** column of **Table 1**, remembering that a 9:3:3:1 ratio is expected:

2. (a) Fill in the missing numbers in the **expected** column of **Table 2**, remembering that a 1:1:1:1 ratio is expected:

   (b) Add the gamete type (parental/recombinant) to the gamete type column in Table 2:

   (c) What type of cross did Morgan perform here?

   _____

3. (a) Use the pedigree chart below to determine if nail-patella syndrome is dominant or recessive, giving reasons for your choice:

   _____

   _____

   _____

   _____

   (b) What evidence is there that nail-patella syndrome is linked to the ABO blood group locus?

   _____

   _____

   _____

   (c) Suggest a likely reason why individual III-3 is not affected despite carrying the B allele:

   _____

   _____

   _____

Morgan performed experiments to investigate linked genes in *Drosophila*. He crossed a heterozygous red-eyed normal-winged (Prpr Vgvg) fly with a homozygous purple-eyed vestigial-winged (prpr vgvg) fly. The table (below) shows the outcome of the cross.

 X

Red eyed normal winged (Prpr Vgvg) | Purple eyed vestigial winged (prpr vgvg)

Table 2: *Drosophila* cross results

Genotype	Observed	Expected	Gamete type
Prpr Vgvg	1339	710	Parental
prpr Vgvg	152		
Prpr vgvg	154		
prpr vgvg	1195		
Total	2840	2840	

Pedigree for nail-patella syndrome

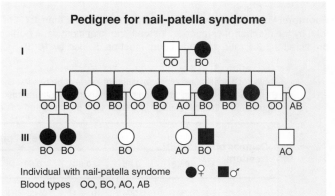

Individual with nail-patella syndome ●♀ ■♂
Blood types   OO, BO, AO, AB

Linked genes can be detected by pedigree analysis. The diagram above shows the pedigree for the inheritance of nail-patella syndrome, which results in small, poorly developed nails and kneecaps in affected people. Other body parts such as elbows, chest, and hips can also be affected. The nail-patella syndrome gene is linked to the ABO blood group locus.

LINK **86** | LINK **83** | **KNOW**

86 Chi-Squared Test in Genetics

Key Idea: The chi-squared test for goodness of fit (χ^2) can be used for testing the outcome of dihybrid crosses against an expected (predicted) Mendelian ratio.

When using the chi-squared test, the null hypothesis predicts the ratio of offspring of different phenotypes according to the expected Mendelian ratio for the cross, assuming independent assortment of alleles (no linkage). Significant departures from the predicted Mendelian ratio indicate linkage of the alleles in question. Raw counts should be used and a large sample size is required for the test to be valid.

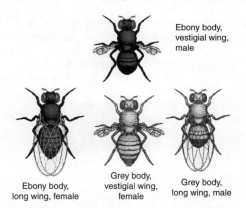

Ebony body, vestigial wing, male

Ebony body, long wing, female

Grey body, vestigial wing, female

Grey body, long wing, male

Images of *Drosophila* courtesy of **Newbyte Educational Software**: *Drosophila* Genetics Lab (www.newbyte.com)

Using χ^2 in Mendelian genetics

In a *Drosophila* genetics experiment, two individuals were crossed (the details of the cross are not relevant here). The predicted Mendelian ratios for the offspring of this cross were 1:1:1:1 for each of the four following phenotypes: grey body-long wing, grey body-vestigial wing, ebony body-long wing, ebony body-vestigial wing. The observed results of the cross were not exactly as predicted. The following numbers for each phenotype were observed in the offspring of the cross:

Observed results of the example *Drosophila* cross

Grey body, long wing	**98**	Ebony body, long wing	**102**
Grey body, vestigial wing	**88**	Ebony body, vestigial wing	**112**

Using χ^2, the probability of this result being consistent with a 1:1:1:1 ratio could be tested. Worked example as follows:

Step 1: Calculate the expected value (E)

In this case, this is the sum of the observed values divided by the number of categories (see note below) $\dfrac{400}{4} = 100$

Step 2: Calculate O – E

The difference between the observed and expected values is calculated as a measure of the deviation from a predicted result. Since some deviations are negative, they are all squared to give positive values. This step is usually performed as part of a tabulation (right, darker blue column).

Category	O	E	O – E	$(O - E)^2$	$\dfrac{(O - E)^2}{E}$
Grey, long wing	98	100	–2	4	0.04
Grey, vestigial wing	88	100	–12	144	1.44
Ebony, long wing	102	100	2	4	0.04
Ebony, vestigial wing	112	100	12	144	1.44

Total = 400 χ^2 $\Sigma = 2.96$

Step 3: Calculate the value of χ^2

$$\chi^2 = \sum \frac{(O - E)^2}{E}$$

Where:
O = the observed result
E = the expected result
Σ = sum of

The calculated χ^2 value is given at the bottom right of the last column in the tabulation.

Step 5a: Using the χ^2 table

On the χ^2 table (part reproduced in Table 1 below) with 3 degrees of freedom, the calculated value for χ^2 of 2.96 corresponds to a probability of between 0.2 and 0.5 (see arrow). *This means that by chance alone a χ^2 value of 2.96 could be expected between 20% and 50% of the time.*

Step 4: Calculating degrees of freedom

The probability that any particular χ^2 value could be exceeded by chance depends on the number of degrees of freedom. This is simply **one less than the total number of categories** (this is the number that could vary independently without affecting the last value). **In this case: 4–1 = 3.**

Step 5b: Using the χ^2 table

The probability of between 0.2 and 0.5 is higher than the 0.05 value which is generally regarded as significant. The null hypothesis cannot be rejected and we have no reason to believe that the observed results differ significantly from the expected (at $P = 0.05$).

Footnote: Many Mendelian crosses involve ratios other than 1:1. For these, calculation of the expected values is not simply a division of the total by the number of categories. Instead, the total must be apportioned according to the ratio. For example, for a total of 400 as above, in a predicted 9:3:3:1 ratio, the total count must be divided by 16 (9+3+3+1) and the expected values will be 225: 75: 75: 25 in each category.

Table 1: Critical values of χ^2 at different levels of probability. By convention, the critical probability for rejecting the null hypothesis (H_0) is 5%. If the test statistic is less than the tabulated critical value for $P = 0.05$ we cannot reject H_0 and the result is not significant. If the test statistic is greater than the tabulated value for $P = 0.05$ we reject H_0 in favour of the alternative hypothesis.

Degrees of freedom	Level of probability (P)									
	0.98	0.95	0.80	0.50	0.20	0.10	0.05	0.02	0.01	0.001
1	0.001	0.004	0.064	0.455	1.64	2.71	3.84	5.41	6.64	10.83
2	0.040	0.103	0.466	1.386	3.22	4.61	5.99	7.82	9.21	13.82
3	0.185	0.352	1.005	2.366	4.64	6.25	7.82	9.84	11.35	16.27
4	0.429	0.711	1.649	3.357	5.99	7.78	9.49	11.67	13.28	18.47
5	0.752	0.145	2.343	4.351	7.29	9.24	11.07	13.39	15.09	20.52

(0.50 column marked χ^2; ← Do not reject H_0 | Reject H_0 →)

© 2016 **BIOZONE** International
ISBN: 978-1-927309-32-2
Photocopying Prohibited

87 Chi-Squared Exercise in Genetics

Key Idea: The following problems examine the use of the chi-squared (χ^2) test in genetics.

A worked example illustrating the use of the chi-squared test for a genetic cross is provided on the previous page.

1. In a tomato plant experiment, two heterozygous individuals were crossed (the details of the cross are not relevant here). The predicted Mendelian ratios for the offspring of this cross were **9:3:3:1** for each of the **four following phenotypes**: purple stem-jagged leaf edge, purple stem-smooth leaf edge, green stem-jagged leaf edge, green stem-smooth leaf edge.

   The observed results of the cross were not exactly as predicted.
   The numbers of offspring with each phenotype are provided below:

Observed results of the tomato plant cross			
Purple stem-jagged leaf edge	12	Green stem-jagged leaf edge	8
Purple stem-smooth leaf edge	9	Green stem-smooth leaf edge	0

   (a) State your null hypothesis for this investigation (H0): _____

   _____

   (b) State the alternative hypothesis (HA): _____

   _____

2. Use the chi-squared (χ^2) test to determine if the differences observed between the phenotypes are significant. The table of critical values of χ^2 at different P values is provided on the previous page.

   (a) Enter the observed values (number of individuals) and complete the table to calculate the χ^2 value:

Category	O	E	O — E	(O — E)²	$\frac{(O-E)^2}{E}$
Purple stem, jagged leaf					
Purple stem, smooth leaf					
Green stem, jagged leaf					
Green stem, smooth leaf					
Σ					Σ

   (b) Calculate χ^2 value using the equation:

   $$\chi^2 = \sum \frac{(O - E)^2}{E} \qquad \chi^2 = \underline{\hspace{2cm}}$$

   (c) Calculate the degrees of freedom: _____

   (d) Using the χ^2 table, state the P value corresponding to your calculated χ^2 value:

   _____

   (e) State your decision: *(circle one)*

   reject H0 / do not reject H0

3. Students carried out a pea plant experiment, where two heterozygous individuals were crossed. The predicted Mendelian ratios for the offspring were **9:3:3:1** for each of the **four following phenotypes**: round-yellow seed, round-green seed, wrinkled-yellow seed, wrinkled-green seed.

   The observed results were as follows:

Round-yellow seed	441	Wrinkled-yellow seed	143
Round-green seed	159	Wrinkled-green seed	57

   Use a separate piece of paper to complete the following:

   (a) State the null and alternative hypotheses (H0 and HA).

   (b) Calculate the χ^2 value.

   (c) Calculate the degrees of freedom and state the P value corresponding to your calculated χ^2 value.

   (d) State whether or not you reject your null hypothesis: reject H0 / do not reject H0 (circle one)

4. Comment on the whether the χ^2 values obtained above are similar. Suggest a reason for any difference:

   _____

   _____

   _____

LINK WEB

86 **87** DATA

88 Problems Involving Dihybrid Inheritance

Key Idea: For dihybrid crosses involving autosomal unlinked genes, the offspring appear in predictable ratios.

Test your understanding of dihybrid inheritance by solving problems involving the inheritance of two genes.

1. In cats, the following alleles are present for coat characteristics: black (**B**), brown (**b**), short (**L**), long (**l**), tabby (**T**), blotched tabby (**tb**). Use the information to complete the dihybrid crosses below:

(a) A black short haired (**BBLl**) male is crossed with a black long haired (**Bbll**) female. Determine the genotypic and phenotypic ratios of the offspring:

Genotype ratio: _____

_____

Phenotype ratio: _____

_____

_____

(b) A tabby, short haired male (**TtbLl**) is crossed with a blotched tabby, short haired (**tbtbLl**) female. Determine ratios of the offspring:

Genotype ratio: _____

_____

Phenotype ratio: _____

_____

_____

2. A plant with orange-striped flowers was cultivated from seeds. The plant was self-pollinated and the F_1 progeny appeared in the following ratios: 89 orange with stripes, 29 yellow with stripes, 32 orange without stripes, 9 yellow without stripes.

(a) Describe the dominance relationships of the alleles responsible for the phenotypes observed: _____

_____

_____

(b) Determine the genotype of the original plant with orange striped flowers: _____

_____

3. In rabbits, spotted coat **S** is dominant to solid colour **s,** while for coat colour, black **B** is dominant to brown **b**. A brown spotted rabbit is mated with a solid black one and all the offspring are black spotted (the genes are not linked).

(a) State the genotypes:

Parent 1: _____

Parent 2: _____

Offspring: _____

(b) Use the Punnett square to show the outcome of a cross between the F_1 (the F_2):

(c) Using ratios, state the phenotypes of the F_2 generation: _____

_____

_____

_____

© 2016 **BIOZONE** International
ISBN: 978-1-927309-32-2
Photocopying Prohibited

4. In guinea pigs, rough coat **R** is dominant over smooth coat **r** and black coat **B** is dominant over white **b**. The genes are not linked.
    A homozygous rough black animal was crossed with a homozygous smooth white:

    (a) State the genotype of the **F₁**: _____

    (b) State the phenotype of the **F₁**: _____

    (c) Use the Punnett square (top right) to show the outcome of a cross between the F₁ (the F₂):

    (d) Using ratios, state the phenotypes of the F₂ generation: _____

    _____

    _____

    (e) Use the Punnett square (right) to show the outcome of a **back cross** of the **F₁** to the rough, black parent:

    (f) Using ratios, state the phenotype of the F₂ generation: _____

    _____

    (g) A rough black guinea pig was crossed with a rough white one produced the following offspring: 28 rough black, 31 rough white, 11 smooth black, and 10 smooth white. Determine the genotypes of the parents:

    _____

5. The Himalayan colour-pointed, long-haired cat is a breed developed by crossing a pedigree (true-breeding), uniform-coloured, long-haired Persian with a pedigree colour-pointed (darker face, ears, paws, and tail) short-haired Siamese.

    The genes controlling hair colouring and length are on separate chromosomes: uniform colour **U**, colour pointed **u**, short hair **S**, long hair **s**.

    Persian   Siamese   Himalayan

    (a) Using the symbols above, indicate the genotype of each breed below its photograph (above, right).

    _____ _____ _____

    (b) State the genotype of the **F₁** (Siamese X Persian): _____

    (c) State the phenotype of the **F₁**: _____

    (d) Use the Punnett square to show the outcome of a cross between the F₁ (the F₂):

    (e) State the ratio of the F₂ that would be Himalayan: _____

    (f) State whether the Himalayan would be true breeding: _____

    (g) State the ratio of the F₂ that would be colour-point, short-haired cats: _____

6. A *Drosophila* male with genotype **Cucu Ebeb** (straight wing, grey body) is crossed with a female with genotype **cucu ebeb** (curled wing, ebony body). The phenotypes of the F₁ were recorded and the percentage of each type calculated. The percentages were: Straight wings, grey body 45%, curled wings, ebony body 43%, straight wings, ebony body 6%, and curled wings grey body 6%.

    Straight wing Cucu Grey body, Ebeb

    (a) Is there evidence of crossing over in the offspring? _____

    (b) Explain your answer: _____

    _____

    _____

    Curled wing cucu Ebony body, ebeb

    (c) Determine the genotypes of the offspring: _____

    _____

89 Gene Interactions

Key Idea: Epistatic genes interact to control the expression of a single characteristic.

Although one gene product (e.g. an enzyme) may independently produce a single phenotypic character, genes frequently interact to produce the phenotype we see. Two or more loci may interact to produce new phenotypes, or an allele at one locus may mask or modify the effect of alleles at other loci. These epistatic gene interactions result in characteristic phenotypic ratios in the offspring that are different from those expected under independent assortment.

In the example of guinea pigs (see *Dihybrid Cross*) the alleles B and b, and L and l act independently on coat colour and length respectively. If the L or l allele is present there is no effect on the phenotype produced by the B or b allele. But consider a situation where the L or l allele works together with the B and b alleles to produce a single phenotype? A simple example of this is the comb type of chickens.

There are four comb types in chickens (right). The four phenotypes are produced by the interactions of two alleles R and P. In a cross between two individuals heterozygous for both alleles (RrPp), the phenotypic ratio is 9:3:3:1, as would be expected in a dihybrid cross involving independent assortment. However, there are many examples of gene interactions that produce different phenotypic ratios. The ratio can be diagnostic in that it can indicate the type of interaction involved.

Single comb	**Pea comb**	**Rose comb**	**Walnut comb**
Genotypes:	Genotypes:	Genotypes:	Genotypes:
rrpp	**rrP_**	**R_pp**	**R_P_**
rrpp	rrPp, rrPP	Rrpp, RRpp	RRPP RrPP, RrPp, RRPp

In chickens, new phenotypes result from interaction between dominant alleles, as well as from the interaction between homozygous recessives.

How do genes interact?

Gene interaction usually occurs when the protein products or enzymes of several genes are all part of the same metabolic process. In the example below, enzyme A (produced from gene A) acts on a precursor substance to produce a colourless intermediate. Enzyme B (from gene B) acts on the intermediate to produce the final product. If either gene A or gene B produces a non-functional enzyme, the end product will be affected. The way gene A or B act on their substrates affects the appearance of the final product and produces different phenotypic ratios. The ratios can be used to identify the type of gene interaction, but they all come under the title of **epistasis**.

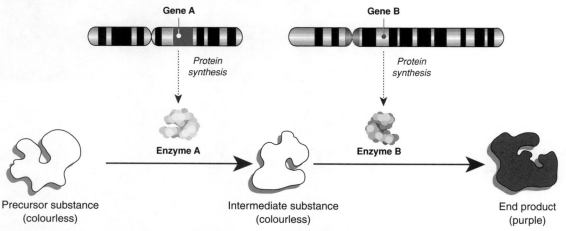

1. (a) For the example of the comb type in chickens determine the ratios of each comb type in a heterozygous cross:

   _____

   (b) What phenotype is produced by the interaction of dominant alleles? _____

   (c) What phenotype is produced by the interaction of recessive alleles? _____

2. In the metabolic process shown above, gene A has the alleles A and a. Allele a produces a non-functional enzyme. Gene B has the alleles B and b. Allele b produces a non-functional enzyme. What is the effect on the end product if:

   (a) Gene A has the allele a and Gene B has the allele B: _____

   (b) Gene A has the allele A and Gene B has the allele b: _____

   (c) Gene A has the allele A and Gene B has the allele B: _____

   (d) Gene A has the allele a and Gene B has the allele b: _____

   (e) On a separate sheet, use a Punnett square to determine the ratio of purple to colourless from a cross AABb x AaBb:

   _____

© 2016 **BIOZONE** International
ISBN: 978-1-927309-32-2
Photocopying Prohibited

WEB LINK LINK

KNOW  89 82 90

Table of gene interactions

This table shows five common dihybrid gene interactions and a dihybrid cross with no gene interaction as a comparison. The important point to note is the change to the expected dihybrid 9:3:3:1 ratio in each case. Note that there is independent assortment at the genotypic level. Epistasis is indicated by the change in the phenotypic ratio. Collaboration is usually not considered an epistatic effect because the phenotypic ratio is unchanged, but it does fit in the broad definition of epistasis being an interaction of two or more genes to control a single phenotype.

No of offspring (out of 16)

Possible genotypes from AaBb x AaBb

Type of gene interaction	AABB 1	AABb 2	AaBB 2	AaBb 4	AAbb 1	Aabb 2	aaBB 1	aaBb 2	aabb 1	F_1 dihybrid ratio	Example Organism	Character
No interaction	Yellow round				Yellow wrinkled		Green round		Green wrinkled	9:3:3:1	Peas	seed colour/coat colour
Collaboration	Walnut				Rose		Pea		Single	9:3:3:1	Chickens	Comb shape
Recessive epistasis	Black				Brown		White			9:3:4	Mice	Coat colour
Duplicate recessive epistasis	Purple				Colourless					9:7	Sweet pea flowers	Colour
Dominant epistasis	White						Yellow		Green	12:3:1	Squash	Fruit colour
Duplicate dominant epistasis	Coloured								Colourless	15:1	Wheat	Kernel colour

3. In a species of freshwater fish, the allele G produces a green pattern on the dorsal fin when in the presence of the allele Y. A fish that is homozygous recessive for the both genes produces no green pattern to the dorsal fin.

(a) Write the genotypes for a fish with a green patterned dorsal fin: _____

_____

(b) Write the genotypes for a fish with no green pattern: _____

_____

(c) Carry out a cross for the heterozygous genotype (GgYy). From the phenotypic ratio, what kind of epistatic interaction is occurring here?

_____

4. In a second species of freshwater fish, the tail can be one of three colours, red, pink, or orange. The colours are controlled by the genes B and H. The following information is known about the breeding of the fish:
   i   Any orange tailed fish crossed together only produce orange tailed fish.
   ii Any red tailed fish crossed with any orange tailed fish may produce offspring with red, pink, or orange tails.
   iii Any pink tailed fish crossed with any orange tailed fish produces offspring that have either all pink tails or 50% with pink tails and 50% with orange tails.

Use the information above and the space below to work out the type of gene interaction that is being examined here:

The gene interaction is: _____

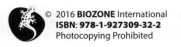

90 Polygenes

Key Idea: Many phenotypes are affected by multiple genes. Some phenotypes (e.g. kernel colour in maize and skin colour in humans) are determined by more than one gene and show **continuous variation** in a population. The production of the skin pigment melanin in humans is controlled by at least three genes. The amount of melanin produced is directly proportional to the number of dominant alleles for either gene (from 0 to 6).

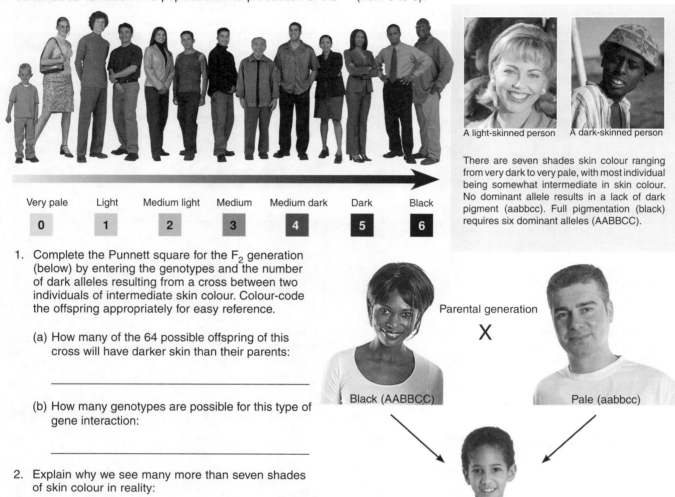

A light-skinned person   A dark-skinned person

There are seven shades skin colour ranging from very dark to very pale, with most individual being somewhat intermediate in skin colour. No dominant allele results in a lack of dark pigment (aabbcc). Full pigmentation (black) requires six dominant alleles (AABBCC).

Very pale	Light	Medium light	Medium	Medium dark	Dark	Black
0	1	2	3	4	5	6

1. Complete the Punnett square for the F₂ generation (below) by entering the genotypes and the number of dark alleles resulting from a cross between two individuals of intermediate skin colour. Colour-code the offspring appropriately for easy reference.

   (a) How many of the 64 possible offspring of this cross will have darker skin than their parents:

   _____

   (b) How many genotypes are possible for this type of gene interaction:

   _____

2. Explain why we see many more than seven shades of skin colour in reality:

   _____

   _____

Parental generation

X

Black (AABBCC)   Pale (aabbcc)

Medium (AaBbCc)

F₂ generation (AaBbCc X AaBbCc)

GAMETES	ABC	ABc	AbC	Abc	aBC	aBc	abC	abc
ABC								
ABc								
AbC								
Abc								
aBC								
aBc								
abC								
abc								

© 2016 **BIOZONE** International
ISBN: 978-1-927309-32-2
Photocopying Prohibited

3. Discuss the differences between **continuous** and **discontinuous variation**, giving examples to illustrate your answer:

    _____

    _____

    _____

    _____

    _____

4. From a sample of no less than 30 adults, collect data for one continuous variable (e.g. height, weight, shoe size, hand span). Record and tabulate your results in the space below, and then plot a frequency histogram on the grid below:

Raw data	Tally chart (frequency table)

Variable: _____

Frequency (y-axis)

(a) Calculate the following for your data and attach your working.

Mean: _____ **Mode:** _____ **Median:** _____

Standard deviation: _____

(b) Describe the pattern of distribution shown by the graph, giving a reason for your answer: _____

    _____

(c) What is the genetic basis of this distribution? _____

    _____

(d) What is the importance of a large sample size when gathering data relating to a continuous variable? _____

    _____

91 Gene Mutations

Key Idea: Gene mutations are localised changes to the DNA base sequence.

Gene mutations are small, localised changes in the base sequence of a DNA strand caused by a mutagen or an error during DNA replication. The changes may involve a single nucleotide (a point mutation) or a change to a triplet. Point mutations can occur by substitution, insertion, or deletion of bases. These changes alter the mRNA transcribed from the mutated DNA. A point mutation may not alter the amino acid sequence because more than one codon can code for the same amino acid. Mutations that result in a change in the amino acid sequence will most often be harmful.

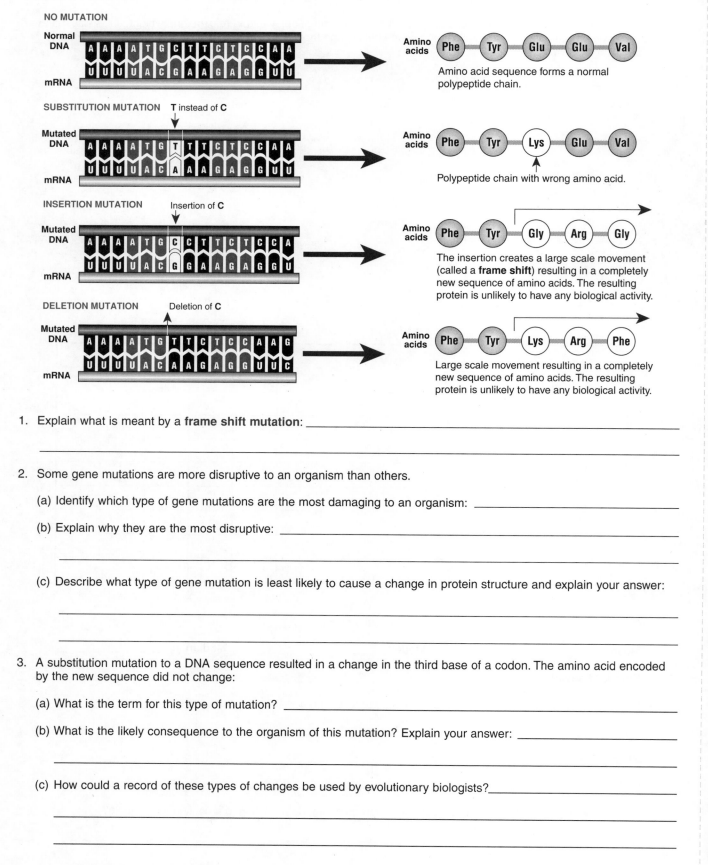

1. Explain what is meant by a **frame shift mutation**: _____
   _____

2. Some gene mutations are more disruptive to an organism than others.

   (a) Identify which type of gene mutations are the most damaging to an organism: _____

   (b) Explain why they are the most disruptive: _____
   _____

   (c) Describe what type of gene mutation is least likely to cause a change in protein structure and explain your answer:
   _____
   _____

3. A substitution mutation to a DNA sequence resulted in a change in the third base of a codon. The amino acid encoded by the new sequence did not change:

   (a) What is the term for this type of mutation? _____

   (b) What is the likely consequence to the organism of this mutation? Explain your answer: _____
   _____

   (c) How could a record of these types of changes be used by evolutionary biologists?_____
   _____
   _____

92 The Nature of Mutation

Key Idea: A mutation is any change to the DNA sequence. Most mutations are harmful, but if a mutation causes no change in the amino acid sequence, it is said to be silent. Occasionally a mutation produces a new and useful protein. A mutation is a change in the genetic sequence of a genome. Only those affecting gametic cells will be heritable. Mutations may occur spontaneously, as a result of errors during meiosis or DNA replication, or they may be induced. Induced mutations are the result of agents called mutagens, which increase the natural mutation rate. These agents include ionising radiation,

some viruses, and chemicals such as formaldehyde, coal tar, and components of tobacco smoke. While changes to DNA are likely to be harmful, there are many documented cases of mutations conferring a survival advantage. Mutations that cause no change in the amino acid sequence are called **silent**. Until recently, it was supposed that these were also **neutral**, i.e. carried without effect until subjected to selection pressure at a later time. However, recent research indicates that even these silent mutations may alter mRNA stability and affect the accuracy of protein synthesis.

The location of mutations

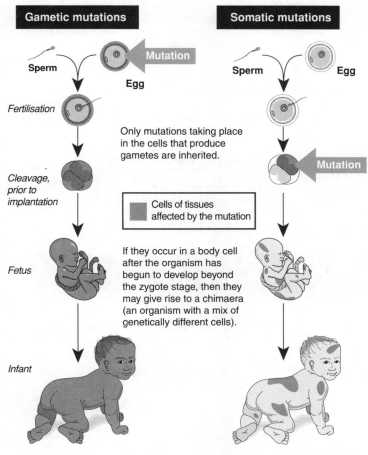

Only mutations taking place in the cells that produce gametes are inherited.

Cells of tissues affected by the mutation

If they occur in a body cell after the organism has begun to develop beyond the zygote stage, then they may give rise to a chimaera (an organism with a mix of genetically different cells).

Gametic mutations occur in the testes of males and the ovaries of females and are inherited.

Somatic mutations occur in body cells. They are not inherited but may affect the person during their lifetime.

The effect of mutagens on DNA

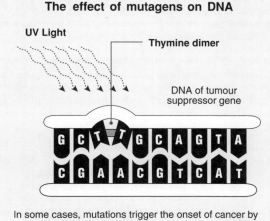

In some cases, mutations trigger the onset of cancer by disrupting the normal controls regulating the cell cycle. After exposure to UV light (a potent mutagen), adjacent thymine bases in DNA become cross-linked to form a 'thymine dimer'. This disrupts the normal base pairing and throws the controlling gene's instructions into chaos.

Mutant phenotype (gold colour)   Normal phenotype (red colour)

The photo above shows an example of a somatic mutation in a red delicious apple. A mutation occurred in the part of the flower that eventually developed into the fleshy part of the apple. The seeds would not be mutant.

1. Using an example, describe how mutagens damage DNA and explain the possible consequences of this: _____
_____
_____

2. Explain how **somatic mutations** differ from **gametic mutations** and comment on the significance of the difference:
_____
_____
_____

3. Explain why the mutation seen in the red delicious apple (above right) will not be inherited: _____
_____
_____

LINK 93   LINK 91   WEB 92   **KNOW**

Albinism: a common harmful mutation

Albinism is caused by any one of a number of gene mutations to enzymes in the metabolic pathway that produces the skin pigment melanin. Mutations to this metabolic pathway are common in most vertebrate taxa, including humans, and most commonly albino individuals are homozygous for the mutation.

Albinos lack pigment in their hair/fur and eyes are so more visible to predators or prey (left). Usually their vision is impaired and they are also more susceptible to the damaging effects of ultraviolet radiation because they lack protective pigmentation.

Beneficial mutations in microbes

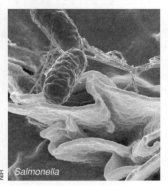 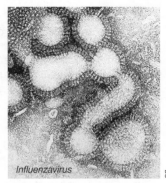

Salmonella

Influenzavirus

Bacteria reproduce asexually by binary fission. They are susceptible to antibiotics (substances that harm them or inhibit their growth) but can acquire antibiotic resistance through mutation. The genes for resistance can be transferred within and between bacterial species. New, multi-resistant bacterial superbugs have arisen in this way.

Viruses, including HIV and *Influenzavirus*, have glycoprotein coated envelopes, which confer virulence but also enable the host to detect the virus and destroy it. The genes encoding these glycoproteins are constantly mutating, so each new viral 'strain' goes undetected by the immune system until well after the infection is established.

Are silent mutations really silent?

So-called **silent mutations** are those that result in no change in the sequence of amino acids making up a protein. The redundancy of the genetic code provides a buffer against the effect of DNA changes affecting the third base. Such mutations have routinely been assumed to be neutral, meaning that they have no effect on the phenotype or on **fitness** (an individual's genetic contribution to the next generation).

Right: A change to the third base of a codon may not change the amino acid encoded, but it does change the exonic sequence.

However, so-called silent changes still affect transcription, splicing, and mRNA stability, even though they do not change the codon information. Disruptions to RNA splicing sequences can cause exon skipping and lead to RNA not being processed properly. Silent variations have been associated with a number of diseases including cystic fibrosis. For example, one silent mutation causes the dopamine receptor D2 gene to be less stable and degrade faster, under-expressing the gene. Experimental evidence with the CFTR gene also shows that silent mutations cause exon skipping, yielding a short CFTR protein.

Normal DNA

| A | A | A | A | T | G | C | T | T | C | T | C | C | A | A | C | G | A | C | T | C |
| U | U | U | U | A | C | G | A | A | G | A | G | G | U | U | G | C | U | G | A | G |

mRNA

Phe — Tyr — Glu — Glu — Val — Ala — Glu · · · Amino acids encoded

Mutant DNA

| A | A | A | A | T | G | C | T | C | C | T | C | C | A | A | C | G | G | C | T | C |
| U | U | U | U | A | C | G | A | G | G | A | G | G | U | U | G | C | C | G | A | G |

mRNA

Phe — Tyr — Glu — Glu — Val — Ala — Glu · · · Amino acids encoded

Partial CFTR exon 12 DNA sequence

AAA GAT GCT GAT TTG TAT TTA GAC TCT CCT TTT GGA TAC

Exon 12 included

Induced silent mutations

AAA GAT GCA GAT TTA TAT TTA GAC TCC CCT TTT GGG/T TAC

Exon 12 left out

4. Giving examples, distinguish between beneficial and harmful mutations: _____

_____

_____

_____

5. (a) Explain what is meant by a silent mutation: _____

_____

   (b) Explain why silent mutations are now no longer seen as always being neutral in their effect: _____

_____

_____

_____

© 2016 **BIOZONE** International
ISBN: 978-1-927309-32-2
Photocopying Prohibited

93 Beneficial Mutations

Key Idea: Beneficial mutations increase the fitness of the organisms that possess them, but they are relatively rare.

A beneficial mutation is one that increases an individual's fitness (ability to survive and produce offspring). Although beneficial mutations are rare compared to those that are harmful, there are a number of well documented beneficial mutations in humans. Some of these mutations are not very common in the human population. This is because the mutations have been in existence for a relatively short time, so the mutations have not had time to become widespread in the human population. Scientists often study mutations that cause disease. By understanding the genetic origin of various diseases it may be possible to develop targeted medical drugs and therapies against them.

The village of Limone, Italy

Apolipoprotein A1-Milano is a well documented mutation to apolipoprotein A1 that helps transport cholesterol through the blood. The mutation causes a change to one amino acid and increases the protein's effectiveness by ten times, dramatically reducing incidence of heart disease. The mutation can be traced back to its origin in Limone, Italy, in 1644. Another mutation to a gene called PCSK9 has a similar effect, lowering the risk of heart disease by 88%.

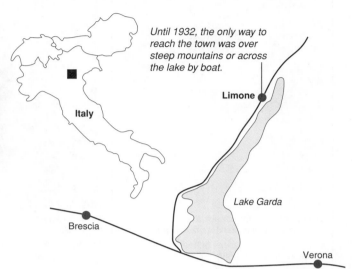

Until 1932, the only way to reach the town was over steep mountains or across the lake by boat.

Italy

Limone

Lake Garda

Brescia

Verona

Lactose is a sugar found in milk. All infant mammals produce an enzyme called lactase that breaks the lactose into the smaller sugars glucose and galactose. As mammals become older, their production of lactase declines and they lose the ability to digest lactose. As adults, they become lactose intolerant and feel bloated after drinking milk. About 10,000 years ago a mutation appeared in humans that maintained lactase production into adulthood. This mutation is now carried in people of mainly European, African and Indian descent.

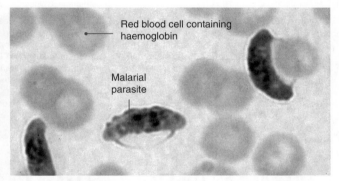

Red blood cell containing haemoglobin

Malarial parasite

Malaria resistance results from a mutation to the haemoglobin gene (Hb^S) that also causes sickle cell disease. This mutation in beneficial in regions where malaria is common. A less well known mutation (Hb^C) to the same gene, discovered in populations in Burkina Faso, Africa, results in a 29% reduction in the likelihood of contracting malaria if the person has one copy of the mutated gene and a 93% reduction if the person has two copies. In addition, the anaemia that person suffers as a result of the mutation is much less pronounced than in the Hb^S mutation.

1. Why is it that many of the recent beneficial mutations in humans have not spread through the entire human population?

_____

_____

_____

2. What selection pressure could act on Apolipoprotein A1-Milano to help it spread through a population?

_____

_____

3. Why would it be beneficial to be able to digest milk in adulthood? _____

_____

_____

LINK
114

LINK
91

WEB
93

KNOW

94 Gene Mutations and Genetic Diseases

Key Idea: Many genetic diseases in humans are the result of mutations to recessive alleles, but some are also caused by dominant or codominant alleles.

There are more than 6000 human diseases attributed to mutations in single genes, although most are uncommon. The three genetic diseases described below occur with relatively high frequency and are the result of recessive, dominant, and codominant allele mutations respectively.

Haemophilia	Huntington disease (HD)	Sickle cell anaemia

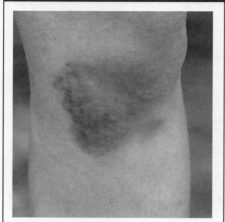

Haemophiliacs haemorrhage (bleed) spontaneously or in response to mild trauma.

Incidence: Three classes of haemophilia:
Haemophilia A:1 in 5000-1 in 10 000.
Haemophilia B: 1 in 20 000-1 in 34 000.
Haemophilia C: 1 in 100 000

Gene type: Haemophilia A and B are recessive X-linked disorders associated with insufficient or inoperative blood clotting factors. Haemophilia A (~80% of cases) is caused by mutation in the F8 (factor VIII) gene, often an inversion. Haemophilia B (~20% of cases) is caused by mutations of the F9 (factor IX) gene. Both are X chromosome linked disorders and, as such, are very rare in females. Haemophilia C is a mild autosomal condition and rare.

Gene location: X chromosome **Factor VIII**
Factor IX

Symptoms: Internal or external bleeding that does not clot easily. Severity of bleeding varies with each person. Joint bleeds are common. It often becomes apparent in children as they learn to walk as bruises that do not fade.

Inheritance: X linked recessive pattern. Affected people are normally male (one allele on the X chromosome). Very rare in females.

American singer-songwriter and folk musician Woody Guthrie died from complications of HD

Incidence: An uncommon disease affecting 3-7 per 100 000 people of European descent. Less common in other ethnicities, including people of Japanese, Chinese, and African descent.

Gene type: Autosomal dominant mutation of the HTT gene caused by a trinucleotide repeat expansion on the short arm of chromosome 4. In the mutation (**mHTT**), the number of CAG repeats increases from the normal 6-30 to 36-125. The severity of the disease increases with the number of repeats. The repeats result in the production of an abnormally long version of the huntingtin protein.

Gene location: Short arm of chromosome 4

HTT

Symptoms: The long huntingtin protein is cut into smaller toxic fragments, which accumulate in nerve cells and eventually kill them. The disease becomes apparent in mid-adulthood, with jerky, involuntary movements and loss of memory, reasoning, and personality.

Inheritance: Autosomal dominance pattern. Affected people may be homozygous or heterozygous for the mutant allele.

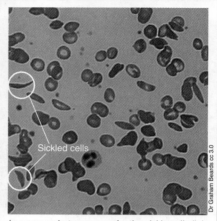

In a person heterozygous for the sickle cell allele, only some of the red blood cells are deformed.

Sickled cells

Incidence: Occurs most commonly in people of African descent. West Africans: 1% (10-45% are carriers). West Indians: 0.5%.

Gene type: Autosomal mutation involving substitution of a single nucleotide in the HBB gene that codes for the beta chain of haemoglobin. The allele is codominant. The substitution causes a change in a single amino acid. The mutated haemoglobin behaves differently when deprived of oxygen, causing distortion of the red blood cells, anaemia, and circulatory problems.

Gene location: Short arm of chromosome 11

HBB

Symptoms: Sickling of the red blood cells, which are removed from circulation, anaemia, pain, damage to tissues and organs.

Inheritance: Autosomal codominance pattern. People who are homozygous for the mutant allele have sickle cell disease. Heterozygotes (carriers) are only mildly affected and show greater resistance to malaria than people without the mutation.

1. For each of genetic disorder below, indicate the following:

    (a) Sickle cell anaemia: Gene name: _____   Chromosome: _____ Mutation type: _____

    (b) Haemophilia: Gene name: _____   Chromosome: _____ Mutation type: _____

    (c) Huntington disease: Gene name: _____   Chromosome: _____ Mutation type: _____

2. Explain why mHTT, which is dominant and lethal, does not disappear from the population: _____

    _____

    _____

3. Suggest why the sickle cell has been maintained in populations, despite being a lethal mutation: _____

    _____

    _____

© 2016 **BIOZONE** International
ISBN: 978-1-927309-32-2
Photocopying Prohibited

95 Cystic Fibrosis Mutation

Key Idea: Cystic fibrosis most often results from a triplet deletion in the CFTR gene, producing a protein that is unable to regulate chloride transport.

Cystic fibrosis (CF) is an inherited disorder caused by a mutation of the CFTR gene. It is one of the most common lethal autosomal recessive conditions affecting people of European descent (4% are carriers). The CFTR gene's protein product is a membrane-based protein that regulates chloride transport in cells. Over 500 mutations of the CFTR gene are known, causing disease symptoms of varying severity. The δ(delta)F508 mutation accounts for more than 70% of all defective CFTR genes. This mutation leads to an abnormal CFTR, which cannot take its proper position in the membrane (below) nor perform its transport function.

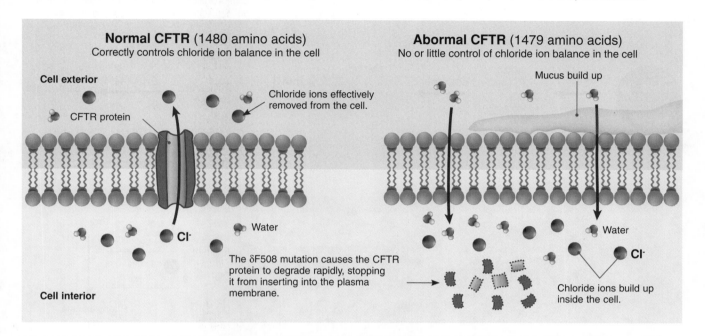

Normal CFTR (1480 amino acids)
Correctly controls chloride ion balance in the cell

Cell exterior

CFTR protein

Chloride ions effectively removed from the cell.

Water

Cl⁻

The δF508 mutation causes the CFTR protein to degrade rapidly, stopping it from inserting into the plasma membrane.

Cell interior

Abormal CFTR (1479 amino acids)
No or little control of chloride ion balance in the cell

Mucus build up

Water

Cl⁻

Chloride ions build up inside the cell.

The CF gene on chromosome 7

The CF gene is located on chromosome 7. The δF508 mutation of the CF gene describes a deletion of the 508th triplet, which in turn causes the loss of a single **amino acid** from the gene's protein product, the cystic fibrosis transmembrane conductance regulator (CFTR). This protein normally regulates the chloride channels in cell membranes, but the mutant form fails to achieve this. The portion of the DNA containing the mutation site is shown below:

p

q

CFTR gene

The CFTR protein consists of 1480 amino acids

CFTR protein

The δF508 mutant form of CFTR fails to take up its position in the membrane. Its absence results in defective chloride transport and leads to a net increase in water absorption by the cell. This accounts for the symptoms of cystic fibrosis, where mucus-secreting glands, particularly in the lungs and pancreas, become fibrous and produce abnormally thick mucus. The widespread presence of CFTR throughout the body also explains why CF is a multisystem condition affecting many organs.

Base 1630

DNA coding strand

C C G T G G T A A T T T C T T T T A T A G T A G A A A C C A C C A

This triplet codes for the 500th amino acid

The 508th triplet is absent in the form with the δF508 mutation

1. (a) Write the mRNA sequence for the transcribing DNA strand above: _____

_____

(b) Use the mRNA-amino acid table on page 278 at the back of this workbook to determine the amino acid sequence coded by the mRNA for the fragment of the normal protein we are studying here:

_____

2. (a) Rewrite the mRNA sequence for the mutant DNA strand: _____

_____

(b) Determine the amino acid sequence coded by the mRNA for the fragment of the δF508 mutant protein:

_____

(c) Which amino acid has been removed from the protein by this mutation? _____

LINK 194   WEB 95   EXT

96 Genes, Enzymes, and Phenotype

Key Idea: Metabolic pathways are interrupted when one or more of the enzymes catalysing the biochemical reactions involved are not expressed correctly.

A metabolic pathway is a series of enzyme-catalysed biochemical reactions. Each step in the pathway relies on the completion of the previous step. An interruption in the pathway caused by an inactive enzyme (usually as a result of a gene mutation) prevents the pathway from progressing and can result in a **metabolic disorder**. Often phenotype is affected, e.g. albinism is caused by an inactive tyrosinase enzyme.

A metabolic pathway

Enzyme 4 is not expressed. The reaction series cannot proceed, so levels of substrate 4 build up and the metabolic pathway does not progress through to the end (production of substrate 5).

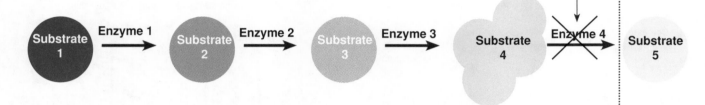

Phenylketonuria (PKU) is caused when the enzyme phenylalanine hydroxylase, needed to metabolise the amino acid **phenylalanine,** is not functional.

Without the enzyme, phenylalanine cannot be converted to the next substrate, tyrosine, and is metabolised to toxic derivatives, which cause central nervous system damage.

Children with PKU tend to have lighter skin and hair than people without the disorder.

Newborn babies are tested for a number of genetic disorders, including PKU, soon after birth. Blood is collected from a heel prick on to a Guthrie card (above) and tested. The prognosis is good if the disease is detected early, and a low phenylalanine diet is followed.

Melanin is the pigment that gives skin, hair, and eyes their colour. It is formed from the metabolism of the amino acid tyrosine. Lack of melanin results in **albinism**, a condition where there is little or no pigmentation (above). The most common cause of albinism is a faulty tyrosinase enzyme that ordinarily converts tyrosine into melanin.

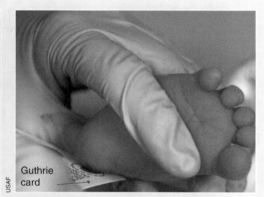
Guthrie card

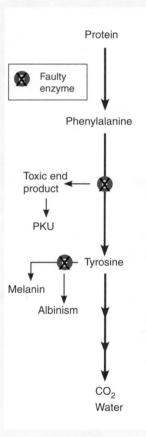

1. What is the initial protein required for the production of melanin?_____

2. Name the faulty enzyme responsible for each of the following conditions:

   (a) Albinism: _____

   (b) Phenylketonuria: _____

3. Explain why people with these two conditions tend to have very pale skin: _____

   _____

   _____

   _____

© 2016 **BIOZONE** International
ISBN: 978-1-927309-32-2
Photocopying Prohibited

97 Gene Induction in Prokaryotes

Key Idea: The presence of the inducer molecule lactose, switches the *lac* operon on so that the genes for lactose metabolism are transcribed.

In prokaryotes, an operon consists of a group of closely linked genes, which act together to control production of the enzymes regulating a metabolic pathway. The operon model **applies only to prokaryotes** because genes in eukaryotic cells are not found as operons. The operon is made up of one or more structural genes, and promoter and operator sequences. Transcription of the structural genes is controlled by the promoter, which initiates transcription, and a region upstream of the structural genes called the operator. A gene outside the operon, called the regulator gene, produces a repressor molecule that can bind to the operator and block the transcription of the structural genes. It is the repressor that switches the structural genes on or off and controls the metabolic pathway. Two mechanisms can operate in the operon model: gene induction and gene repression. Gene induction, described in this activity, occurs when genes are switched on by an inducer binding to the repressor molecule and deactivating it. In the *lac* operon, lactose acts as the inducer for transcription of the genes to metabolise lactose.

Control of gene expression through induction: the *lac* operon

Structure of the operon

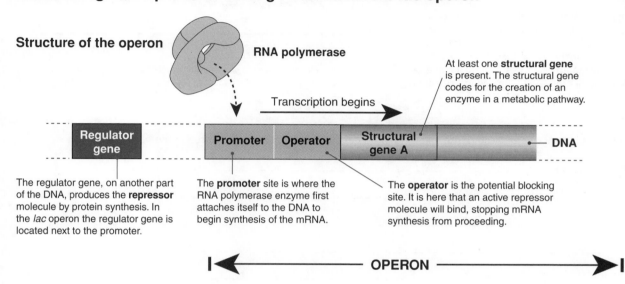

RNA polymerase

Transcription begins

At least one **structural gene** is present. The structural gene codes for the creation of an enzyme in a metabolic pathway.

Regulator gene | Promoter | Operator | Structural gene A | DNA

The regulator gene, on another part of the DNA, produces the **repressor** molecule by protein synthesis. In the *lac* operon the regulator gene is located next to the promoter.

The **promoter** site is where the RNA polymerase enzyme first attaches itself to the DNA to begin synthesis of the mRNA.

The **operator** is the potential blocking site. It is here that an active repressor molecule will bind, stopping mRNA synthesis from proceeding.

 ← OPERON →

Structural genes switched off

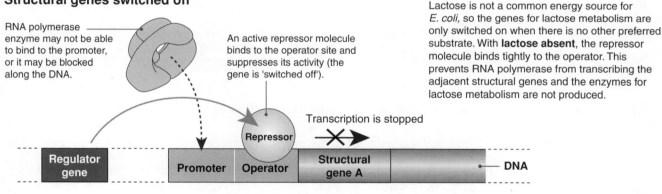

RNA polymerase enzyme may not be able to bind to the promoter, or it may be blocked along the DNA.

An active repressor molecule binds to the operator site and suppresses its activity (the gene is 'switched off').

Lactose is not a common energy source for *E. coli*, so the genes for lactose metabolism are only switched on when there is no other preferred substrate. With **lactose absent**, the repressor molecule binds tightly to the operator. This prevents RNA polymerase from transcribing the adjacent structural genes and the enzymes for lactose metabolism are not produced.

Transcription is stopped

Repressor

Regulator gene | Promoter | Operator | Structural gene A | DNA

Gene induction

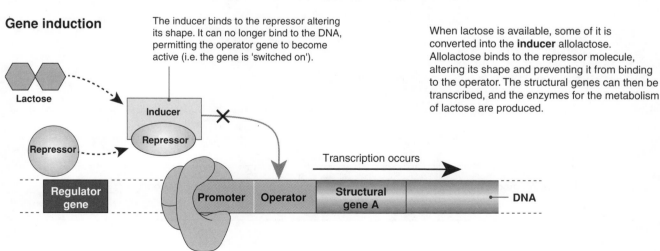

The inducer binds to the repressor altering its shape. It can no longer bind to the DNA, permitting the operator gene to become active (i.e. the gene is 'switched on').

When lactose is available, some of it is converted into the **inducer** allolactose. Allolactose binds to the repressor molecule, altering its shape and preventing it from binding to the operator. The structural genes can then be transcribed, and the enzymes for the metabolism of lactose are produced.

Lactose

Inducer

Repressor

Repressor

Regulator gene | Promoter | Operator | Structural gene A | DNA

Transcription occurs

Diauxie in *E.coli*

Diauxie means two growth phases. **Diauxic growth** describes how microbes grown on a mixed sugar source in batch culture will preferentially metabolise one sugar source before moving on to the second. This sequential metabolism results in two distinct growth phases (right).

In the example (right) *E.coli* is grown on a mixed substrate of glucose and lactose. Diauxie occurs because the presence of glucose in excess suppresses the *lac* operon so that only the enzymes required for glucose metabolism are produced. As the glucose supply diminishes, the *lac* operon becomes activated, and *E.coli* begins to metabolise lactose.

The lag period represents the time taken for the *lac* operon to become active and the synthesis of the enzymes required for lactose metabolism to begin. This mechanism allows *E.coli* to preferentially metabolise the substrate it can grow fastest on, before moving to the second substrate.

The diauxic growth curve of *E.coli* when grown on glucose and lactose

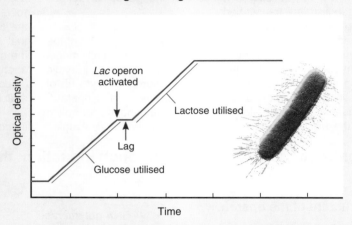

Jacques Monod discovered diauxic growth in 1941 prior to the discovery of the lac operon, which explained the lag phenomenon at the genetic level.

1. Explain the functional role of each of the following in relation to gene regulation in a prokaryote, e.g. *E. coli*:

   (a) Operon: _____

   _____

   (b) Regulator gene: _____

   _____

   (c) Operator: _____

   _____

   (d) Promoter: _____

   _____

   (e) Structural genes: _____

   _____

2. (a) Explain the advantage in having an inducible enzyme system that is regulated by the presence of a substrate:

   _____

   _____

   (b) Suggest when it would not be adaptive to have an inducible system for metabolism of a substrate: _____

   _____

   _____

   (c) Suggest how gene control in a non-inducible system might be achieved:

   _____

   _____

   _____

3. Explain how the operon model explains the diauxic growth of bacteria on two sugar substrates: _____

   _____

© 2016 **BIOZONE** International
ISBN: 978-1-927309-32-2
Photocopying Prohibited

98 Gene Repression in Prokaryotes

Key Idea: Some genes are normally transcribed all the time to produce constitutive end-products (e.g. protein). Repression of these genes controls production of the end-product.

In *E. coli*, the enzyme tryptophan synthetase synthesises the amino acid tryptophan. Tryptophan is a constitutive amino acid (constantly present) so the gene for producing this enzyme is

normally switched on. When tryptophan is present in excess, some of it acts as an effector (or co-repressor), activating the repressor and binding to the operator gene, preventing transcription of the structural gene. Once transcription stops, tryptophan synthetase is no longer produced. This is an example of end-product inhibition (feedback inhibition).

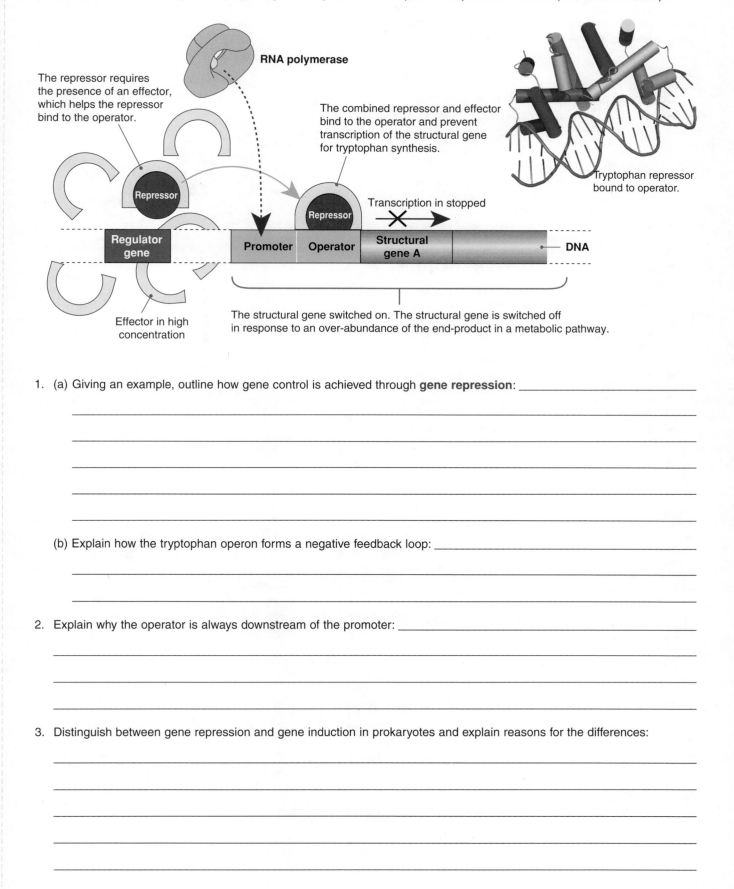

RNA polymerase

The repressor requires the presence of an effector, which helps the repressor bind to the operator.

The combined repressor and effector bind to the operator and prevent transcription of the structural gene for tryptophan synthesis.

Tryptophan repressor bound to operator.

Repressor

Repressor

Transcription in stopped

Regulator gene

Promoter | Operator | Structural gene A

DNA

Effector in high concentration

The structural gene switched on. The structural gene is switched off in response to an over-abundance of the end-product in a metabolic pathway.

1. (a) Giving an example, outline how gene control is achieved through **gene repression**: _____

_____

_____

_____

_____

_____

(b) Explain how the tryptophan operon forms a negative feedback loop: _____

_____

_____

2. Explain why the operator is always downstream of the promoter: _____

_____

_____

_____

3. Distinguish between gene repression and gene induction in prokaryotes and explain reasons for the differences:

_____

_____

_____

_____

_____

© 2016 **BIOZONE** International
ISBN: 978-1-927309-32-2
Photocopying Prohibited

LINK
96 **KNOW**

99 Gene Control in Eukaryotes

Key Idea: Eukaryote transcription occurs when transcription factors bind to an enhancer sequence and RNA polymerase. Although all the cells in your body contain identical copies of your genetic instructions, these cells appear very different (e.g. muscle, nerve, and epithelial cells). These differences reflect differences in gene expression during the cell's development. For example, muscle cells express the genes for the proteins that make up the contractile elements of the muscle fibre. This diversity of cell structure and function reflects precise control over the time, location, and extent of expression of a huge variety of genes. The physical state of the DNA in or near a gene is important in helping to control whether the gene is even available for transcription. To be transcribed, a gene must first be unpacked from its condensed state. Once unpacked, control of gene expression involves the interaction of transcription factors with DNA sequences that control the specific gene. Initiation of transcription is the most important and universally used control point in gene expression.

Control of gene expression in eukaryotes

▶ Eukaryotic genes are very different from prokaryotic genes: they have introns (which are removed after the primary transcript is made) and a relatively large number of control elements (non-coding DNA sequences that help regulate transcription by binding proteins called transcription factors).

▶ Each functional eukaryotic gene has a promoter region at the upstream end of the gene: a DNA sequence where RNA polymerase binds and starts transcription.

▶ Eukaryotic RNA polymerase alone cannot initiate the transcription of a gene; it is dependent on transcription factors in order to recognise and bind to the promoter (step 1).

▶ Transcription is activated when a hairpin loop in the DNA brings the transcription factors (activators) attached to the enhancer sequence in contact with the transcription factors bound to RNA polymerase at the promoter (step 2).

▶ Protein-protein interactions are crucial to eukaryotic transcription. Only when the complete initiation complex is assembled can the polymerase move along the DNA template strand and produce the complementary strand of RNA.

▶ Transcription is deactivated when a terminator sequence is encountered. Terminators are nucleotide sequences that function to stop transcription. Do not confuse these with stop codons, which are the stop signals for translation.

▶ A range of transcription factors and enhancer sequences throughout the genome may selectively activate the expression of specific genes at appropriate stages during cell development.

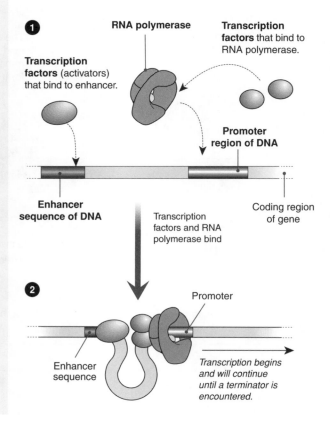

Eukaryotes can control gene expression by inhibiting transcription inhibitors (a double negative pathway). For example, in plants, the hormone gibberellin is involved in stem growth. Gibberellin works by inhibiting the DELLA family of protein repressors which inhibit the binding of transcription factors to the DNA. Auxins also work in a similar way.

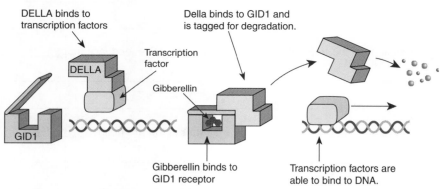

1. What is the function of the promoter region in a eukaryotic gene? _____

_____

2. What is the purpose of the terminator sequence in a eukaryotic gene? _____

_____

3. Explain how transcription of DNA is regulated by gibberellins and DELLA: _____

_____

_____

© 2016 **BIOZONE** International
ISBN: 978-1-927309-32-2
Photocopying Prohibited

100 Chapter Review

Summarise what you know about this topic under the headings and sub-headings provided. You can draw diagrams or mind maps, or write short notes to organise your thoughts. Use the images and hints to help you and refer back to the introduction to check the points covered:

Alleles and meiosis

HINT: What are alleles? What is the role of meiosis is producing variation?

Genes and phenotype

HINT: Explain monohybrid and dihybrid crosses, and linkage and recombination.

Control of gene expression

HINT: Compare and contrast the control of gene expression in prokaryotes and eukaryotes.

REVISE

101 KEY TERMS AND IDEAS: Did You Get It?

1. Test your vocabulary by matching each term to its definition, as identified by its preceding letter code.

alleles _____

diploid _____

dominant _____

genotype _____

meiosis _____

monohybrid cross _____

phenotype _____

Punnett square _____

recessive _____

A Having two homologous copies of each chromosome (2N), usually one from the mother and one from the father.

B Allele that will only express its trait in the absence of the dominant allele.

C Genetic cross between two individuals that differ in one trait of particular interest.

D Sequences of DNA occupying the same gene locus (position) on different, but homologous, chromosomes.

E Observable characteristics in an organism.

F The allele combination of an organism.

G The process of double nuclear division (reduction division) to produce four nuclei, each containing half the original number of chromosomes (haploid).

H A graphical way of illustrating the outcome of a cross.

I Allele that expresses its trait irrespective of the other allele.

2. The following dihybrid cross shows the inheritance of colour and shape in pea seeds. Yellow (**Y**) is dominant over green (**y**) and a round shape (**R**) is dominant over the wrinkled (**r**) form.

(a) Describe the appearance (phenotype) of pea seeds with the genotype YyRr: _____

_____

(b) Complete the Punnett square below when two seeds with the YyRr genotype are crossed. Indicate the number of each phenotype in the boxes on the right.

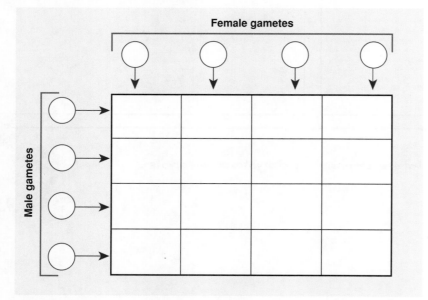

Yellow-round [ ]

Green-round [ ]

Yellow-wrinkled [ ]

Green-wrinkled [ ]

(c) What type of inheritance pattern is this? _____

3. An original DNA sequence is shown right: **GCG TGA TTT GTA GGC GCT CTG**

For each of the following DNA mutations, state the type of mutation that has occurred:

(a) **GCG TGT TTG TAG GCG CTC TG** _____

(b) **GCG TGA TTT GTA AGG CGC TCT G** _____

(c) **GCG TGA TTT GGA GGC GCT CTG** _____

© 2016 **BIOZONE** International
ISBN: 978-1-927309-32-2
Photocopying Prohibited

Topic 17

Selection and evolution

17.1 Variation
Learning outcomes

☐ 1 Distinguish between continuous and discontinuous variation and explain the genetic basis of each.   102

☐ 2 Explain how the environment may affect the phenotype of plants and animals.   103

☐ 3 Use the Student's t test to compare the variation of two different populations.   108 109

☐ 4 Explain why genetic variation is important in selection.   102 114

17.2 Natural and artificial selection
Learning outcomes

☐ 5 Outline the principles of Darwin's theory of evolution by natural selection, i.e. that populations show variation in traits, that traits are heritable, that populations over-produce and offspring compete for resources, and the best adapted variants survive to breed and pass on their alleles to the next generation.   114 116

☐ 6 Explain, using examples, how environmental factors can act as stabilising, disruptive, or directional forces of natural selection.   117-123

☐ 7 Understand the concept of the gene pool and explain how allele frequencies are expressed for populations. Explain how selection, the founder effect, and genetic drift can affect allele frequencies in populations. As extension, identify the effect of genetic bottlenecks on diversity of a population's gene pool.   110 111   115 124   125 126

☐ 8 Use the Hardy-Weinberg principle to calculate allele, genotype, and phenotype frequencies in populations. Explain situations when this principle does not apply.   112 113

☐ 9 Describe how selective breeding has been used to improve milk yield in cattle.   127 128

☐ 10 Outline examples of crop improvement by selective breeding, with reference to: 129 130
- the introduction of disease resistance in wheat and rice.
- the incorporation of mutant genes for gibberellin synthesis into dwarf varieties.
- inbreeding and hybridisation to produce vigorous, uniform varieties of maize.

17.3 Evolution
Learning outcomes

☐ 11 Use examples to illustrate the fact that organisms have changed over time.   131

☐ 12 Discuss the molecular evidence that reveals similarities between closely related organisms with reference to mitochondrial DNA and protein sequence data.   132 133   134 135

☐ 13 Explain allopatric speciation as a result of geographical separation. Contrast with sympatric speciation, which occurs without geographical separation and may occur instantly as a result of genetic isolation (polyploidy).   138-140

☐ 14 Explain the role of pre-zygotic and post-zygotic isolating mechanisms in the evolution of new species.   136 137

☐ 15 Explain why organisms become extinct, with reference to climate change, competition, habitat loss, and humans.   141

102 Types of Variation

Key Idea: The characteristics of sexually reproducing organisms show variation. Those showing continuous variation are controlled by many genes at different loci and are often greatly influenced by environment. Those showing discontinuous variation are controlled by a small number of genes and there are a limited number of phenotypic variants in the population. Both genes and environment contribute to the final phenotype on which natural selection acts.

Variation refers to the diversity of genotypes (allele combinations) and phenotypes (appearances) in a population. Variation in phenotypic characteristics, such as flower colour and birth weight, is a feature of sexually reproducing populations. Some characteristics show discontinuous variation, with only a limited number of phenotypic variants in the population. Others show continuous variation, with a range of phenotypic variants approximating a bell shaped (normal) curve. Both genotype and the environment determine, to different degrees, the final phenotype we see.

Mutations

gene mutations, chromosome mutations

Mutations are the source of all **new** alleles. Existing genes are modified by mutations to form new alleles. Neutral mutations, which are neither detrimental nor beneficial, may escape selection pressure until conditions change.

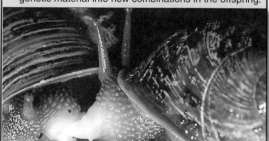

Mutation: Substitute **T** instead of **C**

Original DNA: A A A A T G C T T C T C

Mutant DNA: A A A A T G T T T C T C

Sexual Reproduction

independent assortment, crossing over and recombination, mate selection

Sexual reproduction rearranges and reshuffles the genetic material into new combinations in the offspring.

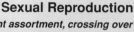

Don Horne

Phenotype

An individual's phenotype is the result of the interaction of genetic and environmental factors during its lifetime (including during development). The expression of genes in an organism can be influenced by both the internal and external environment both during and after development.

Dominant, recessive, codominant, and multiple alleles, DNA modifications (such as methylation), and interactions between genes, combine in their effects.

Genotype

Determines the **genetic potential** of an individual

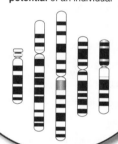

Variation is the essential raw material for natural selection. Different phenotypic variants will have different relative survival and reproductive success (**fitness**) in the prevailing environment and only the most successful variants will proliferate.

Environmental factors

The external and internal environments can influence the expression of the genotype. The external environment may include physical factors such as temperature or light intensity, or biotic factors such as competition. The internal environment, e.g presence or absence of hormones or growth factors during development, may also affect genotypic expression.

1. (a) What is the basis of the genetic variation of sexually reproducing organisms? _____

    _____

    _____

    _____

    _____

    (b) How does the environment contribute to the phenotype we see: _____

    _____

    _____

© 2016 **BIOZONE** International
ISBN: 978-1-927309-32-2
Photocopying Prohibited

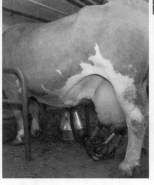

Albinism (above) is the result of the inheritance of recessive alleles for melanin production. Those with the albino phenotype lack melanin pigment in the eyes, skin, and hair.

Comb shape in poultry is a **qualitative trait** and birds have one of four phenotypes depending on which combination of four alleles they inherit. The dash (missing allele) indicates that the allele may be recessive or dominant.

Quantitative traits are characterised by **continuous variation**, with individuals falling somewhere on a normal distribution curve of the phenotypic range. Typical examples include skin colour and height in humans (left), grain yield in corn (above), growth in pigs (above, left), and milk production in cattle (far left). Quantitative traits are determined by genes at many loci (polygenic) but most are also influenced by environmental factors.

Single comb	Walnut comb	Pea comb	Rose comb
rrpp	**R_P_**	**rrP_**	**R_pp**

Flower colour in snapdragons (right) is also a **qualitative trait** determined by two alleles. (red and white) The alleles show incomplete dominance and the heterozygote (C^R C^W) exhibits an intermediate phenotype between the two homozygotes.

C^R C^R

C^W C^W

2. Why is phenotypic variation important in the process of natural selection? _____

_____

_____

3. (a) What is a neutral mutation? _____

 (b) What is the significance of neutral mutations? _____

 _____

 _____

4. Describe the differences between **continuous** and **discontinuous** variation, giving examples to illustrate your answer:

_____

_____

_____

_____

_____

_____

5. Identify each of the following phenotypic characteristics as continuous (quantitative) or discontinuous (qualitative):

 (a) Wool production in sheep: _____ (d) Albinism in mammals: _____

 (b) Hand span in humans: _____ (e) Body weight in mice: _____

 (c) Blood groups in humans: _____ (f) Flower colour in snapdragons: _____

103 The Effect of Environment on Phenotype

Key Idea: The environment can play a big part in an organism's eventual phenotype.

Environmental factors, including physical factors such as temperature and biotic factors such as presence of predators, can influence how genes are expressed. Factors such as heat or chemicals can turn genes on (genes are expressed) or off. When and for how long the genes are expressed can have large effects on an organism's eventual phenotype.

The effect of temperature

The sex of some animals is determined by incubation temperature during embryonic development. Examples include turtles, crocodiles, and the American alligator. In some species, high incubation temperatures produce males and low temperatures produce females. In other species, the opposite is true. Temperature regulated sex determination may be advantageous by preventing inbreeding (since all siblings will tend to be of the same sex).

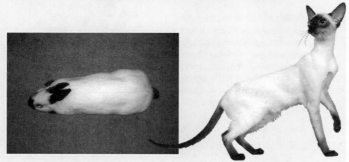

Colour-pointing in breeds of cats and rabbits (e.g. Siamese, Himalyan) is a result of a temperature sensitive mutation in one of the enzymes in the metabolic pathway from tyrosine to melanin. The dark pigment is only produced in the cooler areas of the body (face, ears, feet, and tail), while the rest of the body is a paler version of the same colour, or white.

The effect of other organisms

For some animals, the presence of other individuals of the same species may control sex determination.

Some fish species, including some in the wrasse family (e.g. *Coris sandageri*, right), show this phenomenon. The fish live in groups consisting of a single male with attendant females and juveniles. In the presence of a male, all juveniles become females. When the male dies, the dominant female will undergo changes in physiology and appearance to become a male.

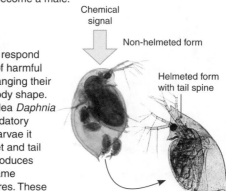

Female

Male

Chemical signal

Non-helmeted form

Helmeted form with tail spine

Some organisms respond to the presence of harmful organisms by changing their morphology or body shape. When the water flea *Daphnia* is exposed to predatory phantom midge larvae it develops a helmet and tail spine and also produces young with the same defensive structures. These responses are mediated through chemicals produced by the predator.

The helmet and spine make *Daphnia* more difficult to attack and handle by the predatory midge.

1. Describe an example to illustrate how genotype and environment contribute to phenotype: _____

_____

_____

_____

2. (a) How is helmet and spine development in *Daphnia* a response to environment? _____

_____

_____

(b) How does the phenotypic response help the animal survive? _____

_____

_____

3. Why are the darker patches of fur in colour-pointed cats and rabbits found only on the face, paws and tail:

_____

_____

_____

© 2016 **BIOZONE** International
ISBN: 978-1-927309-32-2
Photocopying Prohibited

The effect of altitude

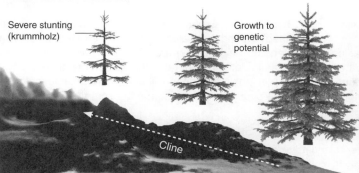

Severe stunting (krummholz)

Growth to genetic potential

Cline

Increasing altitude can stunt the phenotype of plants with the same genotype. In some conifers, e.g. Engelmann spruce, plants at low altitude grow to their full genetic potential, but become progressively more stunted as elevation increases, forming krummholz (gnarled bushy forms) at the highest sites. A continuous gradation in a phenotypic character within a species, associated with a change in an environmental variable, is called a **cline**.

The effect of chemical environment

The chemical environment can influence the expressed phenotype in plants and animals. In hydrangeas, flower colour varies according to soil pH. Flowers are blue in more acidic soils (pH 5.0-5.5), but pink in more alkaline soils (pH 6.0-6.5). The blue colour is due to the presence of aluminium compounds in the flowers and aluminium is more readily available when the soil pH is low.

4. Describe an example of how the chemical environment of a plant can influence phenotype: _____

_____

_____

_____

5. Vegetable growers can produce enormous vegetables for competition. How could you improve the chance that a vegetable would reach its maximum genetic potential?

_____

_____

_____

6. (a) What is a **cline**? _____

_____

_____

(b) What are the physical factors associated with altitude that could affect plant phenotype? _____

_____

_____

_____

(c) On a windswept portion of a coast, two different species of plant (species A and species B) were found growing together. Both had a low growing (prostrate) phenotype. One of each plant type was transferred to a greenhouse where "ideal" conditions were provided to allow maximum growth. In this controlled environment, species B continued to grow in its original prostrate form, but species A changed its growing pattern and became erect in form. Identify the **cause** of the prostrate phenotype in each of the coastal grown plant species and explain your answer:

Plant species A: _____

_____

_____

Plant species B: _____

_____

_____

(d) Which of these species (A or B) would be most likely to exhibit clinal variation? _____

104 Spread of Data

Key Idea: Standard deviation is used to quantify the variability in the data and evaluate the reliability of the mean.

We usually sample populations in order to estimate basic population parameters (such as mean body size in the population) for a quantitative characteristic. It is important to know the central value (e.g. mean) of a set of sample data, but it is also useful to know how the data are spread (dispersed) around that value. The variance (s^2) or its square root, standard deviation (s) are often used as a measure of the spread in data. In general, if the spread of values around the mean is small, the mean will be a more reliable indicator of the true population mean than if the spread is large.

Standard deviation

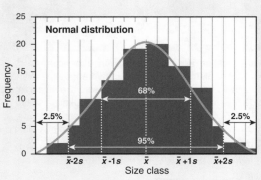

The **standard deviation** is a frequently used measure of the variability (spread) in a set of data. It is usually presented in the form $\bar{x} \pm s$. In a normally distributed set of data, 68% of all data values will lie within one standard deviation (s) of the mean ($\bar{x}$) and 95% of all data values will lie within two standard deviations of the mean (left).

Two different sets of data can have the same mean and range, yet the distribution of data within the range can be quite different. In both the data sets pictured in the histograms below, 68% of the values lie within the range $\bar{x} \pm 1s$ and 95% of the values lie within $\bar{x} \pm 2s$. However, in B, the data values are more tightly clustered around the mean.

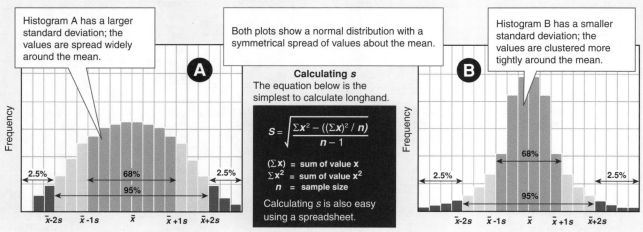

Histogram A has a larger standard deviation; the values are spread widely around the mean.

Both plots show a normal distribution with a symmetrical spread of values about the mean.

Histogram B has a smaller standard deviation; the values are clustered more tightly around the mean.

Calculating s
The equation below is the simplest to calculate longhand.

$$s = \sqrt{\frac{\sum x^2 - ((\sum x)^2 / n)}{n-1}}$$

$(\sum x)$ = sum of value x
$\sum x^2$ = sum of value x^2
n = sample size

Calculating s is also easy using a spreadsheet.

NOTE: you may sometimes see the standard deviation equation written as:

$$s = \sqrt{\frac{\sum (x - \bar{x})^2}{n-1}}$$

This equation gives the same answer as the equation above. The denominator n-1 provides a unbiased sample standard deviation for small sample sizes (large samples can use n).

Birth weights / kg		
3.740	3.810	3.220
3.830	2.640	3.135
3.530	2.980	3.090
3.095	3.350	3.830
1.560	3.780	3.840
3.910	3.260	4.710
4.180	3.800	4.050
3.570	4.170	4.560
3.150	4.400	3.380
3.400	3.770	3.690
3.380	3.825	1.495
2.660	3.130	3.260
3.840	3.400	
3.630	3.260	

1. Two sets of sample data have the same mean. The standard deviation of the first data set is much larger than the standard deviation of the second data set. What does this tell you about the spread of data around the mean for each set?

_____

_____

_____

2. The data on the left are the birth weights of 40 newborn babies.

(a) Calculate the mean for the data: _____

_____

(b) Calculate the standard deviation (s) for the data: _____

(c) State the mean ± 1s: _____

(d) What percentage of values are within 1s of the mean? _____

(e) What does this tell you about the spread of the data? _____

_____

LINK 105   LINK 106

DATA

105 Interpreting Sample Variability

Key Idea: The sampling method can affect the results of the study, especially if it has an unknown bias.

The assumptions we make about a population will be affected by what the sample data tell us. This is why it is important that sample data are **unbiased** (e.g. collected by random sampling) and that the sample set is as large as practicable.

The standard deviation (s) gives an indication of the spread or dispersion in data and serves as a measure of uncertainty. In general, a data set with a small s is more reliable as an indicator of the true population mean than a data set with a large s, but sampling bias can affect our statistical evaluation of the population. This activity will illustrate these principles.

Random sampling, sample size, and dispersion in data

Sample size and sampling bias can both affect the information we obtain when we sample a population. In this exercise you will calculate some descriptive statistics for some sample data.

The complete set of sample data we are working with comprises 689 length measurements of year zero (young of the year) perch (column left). Basic descriptive statistics for the data have been calculated for you below and the frequency histogram has also been plotted.

Look at this data set and then complete the exercise to calculate the same statistics from each of two smaller data sets (tabulated right) drawn from the same population. This exercise shows how random sampling, large sample size, and sampling bias affect our statistical assessment of variation in a population.

Complete sample set n = 689 (random)

Length in mm	Freq
25	1
26	0
27	0
28	0
29	0
30	0
31	0
32	2
33	3
34	3
35	4
36	5
37	10
38	23
39	22
40	33
41	39
42	41
43	41
44	36
45	49
46	32
47	14
48	32
49	27
50	25
51	24
52	17
53	18
54	27
55	21
56	20
57	11
58	18
59	16
60	22
61	13
62	8
63	10
64	5
65	7
66	2
67	3
68	3
69	1
70	0
71	1
	689

Small sample set n = 30 (random)

Length in mm	Freq
25	1
26	0
27	0
28	0
29	0
30	0
31	0
32	0
33	0
34	0
35	2
36	0
37	0
38	3
39	2
40	1
41	3
42	0
43	0
44	0
45	0
46	1
47	0
48	2
49	0
50	0
51	1
52	3
53	0
54	0
55	0
56	0
57	1
58	0
59	3
60	2
61	2
62	0
63	0
64	0
65	0
66	0
67	2
68	1
	30

Small sample set n = 50 (bias)

Length in mm	Freq
46	1
47	0
48	0
49	1
50	0
51	0
52	1
53	1
54	1
55	1
56	0
57	2
58	2
59	4
60	1
61	0
62	8
63	10
64	13
65	2
66	0
67	2
	50

The person gathering this set of data was biased towards selecting larger fish because the mesh size on the net was too large to retain small fish

This population was sampled randomly to obtain this data set

This column records the number of fish of each size

Number of fish in the sample

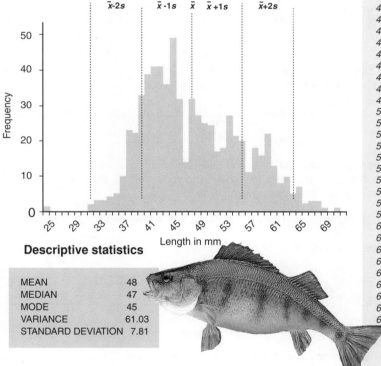

Length of year zero perch

$\bar{x}-2s$ $\bar{x}-1s$ $\bar{x}$ $\bar{x}+1s$ $\bar{x}+2s$

(Frequency vs Length in mm)

Descriptive statistics

MEAN	48
MEDIAN	47
MODE	45
VARIANCE	61.03
STANDARD DEVIATION	7.81

1. For the complete data set ($n = 689$) calculate the percentage of data falling within:

   (a) ± one standard deviation of the mean: _____

   (b) ± two standard deviations of the mean: _____

   (c) Explain what this information tells you about the distribution of year zero perch from this site: _____

   _____

2. Give another reason why you might reach the same conclusion about the distribution: _____

   _____

LINK 106 LINK 104 DATA

Calculating descriptive statistics using *Excel®*

You can use *Microsoft Excel®* or other similar spreadsheet programme to easily calculate descriptive statistics for sample data.

In this first example, the smaller data set ($n = 30$) is shown as it would appear on an *Excel®* spreadsheet, ready for the calculations to be made. Use this guide to enter your data into a spreadsheet and calculate the descriptive statistics as described.

When using formulae in *Excel®*, = indicates that a formula follows. The cursor will become active and you will be able to select the cells containing the data you are interested in, or you can type the location of the data using the format shown. The data in this case are located in the cells B2 through to B31 (B2:B31).

The variables being measured. Both length and weight were measured, but here we are working with only the length data.

Enter the data values in separate cells under an appropriate descriptor

Ignore this WEIGHT column. Sometimes the data we are interested in is part of larger data set.

The cells for the calculations below are B2 to B31

Type in the name of the statistic *Excel®* will calculate. This gives you a reference for the row of values.

Type the formula into the cell beside its label. When you press return, the cell will contain the calculated value.

Karori age zero perch 12-15 F

	A	B	C	D
1		LENGTH	WEIGHT	
2		25	0.15	
3		35	0.44	
4		35	0.44	
5		38	0.57	
6		38	0.57	
7		38	0.57	
8		39	0.61	
9		39	0.61	
10		40	0.67	
11		41	0.72	
12		41	0.72	
13		41	0.72	
14		46	1.03	
15		48	1.18	
16		48	1.18	
17		51	1.43	
18		52	1.52	
			1.52	
			1.52	
			2.04	
			2.27	
			2.27	
		59	2.27	
25		60	2.39	
26		60	2.39	
27		61	2.52	
28		61	2.52	
29		67	3.39	
30		67	3.39	
31		68	3.56	
32				
33				
34	N	=COUNT(B2:B31)		
35	MEAN	=AVERAGE(B2:B31)		
36	MEDIAN	=MEDIAN(B2:B31)		
37	MODE	=MODE(B2:B31)		
38	VARIANCE	=VAR(B2:B31)		
39	STANDARD DEVIATION	=STDEV(B2:B31)		
40				
41				

3. For this set of data, use a spreadsheet to calculate:

(a) Mean: _____

(b) Median: _____

(c) Mode: _____

(d) Sample variance: _____

(e) Standard deviation: _____

Staple the spreadsheet into your workbook.

4. Repeat the calculations for the second small set of sample data ($n = 50$) on the previous page. Again, calculate the statistics as indicated below and staple the spreadsheet into your workbook:

(a) Mean: _____ (b) Median: _____ (c) Mode: _____

(d) Variance: _____ (e) Standard deviation: _____

5. On a separate sheet, plot **frequency histograms** for each of the two small data sets. Label them $n = 30$ and $n = 50$. Staple them into your workbook. If you are proficient in *Excel®* and you have the "Data Analysis" plug in loaded, you can use *Excel®* to plot the histograms for you once you have entered the data.

6. Compare the descriptive statistics you calculated for each data set with reference to the following:

(a) How close the median and mean to each other in each sample set: _____

_____

(b) The size of the standard deviation in each case: _____

_____

(c) How close each small of the sample sets resembles the large sample set of 689 values: _____

_____

_____

7. (a) Compare the two frequency histograms you have plotted for the two smaller sample data sets: _____

_____

_____

(b) Why do you think two histograms look so different? _____

_____

_____

106 Reliability of the Mean

Key Idea: The 95% confidence limit gives a measure of the reliability of the sample mean as an estimate of the true value of the mean of the population.

You have already seen how to use the **standard deviation** (*s*) to quantify the spread or **dispersion** in your data. Usually, you will also want to know how good your sample mean ($\bar{x}$) is as an estimate of the true population mean (μ). This can be indicated by the standard error of the mean (or just **standard error** or **SE**). **SE** is often used as an error measurement simply because it is small, rather than for any good statistical

reason. However, it is does allow you calculate the **95% confidence interval (95% CI)**. By the end of this activity you should be able to:

- Enter data and calculate descriptive statistics using a spreadsheet program such as *Microsoft Excel®*. You can follow this procedure for any set of data.
- Calculate standard error and 95% CIs (and confidence limits) for sample data and plot these data with error bars.
- Interpret the graphically presented data and reach tentative conclusions about the findings of an investigation.

Reliability of the sample mean

When we take measurements from samples of a larger population, we are using those samples as indicators of the trends in the whole population. Therefore, when we calculate a sample mean, it is useful to know how close that value is to the true population mean (μ). This is not merely an academic exercise; it will enable you to make inferences about the aspect of the population in which you are interested. For this reason, statistics based on samples and used to estimate population parameters are called **inferential statistics**.

Ladybird-population

Sample

When we measure a particular attribute from a sample of a larger population and calculate a mean for that attribute, we can calculate how closely our sample mean (the statistic) is to the true population mean for that attribute (the parameter).

Example: If we calculated the mean number of spots from a sample of six ladybird beetles, how reliable is this statistic as an indicator of the mean number of spots in the whole population? We can find out by calculating the **95% confidence interval**.

The standard error (SE)

The standard error (SE) is simple to calculate and is usually a small value. Standard error is given by:

$$SE = \frac{s}{\sqrt{n}}$$

where *s* = the standard deviation, and *n* = sample size.

Standard errors are sometimes plotted as error bars on graphs, but it is more meaningful to plot the **95% confidence intervals** (see box below). All calculations are easily made using a spreadsheet (see following pages).

The 95% confidence interval

SE is required to calculate the 95% confidence interval (CI) of the mean. This is given by:

$$95\% \text{ CI} = SE \times t_{P(n-1)}$$

Do not be alarmed by this calculation; once you have calculated the value of the SE, it is a simple matter to multiply this value by the value of *t* at P = 0.05 (from the *t* table) for the appropriate degrees of freedom (df) for your sample (*n* – 1).

For example: where the SE = 0.6 and the sample size is 10, the calculation of the 95% CI is:

$$95\% \text{ CI} = 0.6 \times 2.262 = \boxed{1.36}$$

Part of the *t* table is given to the right for P = 0.05. Note that, as the sample becomes very large, the value of *t* becomes smaller. For very large samples, *t* is fixed at 1.96, so the 95% CI is slightly less than twice the SE

All these statistics, including a plot of the data with Y error bars, can be calculated using a program such as *Microsoft Excel®*.

Critical values of Student's *t* distribution at P = 0.05.

df	P
	0.05
1	12.71
2	4.303
3	3.182
4	2.776
5	2.571
6	2.447
7	2.365
8	2.306
9	2.262
10	2.228
20	2.086
30	2.042
40	2.021
60	2.000
120	1.980
>120	1.960

Value of *t* at *n*–1 = 9

Maximum value of *t* at this level of P

Relationship of Y against X (± 95% confidence intervals, *n* = 10)

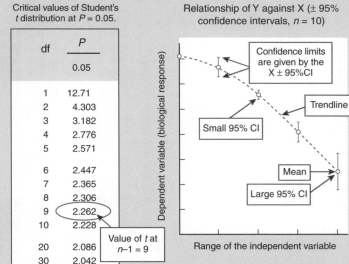

Confidence limits are given by the X ± 95%CI

Trendline

Small 95% CI

Mean

Large 95% CI

Dependent variable (biological response)

Range of the independent variable

Plotting your confidence intervals

Once you have calculated the 95% CI for the means in your data set, you can plot them as error bars on your graph. Note that the **95% confidence limits** are given by the value of the **mean ± 95%CI**. A 95% confidence limit (i.e. P = 0.05) tells you that, on average, 95 times out of 100, the limits will contain the true population mean.

Clover root weevil

The clover root weevil (*Sitona lepidus*) is a pest of white clover pastures. The adults feed on clover leaves, while the larvae feed on clover nodules and roots, causing root loss and a reduction in nitrogen fixation.

Research has indicated that different pastures have different susceptibility to infestation by clover root weevil (left). Armed with this knowledge, two students reasoned that the most susceptible grass type would have the greatest weevil population. The students chose five pasture types, and recorded the number of weevil larvae in each pasture type at six sample sites (sample area 1 m^2). Their results are presented in the table below.

		Environment				
	Sample	Perennial ryegrass	Fescue	White clover	Red clover	Chicory
Number of weevils	1	42	42	48	42	45
	2	45	46	54	46	44
	3	41	38	48	45	45
	4	42	41	52	42	38
	5	49	45	49	44	40
	6	43	44	52	44	47

1. Complete the table below by calculating the mean, standard deviation, standard error, and 95% confidence interval (95% CI) for each of the grass environments.

	Perennial ryegrass	Fescue	White clover	Red clover	Chicory
Mean					
Standard deviation					
Standard error					
95% CI					

2. Select the appropriate graph format and plot the means for each of the grass environments below. Include bars to show the 95% confidence intervals.

3. Study your plot and decide if there are any significant differences between the abundance of clover root weevils in the five environments. Write a conclusion for the investigation below:

_____

_____

_____

107 Which Test to Use?

Key Idea: How your data is analysed depends on the type of data you have collected. Plotting your initial data can help you to decide what statistical analysis to carry out.

Data analysis provides information on the biological significance of your investigation. Never under-estimate the value of plotting your data, even at a very early stage. This will help you decide on the best type of data analysis. Sometimes, statistical analysis may not be required.

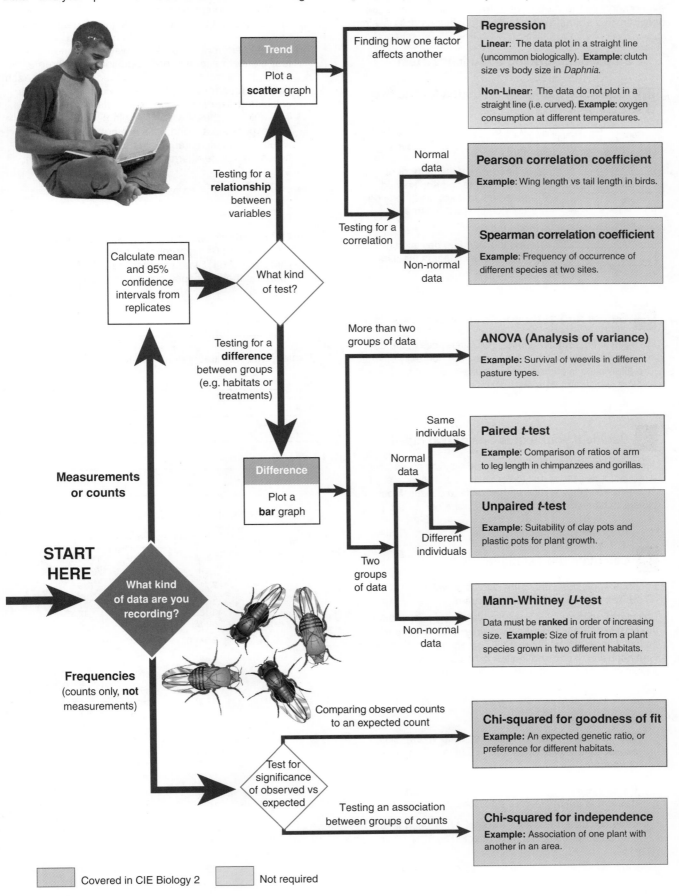

Trend
Plot a **scatter** graph

Finding how one factor affects another

Regression
Linear: The data plot in a straight line (uncommon biologically). **Example**: clutch size vs body size in *Daphnia*.
Non-Linear: The data do not plot in a straight line (i.e. curved). **Example**: oxygen consumption at different temperatures.

Testing for a **relationship** between variables

Testing for a correlation

Normal data

Pearson correlation coefficient
Example: Wing length vs tail length in birds.

Non-normal data

Spearman correlation coefficient
Example: Frequency of occurrence of different species at two sites.

Calculate mean and 95% confidence intervals from replicates

What kind of test?

Testing for a **difference** between groups (e.g. habitats or treatments)

More than two groups of data

ANOVA (Analysis of variance)
Example: Survival of weevils in different pasture types.

Difference
Plot a **bar** graph

Same individuals

Normal data

Paired *t*-test
Example: Comparison of ratios of arm to leg length in chimpanzees and gorillas.

Different individuals

Unpaired *t*-test
Example: Suitability of clay pots and plastic pots for plant growth.

Measurements or counts

Two groups of data

Non-normal data

Mann-Whitney *U*-test
Data must be **ranked** in order of increasing size. **Example**: Size of fruit from a plant species grown in two different habitats.

START HERE

What kind of data are you recording?

Frequencies (counts only, **not** measurements)

Comparing observed counts to an expected count

Chi-squared for goodness of fit
Example: An expected genetic ratio, or preference for different habitats.

Test for significance of observed vs expected

Testing an association between groups of counts

Chi-squared for independence
Example: Association of one plant with another in an area.

Covered in CIE Biology 2   Not required

LINK 162 LINK 161 LINK 158 LINK 108 LINK 86 **REFER**

108 Quantifying Variation Using Student's *t* Test

Key Idea: Differences between two populations can be tested for significance using the Student's *t* test.

The Student's *t* test is commonly used to compare two sample means, e.g. means for a treatment and a control in an experiment, or the means of some measured characteristic between two animal or two plant populations. It is a simple test and useful for distinguishing real but marginal differences between samples. Usefully, the test remains robust even when sample sizes are small. A simple example outlining the steps in the Student's *t* test is provided below. It compares data for a treatment and a control from a hypothetical experiment (the units are not relevant in this case, only the values).

Steps in performing a Student's *t* test

1 Calculate summary statistics for the two data sets

Control (A)	Treatment (B)
6.6	6.3
5.5	7.2
6.8	6.5
5.8	7.1
6.1	7.5
5.9	7.3

$n_A = 6$, $\bar{x}_A = 6.12$, $s_A = 0.496$

$n_B = 6$, $\bar{x}_B = 6.98$, $s_B = 0.475$

n_A and n_B are the number of values in the first and second data sets respectively (these do not need to be the same).

$\bar{x}$ is the mean.

s is the standard deviation (a measure of scatter in the data).

2 Set up and state your null hypothesis (H₀)

H_0: there is no treatment effect. The differences in the data sets are the result of chance and they are not really different. The alternative hypothesis is that there is a treatment effect and the two sets of data are truly different.

3 Decide if your test is one or two tailed

A one-tailed test looks for a difference only in one particular direction. A two-tailed test looks for any difference (+ or –). This tells you what section of the t table to consult. Most biological tests are two-tailed. Very few are one-tailed.

4 Calculate the *t* statistic

For our sample data above the calculated value of *t* is –3.09. The degrees of freedom (df) are $n_1 + n_2 - 2 = 10$.

Calculation of the *t* value uses the variance which is simply the square of the standard deviation (s^2). You may compute *t* using a spreadsheet but manual computation is not difficult (see opposite). It does not matter if the calculated *t* value is a positive or negative (the sign is irrelevant).

The absolute value of the *t* statistic (3.09) well exceeds the critical value for $P = 0.05$ at 10 degrees of freedom.

We can reject H₀ and conclude that the means are different at the 5% level of significance.

If the calculated absolute value of *t* had been less than 2.23, we could not have rejected H_0.

1. (a) In an experiment, data values were obtained from four plants in experimental conditions and three plants in control conditions. The mean values for each data set (control and experimental conditions) were calculated. The *t* value was calculated to be 2.16. The null hypothesis was: "The plants in the control and experimental conditions are not different". State whether the calculated *t* value supports the null hypothesis or its alternative (consult *t* table below):

_____

_____

(b) The experiment was repeated, but this time using 6 control and 6 "experimental" plants. The new *t* value was 2.54. State whether the calculated *t* value supports the null hypothesis or its alternative now:

_____

_____

2. Explain what you understand by statistical significance:

_____

_____

_____

_____

_____

Table of critical values of *t* at different levels of *P*.

Degrees of freedom	Level of Probability		
	0.05	0.01	0.001
1	12.71	63.66	636.6
2	4.303	9.925	31.60
3	3.182	5.841	12.92
4	2.776	4.604	8.610
5	2.571	4.032	6.869
6	2.447	3.707	5.959
7	2.365	3.499	5.408
8	2.306	3.355	5.041
9	2.262	3.250	4.781
10	2.228	3.169	4.587
15	2.131	2.947	4.073
16	2.120	2.921	4.015
17	2.110	2.898	3.965
18	2.101	2.878	3.922
19	2.093	2.861	3.883
20	2.086	2.845	3.850
25	2.060	2.787	3.725
30	2.042	2.750	3.646
40	2.021	2.704	3.551
50	2.009	2.678	3.496
60	2.000	2.660	3.460
100	1.984	2.626	3.390

DATA

3. The table below presents data for heart rate (beats per minute) in samples of ten males and females from a population.
(a) Complete the calculations to perform the t test for these two samples. Some calculations are provided for you.

x (bpm)		x − x̄ (deviation from the mean)		(x − x̄)² (deviation from mean)²	
Male	Female	Male	Female	Male	Female
70	69	-2.3	1	5.29	1
74	62	1.7	-6	2.89	36
80	75				
73	66				
75	68				
82	57				
62	61				
69	84				
70	61				
68	77				

$n_A = 10$ $n_B = 10$

The number of samples in each data set

The sum of each column is called the sum of squares

$\Sigma (x - \bar{x})^2$ $\Sigma (x - \bar{x})^2$

(b) The variance for males: $s^2_A =$

The variance for females: $s^2_B =$

(c) The difference between the means for males and females

$(\bar{x}_A - \bar{x}_B) =$

(d) $t_{(calculated)} =$

(e) Determine the degrees of freedom (d.f.)

d.f. $(n_A + n_B - 2) =$

(f) $P =$

$t_{(critical\ value)} =$

(g) Your decision is: _____

_____

_____

_____

_____

_____

Step 1: Summary statistics

Tabulate the data as shown in the first 2 columns of the table (left). Calculate the mean and give the n value for each data set. Compute the standard deviation if you wish.

Males $\bar{x}_A = 72.3$ Females $\bar{x}_B = 68.0$
$n_A = 10$ $n_B = 10$
$s_A = 5.87$ $s_B = 8.47$

Step 2: State your null hypothesis

Step 3: Test is one tailed / two tailed (delete one)

Step 4: Calculating t

4a: Calculate sums of squares

Complete the computations outlined in the table left. The sum of each of the final two columns (left) is called the sum of squares.

4b: Calculate the variances

Calculate the variance (s^2) for each data set. This is the sum of squares ÷ by $n - 1$ (number of samples in each data set − 1). In this case the n values are the same, but they need not be.

$$s^2_A = \frac{\Sigma(x - \bar{x})^2}{n_A - 1} \text{(A)} \qquad s^2_B = \frac{\Sigma(x - \bar{x})^2}{n_B - 1}\text{(B)}$$

4c: Differences between the means

Calculate the difference between the means

$$(\bar{x}_A - \bar{x}_B)$$

4d: Calculate t

$$t = \frac{(\bar{x}_A - \bar{x}_B)}{\sqrt{\dfrac{s^2_A}{n_A} + \dfrac{s^2_B}{n_B}}}$$

4e: Determine the degrees of freedom

Degrees of freedom (d.f.) = $n_A + n_B - 2$ where n_A and n_B are the number of counts in each of populations A and B.

Step 5: Consult the t table

Consult the t-tables (opposite) for the critical t value at the appropriate degrees of freedom and the acceptable probability level (e.g. P = 0.05).

5a: Make your decision

Make your decision whether or not to reject H_0. If t_{calc} is large enough you may be able to reject H_0 at a lower P value (e.g. 0.001), increasing confidence in the alternative hypothesis.

109 Quantitative Investigation of Variation

Key Idea: The Student's *t* test can be used to test the significance of differences between populations for a variable phenotypic character.
White clover (*Trifolium repens*) is a common pasture plant.

It has white flowers and distinctive leaves with three (or occasionally four) leaflets. The leaves are held on petioles that can be 150 mm or more long if left undisturbed. In pasture that is regularly grazed petiole length can be shorter.

Two paddocks containing white clover were grazed by cattle under different regimes during the peak growing season (late winter to early summer). Paddock A was grazed for one day every week whereas paddock B was grazed for one day every four weeks. At the end of the trial, quadrats were used to select random samples of clover and the lengths of the petioles were measured to evaluate the effect of grazing on morphology (in this case petiole length). The results are shown below. Use the Student's *t* test to determine the significance of the differences between the two populations (grazing regimes). The calculation steps are given in the blue boxes. Steps for calculating the summary statistics with a calculator are in the grey boxes.

Leaflets

Petiole

Clover leaf

x (length / mm)		x − x̄ (deviation from the mean)		(x − x̄)² (deviation from mean)²	
Paddock A	Paddock B	Paddock A	Paddock B	Paddock A	Paddock B
83	30	40.2	-77.5	1616.04	6006.25
70	87	27.2	-20.5	739.84	420.25
32	48				
61	92				
70	54				
45	33				
28	135				
34	60				
37	81				
20	139				
25	90				
30	78				
31	125				
35	174				
80	167				
22	184				
62	80				
35	125				
25	163				
44	197				
30	116				

The sum of each column is called the sum of squares

$\Sigma (x - \bar{x})^2$ $\Sigma (x - \bar{x})^2$

Step 1: Summary statistics

Tabulate the data as shown in the first 2 columns of the table (left). Calculate the mean and give the n value for each data set. Compute the standard deviation if you wish.

Popn A $\bar{x}_A =$ _____   Popn B $\bar{x}_B =$ _____
$n_A =$ _____ $n_B =$ _____
$s_A^* =$ _____ $s_B^* =$ _____

* These can be calculated using the variance equation or a standard scientific calculator (see below).

Step 2: State your null hypothesis

Step 3: Test is one tailed / two tailed (delete one)

Summary statistics on a calculator

Most standard scientific calculators will be able to provide you with the number of sample entrants (n), the mean (x̄) and the standard deviation (s) once you have entered the data. The procedure shown below is for a Casio fx-82 calculator, a standard classroom calculator. In most Casio models the procedure is similar. Consult the calculator's manual if necessary.

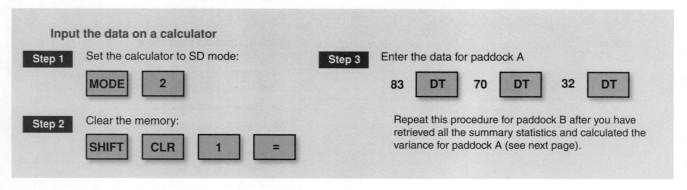

Input the data on a calculator

Step 1 Set the calculator to SD mode:

MODE 2

Step 2 Clear the memory:

SHIFT CLR 1 =

Step 3 Enter the data for paddock A

83 DT 70 DT 32 DT

Repeat this procedure for paddock B after you have retrieved all the summary statistics and calculated the variance for paddock A (see next page).

LINK
DATA 108

© 2016 **BIOZONE** International
ISBN: 978-1-927309-32-2
Photocopying Prohibited

Step 4: Calculating t

4a: Calculate sums of squares

Complete the computations outlined in the table left. The sum of each of the final two columns (left) is called the sum of squares.

4b: Calculate the variances

Calculate the variance (s^2) for each data set. This is the sum of squares ÷ by $n - 1$ (number of samples in each data set $- 1$). In this case the n values are the same, but they need not be.

$$s^2_A = \frac{\sum(x - \bar{x})^2}{n_A - 1}_{(A)} \qquad s^2_B = \frac{\sum(x - \bar{x})^2}{n_B - 1}_{(B)}$$

4c: Differences between the means

Calculate the difference between the means

$$(\bar{x}_A - \bar{x}_B)$$

4d: Calculate t

$$t = \frac{(\bar{x}_A - \bar{x}_B)}{\sqrt{\dfrac{s^2_A}{n_A} + \dfrac{s^2_B}{n_B}}}$$

4e: Determine the degrees of freedom

Degrees of freedom (d.f.) $= n_A + n_B - 2$ where n_A and n_B are the number of counts in each of populations A and B.

Step 5: Consult the t table

Consult the t-tables in the previous activity for the critical t value at the appropriate degrees of freedom and probability level (e.g. P = 0.05).

5a: Make your decision

Make your decision whether or not to reject H_0. If t_{calc} is large enough you may be able to reject H_0 at a lower P value (e.g. 0.001), increasing confidence in the alternative hypothesis.

Retrieving the summary statistics

| SHIFT | 1 | 3 | = | (calculates n) |

| SHIFT | 2 | 1 | = | (calculates x̄) |

| SHIFT | 2 | 3 | = | (calculates s) |

Calculate the variance

| SHIFT | 2 | 3 | x^2 | = |

1. The variance for population A: $s^2_A =$ _____

   The variance for population B: $s^2_B =$ _____

2. The difference between the population means:

   $(\bar{x}_A - \bar{x}_B) =$ _____

3. (a) Calculate t.

   (b) $t_{(calculated)} =$ _____

4. Determine the degrees of freedom (d.f.)

   d.f. $(n_A + n_B - 2) =$ _____

   _____

5. $P =$ _____

   $t_{(critical\ value)} =$ _____

6. Your decision is: _____

7. Write a conclusion for the investigation: _____

   _____

   _____

8. To further the investigation, it was decided to find out if the regular grazing affected the rate of dry matter increase in the clover. Suggest a way in which this could done:

   _____

   _____

   _____

110 Gene Pools and Evolution

Key Idea: The proportions of alleles in a gene pool can be altered by the processes that increase or decrease variation. This activity portrays two populations of a beetle species. Each beetle is a 'carrier' of genetic information, represented by the alleles (A and a) for a gene that controls colour and has a dominant/recessive inheritance pattern. There are normally two phenotypes: black and pale. Mutations may create new alleles. Some of the **microevolutionary processes** (natural selection, genetic drift, gene flow, and mutation) that affect the genetic composition (**allele frequencies**) of gene pools are shown below. Simulate the effect of these using the *Gene Pool Exercise*.

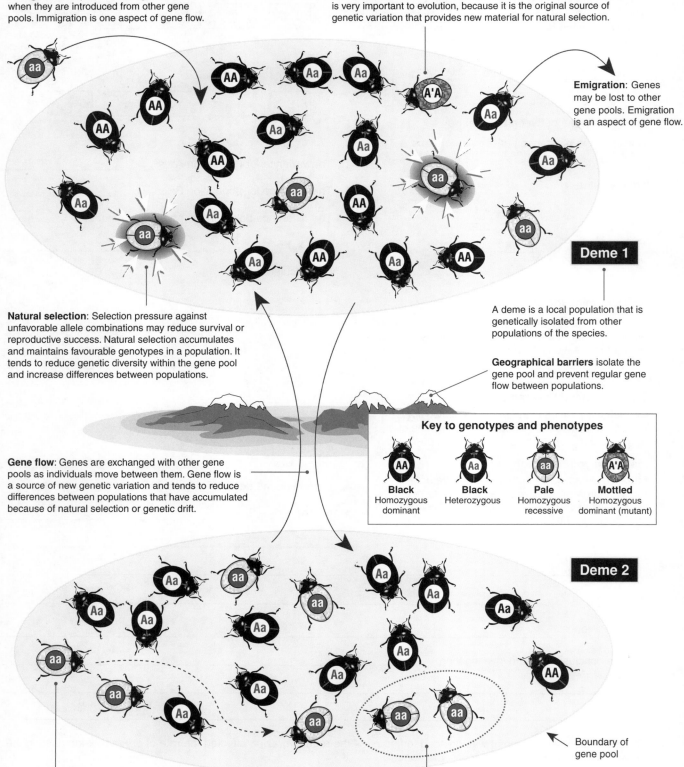

Immigration: Populations can gain alleles when they are introduced from other gene pools. Immigration is one aspect of gene flow.

Mutations: Spontaneous mutations can create new alleles. Mutation is very important to evolution, because it is the original source of genetic variation that provides new material for natural selection.

Emigration: Genes may be lost to other gene pools. Emigration is an aspect of gene flow.

Natural selection: Selection pressure against unfavorable allele combinations may reduce survival or reproductive success. Natural selection accumulates and maintains favourable genotypes in a population. It tends to reduce genetic diversity within the gene pool and increase differences between populations.

A deme is a local population that is genetically isolated from other populations of the species.

Geographical barriers isolate the gene pool and prevent regular gene flow between populations.

Gene flow: Genes are exchanged with other gene pools as individuals move between them. Gene flow is a source of new genetic variation and tends to reduce differences between populations that have accumulated because of natural selection or genetic drift.

Key to genotypes and phenotypes

- **AA** Black — Homozygous dominant
- **Aa** Black — Heterozygous
- **aa** Pale — Homozygous recessive
- **A'A** Mottled — Homozygous dominant (mutant)

Deme 1

Deme 2

Boundary of gene pool

Mate choice (non-random mating): Individuals may not select their mate randomly and may seek out particular phenotypes, increasing the frequency of the associated alleles in the population.

Genetic drift: Chance events cause the allele frequencies of small populations to 'drift' (change) randomly from generation to generation. Genetic drift has a relatively greater effect on the genetics of small populations and can be important in their evolution. Small populations may occur as a result of the **founder effect** (where a small number of individuals colonise a new area) or **genetic bottlenecks** (where the population size is dramatically reduced by a catastrophic event).

© 2016 BIOZONE International
ISBN: 978-1-927309-32-2
Photocopying Prohibited

1. For each of the two demes shown on the previous page (treating the mutant in deme 1 as a AA):

   (a) Count up the numbers of **allele types** (**A** and **a**).

   (b) Count up the numbers of **allele combinations** (**AA, Aa, aa**).

2. Calculate the frequencies as percentages (%) for the allele types and combinations:

Deme 1		Number counted	%
Allele types	A		
	a		
Allele combinations	AA		
	Aa		
	aa		

Deme 2		Number counted	%
Allele types	A		
	a		
Allele combinations	AA		
	Aa		
	aa		

3. One of the fundamental concepts for population genetics is that of **genetic equilibrium**, stated as: *"For a very large, randomly mating population, the proportion of dominant to recessive alleles remains constant from one generation to the next"*. If a gene pool is to remain unchanged, it must satisfy all of the criteria below that favour gene pool stability. Few populations meet all (or any) of these criteria and their genetic makeup must therefore by continually changing. For each of the five factors (a-e) below, state briefly **how** and **why** each would affect the allele frequency in a gene pool:

   (a) Population size: _____

   _____

   _____

   _____

   (b) Mate selection: _____

   _____

   _____

   _____

   (c) Gene flow between populations: _____

   _____

   _____

   _____

   (d) Mutations: _____

   _____

   _____

   _____

   (e) Natural selection: _____

   _____

   _____

   _____

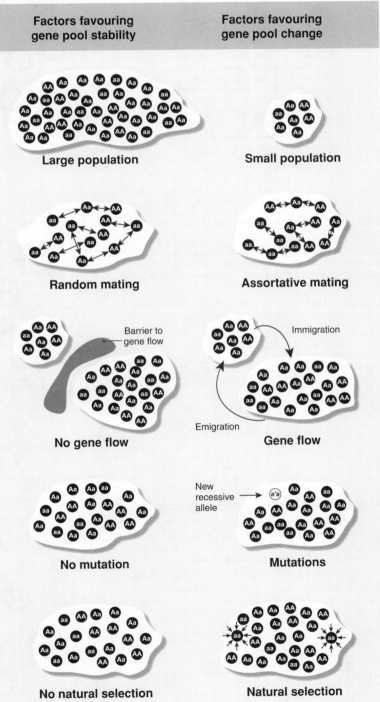

Factors favouring gene pool stability | **Factors favouring gene pool change**

Large population | Small population

Random mating | Assortative mating

No gene flow | Gene flow

No mutation | Mutations

No natural selection | Natural selection

4. Identify the factors that tend to:

   (a) Increase genetic variation in populations:

   _____

   _____

   (b) Decrease genetic variation in populations:

   _____

   _____

111 Changes in a Gene Pool

Key Idea: Natural selection and migration can alter the allele frequencies in gene pools.

The diagram below shows an hypothetical population of beetles undergoing changes as it is subjected to two 'events'. The three phases represent a progression in time (i.e. the same gene pool, undergoing change). The beetles have two phenotypes (black and pale) determined by the amount of pigment deposited in the cuticle. The gene controlling this character is represented by two alleles **A** and **a**. Your task is to analyse the gene pool as it undergoes changes.

1. For each phase in the gene pool below fill in the tables provided as follows; (some have been done for you):

   (a) Count the number of A and a alleles separately. Enter the count into the top row of the table (left hand columns).
   (b) Count the number of each type of allele combination (AA, Aa and aa) in the gene pool. Enter the count into the top row of the table (right hand columns).
   (c) For each of the above, work out the frequencies as percentages (bottom row of table):

$$\text{Allele frequency} = \text{No. counted alleles} \div \text{Total no. of alleles} \times 100$$

Phase 1: Initial gene pool

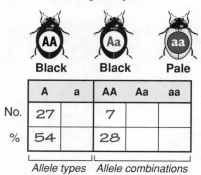

	A	a	AA	Aa	aa
No.	27		7		
%	54		28		

Allele types — *Allele combinations*

Two pale individuals died. Their alleles are removed from the gene pool.

Phase 2: Natural selection

In the same gene pool at a later time there was a change in the allele frequencies. This was due to the loss of certain allele combinations due to natural selection. Some of those with a genotype of aa were eliminated (poor fitness).

These individuals (surrounded by small white arrows) are not counted for allele frequencies; they are dead!

	A	a	AA	Aa	aa
No.					
%					

This individual is entering the population and will add its alleles to the gene pool.

This individual is leaving the population, removing its alleles from the gene pool.

Phase 3: Immigration and emigration

This particular kind of beetle exhibits wandering behaviour. The allele frequencies change again due to the introduction and departure of individual beetles, each carrying certain allele combinations.

Individuals coming into the gene pool (AA) are counted for allele frequencies, but those leaving (aa) are not.

	A	a	AA	Aa	aa
No.					
%					

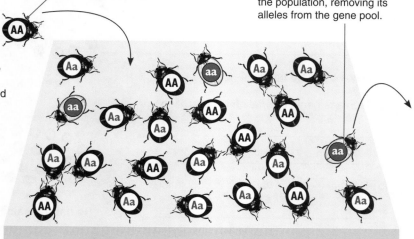

© 2016 **BIOZONE** International
ISBN: **978-1-927309-32-2**
Photocopying Prohibited

112 Hardy-Weinberg Calculations

Key Idea: The Hardy-Weinberg equation is a mathematical model used to calculate allele and genotype frequencies in populations.

The Hardy-Weinberg equation provides a simple mathematical model of genetic equilibrium in a gene pool, but its main application in population genetics is in calculating allele and genotype frequencies in populations, particularly as a means of studying changes and measuring their rate.

Punnett square

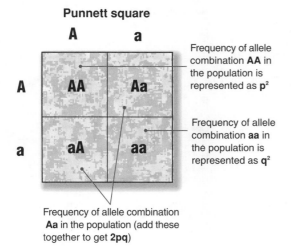

Frequency of allele combination **AA** in the population is represented as p^2

Frequency of allele combination **aa** in the population is represented as q^2

Frequency of allele combination **Aa** in the population (add these together to get **2pq**)

$$ (p + q)^2 \quad = \quad p^2 + 2pq + q^2 \quad = 1 $$

Frequency of allele types

p = Frequency of allele A
q = Frequency of allele a

Frequency of allele combinations

p^2 = Frequency of AA (homozygous dominant)
2pq = Frequency of Aa (heterozygous)
q^2 = Frequency of aa (homozygous recessive)

The Hardy-Weinberg equation is applied to populations with a simple genetic situation: dominant and recessive alleles controlling a single trait. The frequency of all of the dominant (A) and recessive alleles (a) equals the total genetic complement, and adds up to 1 or 100% of the alleles present (i.e. p + q = 1).

How To solve Hardy-Weinberg problems

In most populations, the frequency of two alleles of interest is calculated from the proportion of homozygous recessives (q^2), as this is the only genotype identifiable directly from its phenotype. If only the dominant phenotype is known, q^2 may be calculated (1 – the frequency of the dominant phenotype). The following steps outline the procedure for solving a Hardy-Weinberg problem:

Remember that all calculations must be carried out using proportions, NOT PERCENTAGES!

1. Examine the question to determine what piece of information you have been given about the population. In most cases, this is the percentage or frequency of the homozygous recessive phenotype q^2, or the dominant phenotype $p^2 + 2pq$ (see note above).

2. The first objective is to find out the value of p or q, If this is achieved, then every other value in the equation can be determined by simple calculation.

3. Take the square root of q^2 to find q.

4. Determine p by subtracting q from 1 (i.e. p = 1 – q).

5. Determine p^2 by multiplying p by itself (i.e. $p^2 = p \times p$).

6. Determine 2pq by multiplying p times q times 2.

7. Check that your calculations are correct by adding up the values for $p^2 + q^2 + 2pq$ (the sum should equal 1 or 100%).

Worked example

Among white-skinned people in the USA, approximately 70% of people can taste the chemical phenylthiocarbamide (PTC) (the dominant phenotype), while 30% are non-tasters (the recessive phenotype).

Determine the frequency of:		*Answers*
(a) Homozygous recessive phenotype(q^2).		30% - provided
(b) The dominant allele (**p**).		45.2%
(c) Homozygous tasters (**p^2**).		20.5%
(d) Heterozygous tasters (**2pq**).		49.5%

Data: The frequency of the dominant phenotype (70% tasters) and recessive phenotype (30% non-tasters) are provided.

Working:

Recessive phenotype: q^2 = 30%
      use 0.30 for calculation

    therefore: **q**   = 0.5477
      square root of 0.30

    therefore: **p**   = 0.4523
      1 – q = p
      1 – 0.5477 = 0.4523

Use p and q in the equation (top) to solve any unknown:

Homozygous dominant   **p^2**   = 0.2046
      (p x p = 0.4523 x 0.4523)

Heterozygous: **2pq** = 0.4953

---

1. A population of hamsters has a gene consisting of 90% M alleles (black) and 10% m alleles (grey). Mating is random.

   Data: Frequency of recessive allele (10% m) and dominant allele (90% M).

   Determine the proportion of offspring that will be black and the proportion that will be grey (show your working):

   _____

   _____

Recessive allele:	q =	
Dominant allele:	p =	
Recessive phenotype:	q^2 =	
Homozygous dominant:	p^2 =	
Heterozygous:	2pq =	

LINK WEB
113 112 DATA

2. You are working with pea plants and found 36 plants out of 400 were dwarf.
   Data: Frequency of recessive phenotype (36 out of 400 = 9%)

   (a) Calculate the frequency of the tall gene: _____

   (b) Determine the number of heterozygous pea plants:

   _____

   _____

Recessive allele:	q =	
Dominant allele:	p =	
Recessive phenotype:	q^2 =	
Homozygous dominant:	p^2 =	
Heterozygous:	2pq =	

3. In humans, the ability to taste the chemical phenylthiocarbamide (PTC) is inherited as a simple dominant characteristic. Suppose you found out that 360 out of 1000 college students could not taste the chemical.
   Data: Frequency of recessive phenotype (360 out of 1000).

   (a) State the frequency of the gene for tasting PTC:

   _____

   (b) Determine the number of heterozygous students in this population:

   _____

Recessive allele:	q =	
Dominant allele:	p =	
Recessive phenotype:	q^2 =	
Homozygous dominant:	p^2 =	
Heterozygous:	2pq =	

4. A type of deformity appears in 4% of a large herd of cattle. Assume the deformity was caused by a recessive gene.
   Data: Frequency of recessive phenotype (4% deformity).

   (a) Calculate the percentage of the herd that are carriers of the gene:

   _____

   (b) Determine the frequency of the dominant gene in this case:

   _____

Recessive allele:	q =	
Dominant allele:	p =	
Recessive phenotype:	q^2 =	
Homozygous dominant:	p^2 =	
Heterozygous:	2pq =	

5. Assume you placed 50 pure bred black guinea pigs (dominant allele) with 50 albino guinea pigs (recessive allele) and allowed the population to attain genetic equilibrium (several generations have passed).
   Data: Frequency of recessive allele (50%) and dominant allele (50%).

   Determine the proportion (%) of the population that becomes white:

   _____

Recessive allele:	q =	
Dominant allele:	p =	
Recessive phenotype:	q^2 =	
Homozygous dominant:	p^2 =	
Heterozygous:	2pq =	

6. It is known that 64% of a large population exhibit the recessive trait of a characteristic controlled by two alleles (one is dominant over the other).
   Data: Frequency of recessive phenotype (64%). Determine the following:

   (a) The frequency of the recessive allele: _____

   (b) The percentage that are heterozygous for this trait: _____

   (c) The percentage that exhibit the dominant trait: _____

   (d) The percentage that are homozygous for the dominant trait: _____

   (e) The percentage that has one or more recessive alleles: _____

7. Albinism is recessive to normal pigmentation in humans. The frequency of the albino allele was 10% in a population.
   Data: Frequency of recessive allele (10% albino allele).

   Determine the proportion of people that you would expect to be albino:

   _____

   _____

   _____

Recessive allele:	q =	
Dominant allele:	p =	
Recessive phenotype:	q^2 =	
Homozygous dominant:	p^2 =	
Heterozygous:	2pq =	

© 2016 **BIOZONE** International
ISBN: 978-1-927309-32-2
Photocopying Prohibited

113 Analysis of a Squirrel Gene Pool

Key Idea: Allele frequencies for real populations can be calculated using the Hardy-Weinberg equation. Analysis of those allele frequencies can show how the population's gene pool changes over time.

In Olney, Illinois, there is a unique population of albino (white) and grey squirrels. Between 1977 and 1990, students at Olney Central College carried out a study of this population. They recorded the frequency of grey and albino squirrels. The albinos displayed a mutant allele expressed as an albino phenotype only in the homozygous recessive condition. The data they collected are provided in the table below. Using the **Hardy-Weinberg equation**, it was possible to estimate the frequency of the normal 'wild' allele (G) providing grey fur colouring, and the frequency of the mutant albino allele (g) producing white squirrels when homozygous.

Thanks to **Dr. John Stencel**, Olney Central College, Olney, Illinois, US, for providing the data for this exercise.

Grey squirrel, usual colour form   Albino form of grey squirrel

Population of grey and white squirrels in Olney, Illinois (1977-1990)

Year	Grey	White	Total	GG	Gg	gg	Freq. of g	Freq. of G
1977	602	182	784	26.85	49.93	23.21	48.18	51.82
1978	511	172	683	24.82	50.00	25.18	50.18	49.82
1979	482	134	616	28.47	49.77	21.75	46.64	53.36
1980	489	133	622	28.90	49.72	21.38	46.24	53.76
1981	536	163	699	26.74	49.94	23.32	48.29	51.71
1982	618	151	769	31.01	49.35	19.64	44.31	55.69
1983	419	141	560	24.82	50.00	25.18	50.18	49.82
1984	378	106	484	28.30	49.79	21.90	46.80	53.20
1985	448	125	573	28.40	49.78	21.82	46.71	53.29
1986	536	155	691	27.71	49.86	22.43	47.36	52.64
1987	No data collected this year							
1988	652	122	774	36.36	47.88	15.76	39.70	60.30
1989	552	146	698	29.45	49.64	20.92	45.74	54.26
1990	603	111	714	36.69	47.76	15.55	39.43	60.57

1. **Graph population changes**: Use the data in the first 3 columns of the table above to plot a line graph. This will show changes in the phenotypes: numbers of grey and white (albino) squirrels, as well as changes in the total population. Plot: **grey**, **white**, and **total** for each year:

(a) Determine by how much (as a %) total population numbers have fluctuated over the sampling period:

_____

(b) Describe the overall trend in total population numbers and any pattern that may exist:

_____

_____

_____

_____

_____

_____

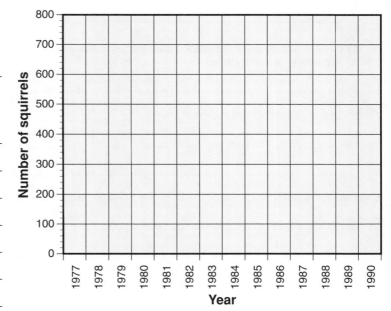

2. Graph genotype changes: Use the data in the genotype columns of the table on the opposite page to plot a line graph. This will show changes in the allele combinations (**GG**, **Gg**, **gg**). Plot: **GG**, **Gg**, and **gg** for each year:

Describe the overall trend in the frequency of:

(a) Homozygous dominant (**GG**) genotype:

_____

_____

(b) Heterozygous (**Gg**) genotype:

_____

_____

(c) Homozygous recessive (**gg**) genotype:

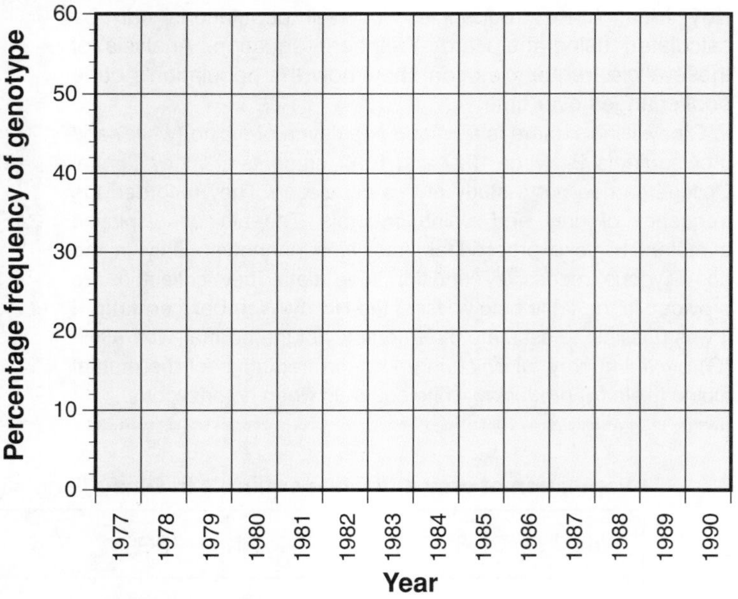

_____

_____

_____

Graph: y-axis "Percentage frequency of genotype" 0–60; x-axis "Year" 1977–1990

3. Graph allele changes: Use the data in the last two columns of the table on the previous page to plot a line graph. This will show changes in the allele frequencies for each of the dominant (**G**) and recessive (**g**) alleles. Plot: the frequency of **G** and the frequency of **g**:

(a) Describe the overall trend in the frequency of the dominant allele (**G**):

_____

_____

_____

(b) Describe the overall trend in the frequency of the recessive allele (**g**):

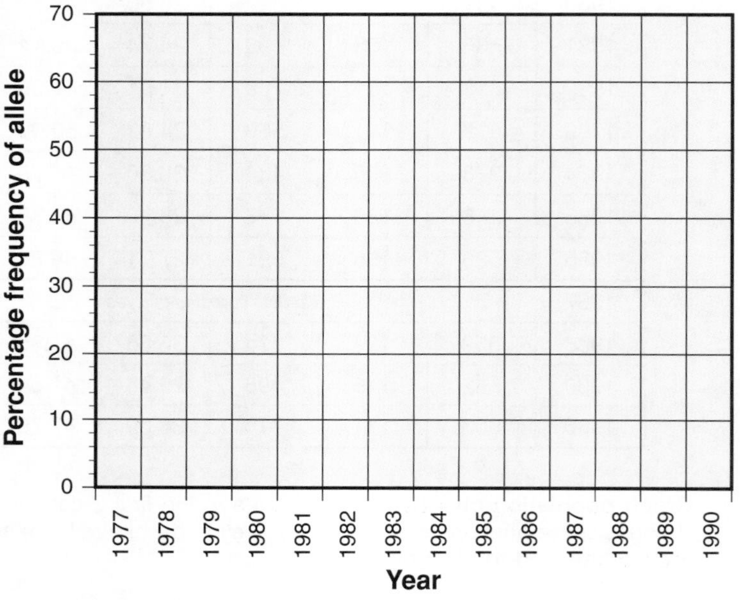

_____

_____

_____

_____

_____

Graph: y-axis "Percentage frequency of allele" 0–70; x-axis "Year" 1977–1990

4. (a) State which of the three graphs best indicates that a significant change may be taking place in the gene pool of this population of squirrels:

_____

(b) Give a reason for your answer: _____

_____

_____

5. Describe a possible cause of the changes in allele frequencies over the sampling period: _____

_____

_____

_____

114 Mechanism of Natural Selection

Key Idea: Natural selection is the mechanism by which organisms that are better adapted to their environment survive to produce a greater number of offspring.

Evolution is the change in inherited characteristics in a population over generations. Evolution is the consequence of interaction between four factors: (1) The potential for populations to increase in numbers, (2) Genetic variation as a result of mutation and sexual reproduction, (3) competition for resources, and (4) proliferation of individuals with better survival and reproduction.

Natural selection is the term for the mechanism by which better adapted organisms survive to produce a greater number of viable offspring. This has the effect of increasing their proportion in the population so that they become more common. This is the basis of Darwin's theory of evolution by natural selection.

We can demonstrate the basic principles of evolution using the analogy of a 'population' of M&M's candy.

#1

In a bag of M&M's, there are many colours, which represents the variation in a population. As you and a friend eat through the bag of candy, you both leave the blue ones, which you both dislike, and return them to bag.

#2

The blue candy becomes more common...

#3

Eventually, you are left with a bag of blue M&M's. Your selective preference for the other colours changed the make-up of the M&M's population. This is the basic principle of selection that drives evolution in natural populations.

Darwin's theory of evolution by natural selection

Darwin's theory of evolution by natural selection is outlined below. It is widely accepted by the scientific community today and is one of founding principles of modern science.

Overproduction
Populations produce too many young: many must die

Populations generally produce more offspring than are needed to replace the parents. Natural populations normally maintain constant numbers. A certain number will die without reproducing.

Variation
Individuals show variation: some variations more favourable than others

Individuals have different **phenotypes** (appearances) and therefore **genotypes** (genetic makeup). Some phenotypes have better survival and reproductive success in the environment.

Natural selection
Natural selection favours the individuals best suited to the prevailing environment (the environment at the time)

Individuals in the population compete for limited resources. Those with favourable variations will be more likely to survive. Relatively more of those without favourable variations will die.

Inherited
Variations are inherited: the best suited variants leave more offspring

The variations (both favourable and unfavourable) are passed on to offspring. Each generation will contain proportionally more descendants of individuals with favourable characters.

---

1. Identify the four factors that interact to bring about evolution in populations: _____

   _____

   _____

   _____

© 2016 **BIOZONE** International
ISBN: 978-1-927309-32-2
Photocopying Prohibited

LINK **117** LINK **116** LINK **115** KNOW

Variation, selection, and population change

Natural populations, like the ladybug population above, show genetic variation. This is a result of **mutation** (which creates new alleles) and sexual reproduction (which produces new combinations of alleles). Some variants are more suited to the environment of the time than others. These variants will leave more offspring, as described for the hypothetical population (right).

1. Variation through mutation and sexual reproduction:
In a population of brown beetles, mutations independently produce red colouration and 2 spot marking on the wings. The individuals in the population compete for limited resources.

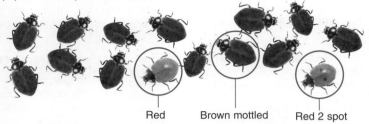

Red   Brown mottled   Red 2 spot

2. Selective predation:
Brown mottled beetles are eaten by birds but red ones are avoided.

3. Change in the genetics of the population:
Red beetles have better survival and fitness and become more numerous with each generation. Brown beetles have poor fitness and become rare.

2. What produces the genetic variation in populations? _____

3. Define evolution: _____

_____

4. Explain how the genetic make-up of a population can change over time: _____

_____

_____

_____

_____

_____

_____

5. Complete the table below by calculating the percentage of beetles in the example above right.

Beetle population	% Brown beetles	% Red beetles	% Red beetles with spots
1			
2			
3			

© 2016 **BIOZONE** International
ISBN: 978-1-927309-32-2
Photocopying Prohibited

115 Gene Pool Exercise

The set of all the versions of all the genes in a population (it genetic make-up) is called the **gene pool**. Cut out the squares below and use them to model the events described in *Modeling Natural Selection*.

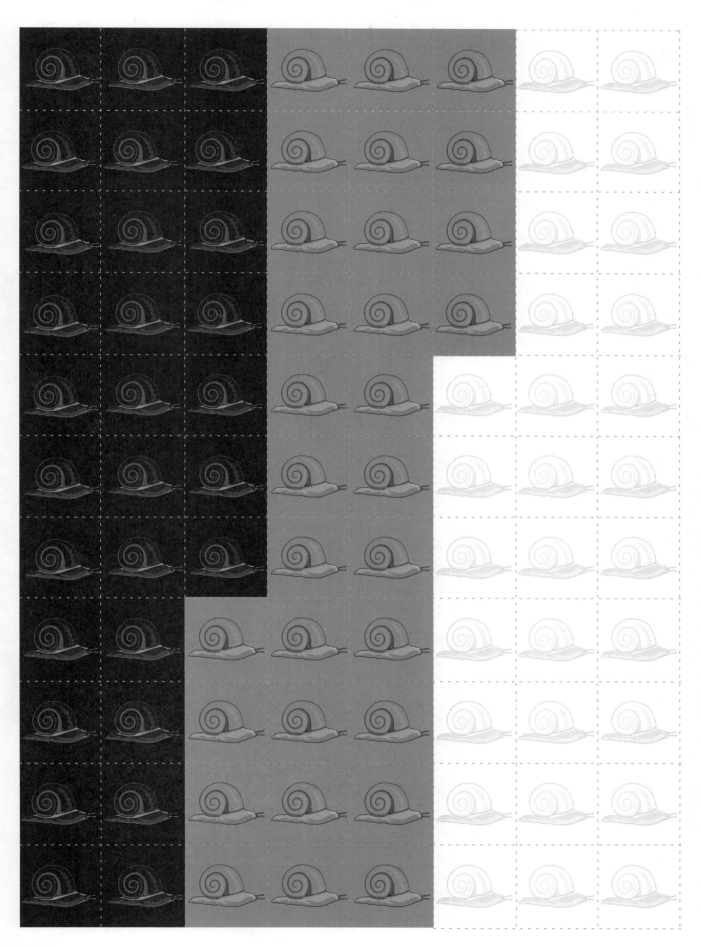

PRAC

116 Modelling Natural Selection

Key Idea: The way that natural selection acts on phenotypes can be modelled for a hypothetical population in which individuals differ with respect to one phenotypic character.

Natural selection can be modelled in a simple activity based on predation. You can carry out the following activity by yourself, or work with a partner to increase the size of the population. The black, grey, and white squares on the preceding pages represent phenotypes of a population. Cut them out and follow the instructions below to model natural selection. You will also need a sheet of white paper and a sheet of black paper.

1. Cut out the squares on the preceding pages and record the number of black, grey, and white squares.

2. For the first half of the activity you will also need a black sheet of paper or material that will act as the environment (A3 is a good size). For the second half of the activity you will need a white sheet of paper.

3. Place 10 black, 10 white, and 22 grey squares in a bag and shake them up to mix them. Keep the other squares for making up population proportions later. Write the values in the numbers row of generation 1 below.

4. Work out the proportion of each phenotype in the population (e.g. 10/42 = 0.24) and place these values in the table below. This represents your starting population (you can combine populations with a partner to increase the population size for more reliable results).

5. Now take the squares out of the bag and randomly distribute them over the sheet of black paper (this works best if your partner does this while you aren't looking).

6. You will act the part of a predator on the snails. For 15 seconds, pick up the squares that stand out (are obvious) on the black paper using your thumb and forefinger. These squares represent animals in the population that have been preyed upon and killed. Place them to one side. The remaining squares represent the population that survived to reproduce.

7. Count the remaining phenotypes. In this population, black carries the alleles BB, grey the alleles Bb, and white the alleles bb. On a separate sheet, calculate the frequency of the B and b alleles in the remaining population (hint: if there are 5 black and 10 grey snails then there are 20 B alleles).

8. These frequencies are what is passed on to the next generation. To produce the next generation, the number of black, grey, and white snails must be calculated. This can be done using the original population number and Hardy - Weinberg equations ($p^2 + 2pq + q^2 = 1$ and $p + q = 1$).

9. For example. If there are 24 snails left with the numbers 5 black, 10 grey, and 9 white then the frequency of B (p) = (5 x 2 + 10) / (24 x 2) = 0.4167 and b (q) = 0.5833. The number of black snails in the next generation will therefore be p^2 x 42 = 0.4167^2 x 42 = 7.3 = 7 (you can't have 0.3 of a snail).

10. Record the number of black, grey, and white snails in the table below in generation 2, along with their phenotype frequencies.

11. Repeat steps 4 to 10 for generation 2, and 3 more generations (5 generations in total or more if you wish).

12. On separate graph paper, draw a line graph of the proportions of each colour over the five generations. Which colours have increased, which have decreased?

13. Now repeat the whole activity using a white sheet background instead of the black sheet. What do you notice about the proportions this time?

Generation		Black	Grey	White
1	Number			
	Proportion			
2	Number			
	Proportion			
3	Number			
	Proportion			
4	Number			
	Proportion			
5	Number			
	Proportion			

LINK
117 PRAC

117 Types of Natural Selection

Key Idea: Natural selection acts on phenotypes and can favour for the most common phenotype or cause a shift in the most common phenotype in one or more directions.

Natural selection operates on the phenotypes of individuals, produced by their particular combinations of alleles. It results in the differential survival of some genotypes (and their phenotypes) over others. Over time, natural selection may lead to a permanent change in the genetic makeup of a population. Natural selection is always linked to phenotypic suitability in the prevailing environment so it is a dynamic process. It may favour existing phenotypes or shift the phenotypic median, as is shown in the diagrams below. The top row of diagrams below represents the population phenotypic spread before selection, and the bottom row the spread afterwards.

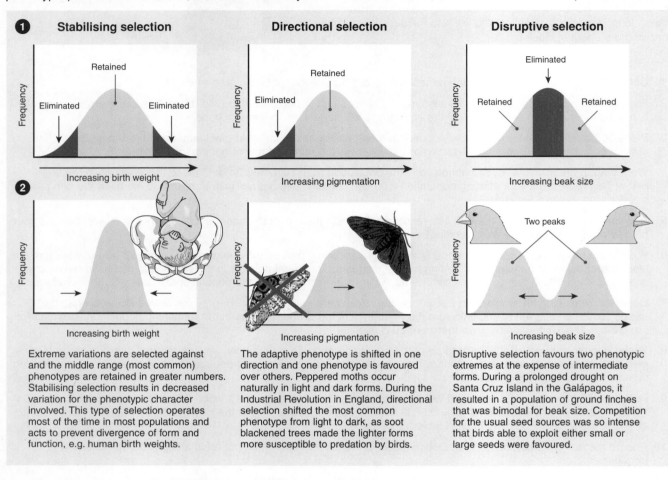

① Stabilising selection

Directional selection

Disruptive selection

②

Extreme variations are selected against and the middle range (most common) phenotypes are retained in greater numbers. Stabilising selection results in decreased variation for the phenotypic character involved. This type of selection operates most of the time in most populations and acts to prevent divergence of form and function, e.g. human birth weights.

The adaptive phenotype is shifted in one direction and one phenotype is favoured over others. Peppered moths occur naturally in light and dark forms. During the Industrial Revolution in England, directional selection shifted the most common phenotype from light to dark, as soot blackened trees made the lighter forms more susceptible to predation by birds.

Disruptive selection favours two phenotypic extremes at the expense of intermediate forms. During a prolonged drought on Santa Cruz Island in the Galápagos, it resulted in a population of ground finches that was bimodal for beak size. Competition for the usual seed sources was so intense that birds able to exploit either small or large seeds were favoured.

1. (a) In which type of environment is stabilising selection most likely to operate: stable / changing (delete one)

   (b) Explain why this is the case: _____

   _____

   _____

2. (a) In which type of environment is directional selection most likely to operate: stable / changing (delete one)

   (b) Explain why this is the case: _____

   _____

   _____

3. Disruptive selection can be important in the formation of new species:

   (a) Describe the evidence from the ground finches on Santa Cruz Island that provides support for this statement:

   _____

   _____

   (b) Predict the consequences of the end of the drought and an increased abundance of medium size seeds as food:

   _____

WEB 117   LINK 118   LINK 119   LINK 120

© 2016 **BIOZONE** International
ISBN: 978-1-927309-32-2
Photocopying Prohibited

118 Directional Selection in Darwin's Finches

Key Idea: The effect of directional selection on a population can be verified by making measurements of phenotypic traits. Natural selection acts on the phenotypes of a population. Individuals with phenotypes that increase their fitness produce more offspring, increasing the proportion of the genes corresponding to that phenotype in the next generation. Many population studies have shown natural selection can cause phenotypic changes in a population relatively quickly.

The finches on the Galápagos island (Darwin's finches) are famous in that they are commonly used as examples of how evolution produces new species. In this activity you will analyse data from the measurement of beaks depths of the medium ground finch (*Geospiza fortis*) on the island of Daphne Major near the centre of the Galápagos Islands. The measurements were taken in 1976 before a major drought hit the island and in 1978 after the drought (survivors and survivors' offspring).

Beak depth / mm	No. 1976 birds	No. 1978 survivors	Beak depth of offspring / mm	Number of birds
7.30-7.79	1	0	7.30-7.79	2
7.80-8.29	12	1	7.80-8.29	2
8.30-8.79	30	3	8.30-8.79	5
8.80-9.29	47	3	8.80-9.29	21
9.30-9.79	45	6	9.30-9.79	34
9.80-10.29	40	9	9.80-10.29	37
10.30-10.79	25	10	10.30-10.79	19
10.80-11.29	3	1	10-80-11.29	15
11.30+	0	0	11.30+	2

1. Use the data above to draw two separate sets of histograms:

    (a) On the left hand grid draw side-by-side histograms for the number of 1976 birds per beak depth and the number of 1978 survivors per beak depth.

    (b) On the right hand grid draw a histogram of the beak depths of the offspring of the 1978 survivors.

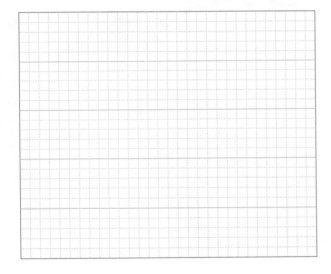
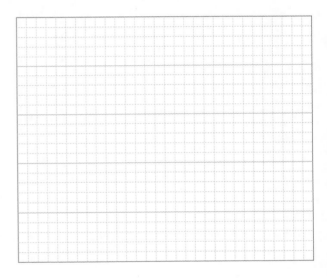

2. (a) Mark the approximate mean beak depth on the graphs of the 1976 beak depths and the 1978 offspring.

    (b) How much has the average moved from 1976 to 1978? _____

    (c) Is beak depth heritable? What does this mean for the process of natural selection in the finches?

    _____

    _____

3. The 1976 drought resulted in plants dying back and not producing seed. Based on the graphs, what can you say about competition between the birds for the remaining seeds, i.e. in what order were the seeds probably used up?

    _____

    _____

    _____

LINK 119 LINK 117 WEB 118 DATA

119 Directional Selection in Moths

Key Idea: Directional selection pressures on the peppered moth during the Industrial Revolution shifted the common phenotype from the grey form to the melanic (dark) form. Natural selection may act on the frequencies of phenotypes (and hence genotypes) in populations in one of three different ways (through stabilising, directional, or disruptive selection).

Colour change in the **peppered moth** (*Biston betularia*) during the Industrial Revolution is often used to show **directional selection** in a polymorphic population (polymorphic means having two or more forms). Intensive coal burning during this time caused trees to become dark with soot, and the dark form (morph) of peppered moth became dominant.

The gene controlling colour in the peppered moth, is located on a single locus. The allele for the melanic (dark) form (**M**) is dominant over the allele for the grey (light) form (**m**).

Olaf Leillinger

Melanic form
Genotype: MM or Mm

The peppered moth, *Biston betularia*, has two forms: a grey mottled form, and a dark melanic form. During the Industrial Revolution, the relative abundance of the two forms changed to favour the dark form. The change was thought to be the result of selective predation by birds. It was proposed that the grey form was more visible to birds in industrial areas where the trees were dark. As a result, birds preyed upon them more often, resulting in higher numbers of the dark form surviving.

Olaf Leillinger

Grey form
Genotype: mm

Museum collections of the peppered moth over the last 150 years show a marked change in the frequency of the melanic form (above right). Moths collected in 1850, prior to the major onset of the Industrial Revolution in England, were mostly the grey form (above left). Fifty years later the frequency of the darker melanic forms had increased.

In the 1940s and 1950s, coal burning was still at intense levels around the industrial centres of Manchester and Liverpool. During this time, the melanic form of the moth was still very dominant. In the rural areas further south and west of these industrial centres, the occurrence of the grey form increased dramatically. With the decline of coal burning factories and the introduction of the Clean Air Act in cities, air quality improved between 1960 and 1980. Sulfur dioxide and smoke levels dropped to a fraction of their previous levels. This coincided with a sharp fall in the relative numbers of melanic moths (right).

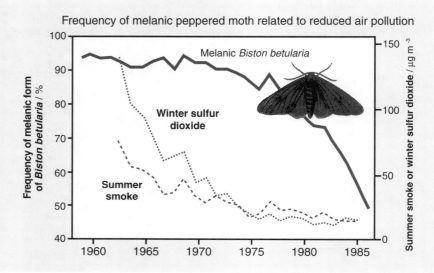

Frequency of melanic peppered moth related to reduced air pollution

1. The populations of peppered moth in England have undergone changes in the frequency of an obvious phenotypic character over the last 150 years. What is the phenotypic character?

   _____

2. Describe how the selection pressure on the grey form has changed with change in environment over the last 150 years:

   _____
   _____
   _____

3. Describe the relationship between allele frequency and phenotype frequency: _____

   _____
   _____

4. The level of pollution dropped around Manchester and Liverpool between 1960 and 1985. How did the frequency of the darker melanic form change during this period?

   _____

© 2016 **BIOZONE** International
ISBN: 978-1-927309-32-2
Photocopying Prohibited

120 Disruptive Selection in Darwin's Finches

Key Idea: Disruptive selection in the finch *Geospiza fortis* produces a bimodal distribution for beak size.

The Galápagos Islands, 970 km west of Ecuador, are home to the finch species *Geospiza fortis*. A study during a prolonged drought on Santa Cruz Island showed how **disruptive selection** can change the distribution of genotypes in a population. During the drought, large and small seeds were more abundant than the preferred intermediate seed size.

Beak sizes of *G. fortis* were measured over a three year period (2004-2006), at the start and end of each year. At the start of the year, individuals were captured, banded, and their beaks were measured.

The presence or absence of banded individuals was recorded at the end of the year when the birds were recaptured. Recaptured individuals had their beaks measured.

The proportion of banded individuals in the population at the end of the year gave a measure of fitness. Absent individuals were presumed dead (fitness = 0).

Fitness related to beak size showed a bimodal distribution (left) typical of disruptive selection.

Beak size vs fitness in *Geospiza fortis*

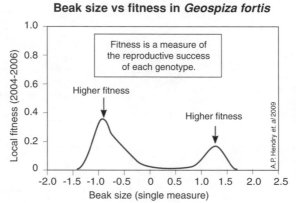

Fitness is a measure of the reproductive success of each genotype.

Higher fitness

Higher fitness

Fitness showed a bimodal distribution (arrowed) being highest for smaller and larger beak sizes.

Measurements of the beak length, width, and depth were combined into one **single measure**.

Beak size pairing in *Geospiza fortis*

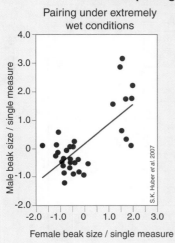

Pairing under extremely wet conditions

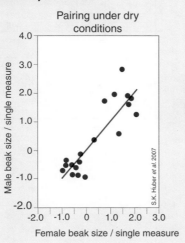

Pairing under dry conditions

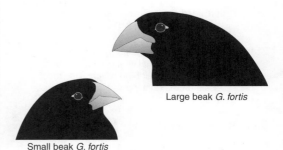

Large beak *G. fortis*

Small beak *G. fortis*

A 2007 study found that breeding pairs of birds had similar beak sizes. Male and females with small beaks tended to breed together, and males and females with large beaks tended to breed together. Mate selection maintained the biomodal distribution in the population during extremely wet conditions. If beak size wasn't a factor in mate selection, the beak size would even out.

1. (a) How did the drought affect seed size on Santa Cruz Island? _____

_____

(b) How did the change in seed size during the drought create a selection pressure for changes in beak size?

_____

_____

_____

2. How does beak size relate to fitness (differential reproductive success) in *G. fortis*? _____

_____

_____

_____

3. (a) Is mate selection in *G. fortis* random / non-random? (delete one)

(b) Give reasons for your answer: _____

_____

_____

© 2016 **BIOZONE** International
ISBN: 978-1-927309-32-2
Photocopying Prohibited

LINK **118** LINK **117** WEB **120** KNOW

121 Selection for Human Birth Weight

Key Idea: Stabilising selection operates to keep human birth weight within relatively narrow constraints.

Selection pressures operate on populations in such a way as to reduce mortality. In a study of human birth weights it is possible to observe the effect of selection pressures

operating to constrain human birth weight within certain limits. This is a good example of **stabilising selection**. This activity explores the selection pressures acting on the birth weight of human babies. Carry out the steps below:

Step 1: Collect the birth weights from 100 birth notices from your local newspaper (or 50 if you are having difficulty getting enough; this should involve looking back through the last 2-3 weeks of birth notices). If you cannot obtain birth weights in your local newspaper, a set of 100 sample birth weights is provided in the Model Answers booklet.

Step 2: Group the weights into each of the 12 weight classes (of 0.5 kg increments). Determine what percentage (of the total sample) fall into each weight class (e.g. 17 babies weigh 2.5-3.0 kg out of the 100 sampled = 17%)

Step 3: Graph these in the form of a histogram for the 12 weight classes (use the graphing grid provided right). Be sure to use the scale provided on the left vertical (y) axis.

Step 4: Create a second graph by plotting percentage mortality of newborn babies in relation to their birth weight. Use the scale on the right y axis and data provided (below).

Step 5: Draw a line of 'best fit' through these points.

Mortality of newborn babies related to birth weight

Weight / kg	Mortality / %
1.0	80
1.5	30
2.0	12
2.5	4
3.0	3
3.5	2
4.0	3
4.5	7
5.0	15

Source: Biology: The Unity & Diversity of Life (4th ed), by Starr and Taggart

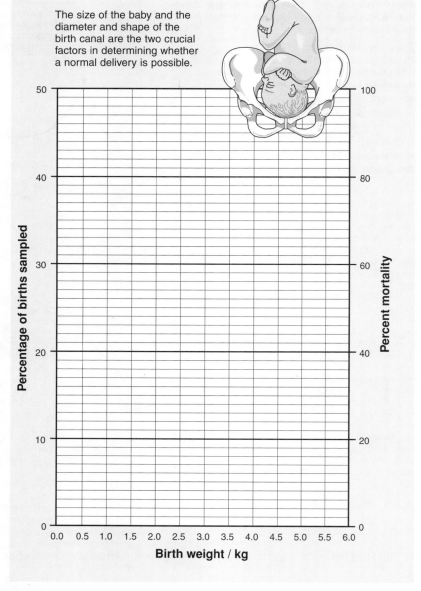

The size of the baby and the diameter and shape of the birth canal are the two crucial factors in determining whether a normal delivery is possible.

1. Describe the shape of the histogram for birth weights: _____

2. What is the optimum birth weight in terms of the lowest newborn mortality?_____

3. Describe the relationship between newborn mortality and birth weight: _____

   _____

4. Describe the selection pressures that are operating to control the range of birth weight: _____

   _____

   _____

5. How might have modern medical intervention during pregnancy and childbirth altered these selection pressures?

   _____

   _____

© 2016 **BIOZONE** International
ISBN: 978-1-927309-32-2
Photocopying Prohibited

122 Natural Selection in Pocket Mice

Key Idea: The need to blend into their surroundings to avoid predation is an important selection pressure acting on the coat colour of rock pocket mice.

Rock pocket mice are found in the deserts of southwestern United States and northern Mexico. They are nocturnal, foraging at night for seeds, while avoiding owls (their main predator). During the day they shelter from the desert heat in their burrows. The coat colour of the mice varies from light brown to very dark brown. Throughout the desert environment in which the mice live there are outcrops of dark volcanic rock. The presence of these outcrops and the mice that live on them present an excellent study in natural selection.

▶ The coat colour of the Arizona rock pocket mice is controlled by the Mc1r gene (a gene that in mammals is commonly associated with the production of the dark pigment melanin).

There are variations for the gene that controls coat colour. These variations are called alleles. Homozygous dominant (**DD**) and heterozygous mice (**Dd**) have dark coats, while homozygous recessive mice (**dd**) have light coats. The coat colour of mice in New Mexico is not related to the Mc1r gene.

▶ 107 rock pocket mice from 14 sites were collected and their coat colour and the rock colour they were found on were recorded by measuring the percentage of light reflected from their coat (low percentage reflectance equals a dark coat). The data are presented right:

Site	Rock type (V volcanic)	Percent reflectance / %	
		Mice coat	Rock
KNZ	V	4	10.5
ARM	V	4	9
CAR	V	4	10
MEX	V	5	10.5
TUM	V	5	27
PIN	V	5.5	11
AFT		6	30
AVR		6.5	26
WHT		8	42
BLK	V	8.5	15
FRA		9	39
TIN		9	39
TUL		9.5	25
POR		12	34.5

1. (a) What are the genotypes of the dark coloured mice? _____

   (b) What is the genotype of the light coloured mice? _____

2. Using the data in the table above and the grids below and on the next page, draw column graphs of the percent reflectance of the mice coats and the rocks at each of the 14 collection sites.

3. (a) What do you notice about the reflectance of the rock pocket mice coat colour and the reflectance of the rocks they were found on?

_____

(b) Suggest a cause for the pattern in 3(a). How do the phenotypes of the mice affect where the mice live?

_____

_____

_____

(c) What are two exceptions to the pattern you have noticed in 3(a)? _____

_____

_____

_____

(d) How might these exceptions have occurred? _____

_____

_____

_____

4. What type of selection appears to be operating in each of the environments (dark and light rock)? Explain:

_____

_____

_____

5. The rock pocket mice populations in Arizona use a different genetic mechanism to control coat colour than the New Mexico populations. What does this tell you about the evolution of the genetic mechanism for coat colour?

_____

_____

_____

© 2016 BIOZONE International
ISBN: 978-1-927309-32-2
Photocopying Prohibited

123 Selection for Skin Colour in Humans

Key Idea: Skin colour is an evolutionary response to the need to synthesise vitamin D which requires sunlight, and to conserve folate which breaks down in sunlight.

Pigmented skin of varying tones is a feature of humans that evolved after early humans lost the majority of their body hair. However, the distribution of skin colour globally is not random; people native to equatorial regions have darker skin tones than people from higher latitudes. For many years, biologists postulated that this was because darker skins had evolved to protect against skin cancer. The problem with this explanation

was that skin cancer is not tied to evolutionary fitness because it affects post-reproductive individuals and cannot therefore provide a mechanism for selection. More complex analyses of the physiological and epidemiological evidence has shown a more complex picture in which selection pressures on skin colour are finely balanced to produce a skin tone that regulates the effects of the sun's ultraviolet radiation on the nutrients vitamin D and folate, both of which are crucial to successful human reproduction, and therefore evolutionary fitness. The selection is stabilising within each latitudinal region.

Skin colour in humans: A product of natural selection

Alaska   France   The Netherlands   Iraq   China   Japan

80°   80°
No data

Insufficient UV most of year

40°   Insufficient UV one month   40°

0°   Sufficient UV all year   0°
Sufficient UV all year

40°   Insufficient UV one month   40°

Insufficient UV most of year

Adapted from Jablonski & Chaplin,
Sci. Am. Oct. 2002

Peru   Liberia   Burundi   Botswana   Southern India   Malaysia

Human skin colour is the result of two opposing selection pressures. Skin pigmentation has evolved to protect against destruction of folate from ultraviolet light, but the skin must also be light enough to receive the light required to synthesise vitamin D. Vitamin D synthesis is a process that begins in the skin and is inhibited by dark pigment. Folate is needed for healthy neural development in humans and a deficiency is associated with fatal neural tube defects. Vitamin D is required for the absorption of calcium from the diet and therefore normal skeletal development.

Women also have a high requirement for calcium during pregnancy and lactation. Populations that live in the tropics receive enough ultraviolet (UV) radiation to synthesise vitamin D all year long. Those that live in northern or southern latitudes do not. In temperate zones, people lack sufficient UV light to make vitamin D for one month of the year. Those nearer the poles lack enough UV light for vitamin D synthesis most of the year (above). Their lighter skins reflect their need to maximise UV absorption (the photos show skin colour in people from different latitudes).

LINK 117   LINK 90   WEB 123   KNOW

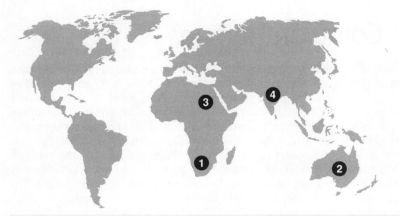

Long-term resident Recent immigrant

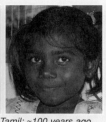

① Southern Africa: ~ 20-30°S

Khoisan-Namibia   *Zulu: 1000 years ago*

② Australia: ~ 10-35°S

Aborigine   *European: 300 years ago*

③ Banks of the Red Sea: ~ 15-30°N

Nuba-Sudan   *Arab: 2000 years ago*

④ India: ~ 10-30°S

West Bengal   *Tamil: ~100 years ago*

The skin of people who have inhabited particular regions for millennia has adapted to allow sufficient vitamin D production while still protecting folate stores. In the photos above, some of these original inhabitants are illustrated to the left of each pair and compared with the skin tones of more recent immigrants (to the right of each pair, with the number of years since immigration). The numbered locations are on the map.

1. (a) Describe the role of folate in human physiology: _____

   (b) Describe the role of vitamin D in human physiology: _____

2. (a) Early hypotheses to explain skin colour linked pigmentation level only to the degree of protection it gave from UV-induced skin cancer. Explain why this hypothesis was inadequate in accounting for how skin colour evolved:

   _____

   _____

   (b) Explain how the new hypothesis for the evolution of skin colour overcomes these deficiencies:_____

   _____

   _____

   _____

   _____

3. Explain why, in any given geographical region, women tend to have lighter skins (by 3-4% on average) than men:

   _____

   _____

4. The Inuit people of Alaska and northern Canada have a diet rich in vitamin D and their skin colour is darker than predicted on the basis of UV intensity at their latitude. Explain this observation:

   _____

   _____

5. (a) What health problems might be expected for people of African origin now living in northern UK?_____

   _____

   (b) How could these people avoid these problems in their new higher latitude environment? _____

   _____

   _____

124 Genetic Drift

Key Idea: Genetic drift is the term for the random changes in allele frequency that occur in all populations. It has a more pronounced effect in small populations.

Not all individuals, for various reasons, will be able to contribute their genes to the next generation. In a small population, the effect of a few individuals not contributing their alleles to the next generation can have a great effect on allele frequencies. Alleles may even become **lost** from the gene pool altogether (frequency becomes 0%) or **fixed** as the only allele for the gene present (frequency becomes 100%). The random change in allele frequencies is called **genetic drift**.

The genetic makeup (allele frequencies) of the population changes randomly over a period of time

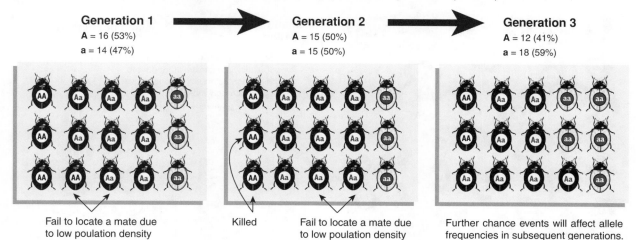

Generation 1
A = 16 (53%)
a = 14 (47%)

Generation 2
A = 15 (50%)
a = 15 (50%)

Generation 3
A = 12 (41%)
a = 18 (59%)

Fail to locate a mate due to low poulation density

Killed   Fail to locate a mate due to low poulation density

Further chance events will affect allele frequencies in subsequent generations.

This diagram shows the gene pool of a hypothetical small population over three generations. For various reasons, not all individuals contribute alleles to the next generation. With the random loss of the alleles carried by these individuals, the allele frequency changes from one generation to the next. The change in frequency is directionless as there is no selecting force. The allele combinations for each successive generation are determined by how many alleles of each type are passed on from the preceding one.

Computer simulation of genetic drift

Below are displayed the change in allele frequencies in a computer simulation showing random genetic drift. The breeding population progressively gets smaller from left to right. Each simulation was run for 140 generations.

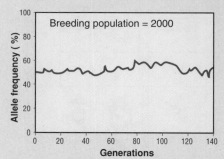

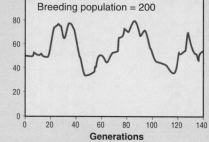

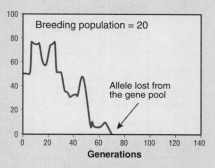

Allele lost from the gene pool

Large breeding population

Fluctuations are minimal in large breeding populations because the large numbers buffer the population against random loss of alleles. On average, losses for each allele type will be similar in frequency and little change occurs.

Small breeding population

Fluctuations are more severe in smaller breeding populations because random changes in a few alleles cause a greater percentage change in allele frequencies.

Very small breeding population

Fluctuations in very small breeding populations are so extreme that the allele can become fixed (frequency of 100%) or lost from the gene pool altogether (frequency of 0%).

1. (a) What is genetic drift? _____

_____

(b) Why is the effect of genetic drift more pronounced in small populations? _____

_____

2. Suggest why genetic drift is an important process in the evolution of small populations: _____

_____

_____

LINK **126** LINK **125** WEB **124** KNOW

125 The Founder Effect

Key Idea: The founder effect can result in differences in allele frequencies between a parent and founder populations.

If a small number of individuals from a large population becomes isolated from their original parent population, their sample of alleles is unlikely to represent the allele proportions of the parent population. This phenomenon is called the **founder effect** and it can result in the colonising (founder) population evolving in a different direction to the parent population. This is particularly the case if the founder population is subjected to different selection pressures in a new environment and if the population is missing alleles that are present in the parent population.

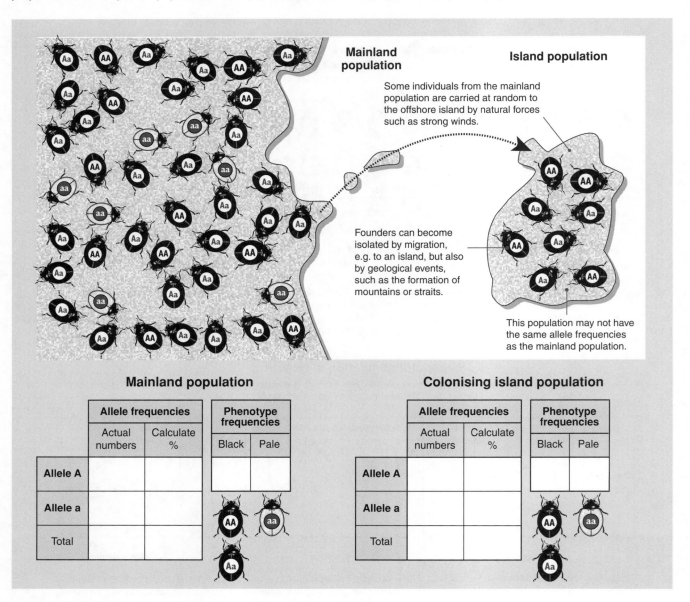

Mainland population

	Allele frequencies		Phenotype frequencies	
	Actual numbers	Calculate %	Black	Pale
Allele A				
Allele a				
Total				

Colonising island population

	Allele frequencies		Phenotype frequencies	
	Actual numbers	Calculate %	Black	Pale
Allele A				
Allele a				
Total				

1. Compare the mainland population to the population which ended up on the island (use the spaces in the tables above):
   (a) Count the **phenotype** numbers for the two populations (i.e. the number of black and pale beetles).
   (b) Count the **allele** numbers for the two populations: the number of dominant alleles (A) and recessive alleles (a). Calculate these as a percentage of the total number of alleles for each population.

2. How are the allele frequencies of the two populations different? _____

   _____

   _____

3. Describe some possible ways in which various types of organism can be **carried** to an offshore island:

   (a) Plants: _____

   (b) Land animals: _____

   (c) Non-marine birds: _____

© 2016 **BIOZONE** International
ISBN: 978-1-927309-32-2
Photocopying Prohibited

Microgeographic isolation in garden snails

The European garden snail (*Cornu aspersum*, formerly *Helix aspersa*) is widely distributed throughout the world, both naturally and by human introduction. However because of its relatively slow locomotion and need for moist environments it can be limited in its habitat and this can lead to regional variation. The study below illustrates an investigation carried out on two snail populations in the city of Bryan, Texas. The snail populations covered two adjacent city blocks surrounded by tarmac roads.

The snails were found in several colonies in each block. Allele frequencies for the gene *MDH-1* (alleles A and a) were obtained and compared. Statistical analysis of the allele frequencies of the two populations showed them to be significantly different ($P \ll 0.05$). Note: A Mann-Whitney U test was used in this instance. It is similar to a Student's t test, but does not assume a normal distribution of data (it is non-parametric).

Block A   **Block B**

Road (not to sclae)

Source: Evolution, Vol 29, No. 3, 1975

Snail colony (circle size is proportional to colony size).   Building

	Colony	1	2	3	4	5	6	7	8	9	10	11	12	13	14	15
Block A	*MDH-1* A %	39	39	36	42	39	47	32	42	44	42	44	50	50	58	75
	MDH-1 a %															
Block B	*MDH-1* A %	81	61	75	68	70	61	70	60	58	61	54	54	47		
	MDH-1 a %															

4. Complete the table above by filling in the frequencies of the *MDH-1* a allele:

5. Suggest why these snail populations are effectively geographically isolated: _____

_____

_____

_____

6. Both the *MDH-1* alleles produce fully operative enzymes. Suggest why the frequencies of the alleles have become significantly different.

_____

_____

_____

7. Identify the colony in block A that appears to be isolated from the rest of the block itself: _____

126 Genetic Bottlenecks

Key Idea: Genetic bottlenecks occur when population numbers and diversity fall dramatically. Although a population's numbers may recover, its genetic diversity often does not.

Populations may sometimes be reduced to low numbers by predation, disease, or periods of climatic change. These large scale reductions are called genetic (or population) bottlenecks. The sudden population decline is not necessarily selective and it may affect all phenotypes equally. Large scale catastrophic events, such as fire or volcanic eruptions, are examples of

such non-selective events. Affected populations may later recover, having squeezed through a 'bottleneck' of low numbers. The diagram below illustrates how population numbers may be reduced as a result of a catastrophic event. Following such an event, the gene pool of the surviving remnant population may be markedly different to that of the original gene pool. Genetic drift may cause further changes to allele frequencies. The small population may return to previous levels but with a reduced genetic diversity.

Change in population numbers and diversity

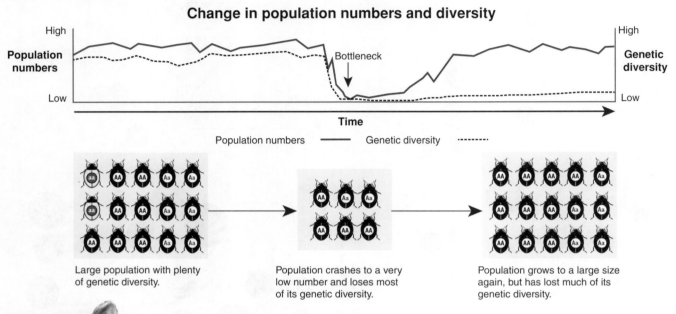

Population numbers ——— Genetic diversity ┈┈┈┈┈

Large population with plenty of genetic diversity.

Population crashes to a very low number and loses most of its genetic diversity.

Population grows to a large size again, but has lost much of its genetic diversity.

Modern examples of genetic bottlenecks

Cheetahs: The world population of cheetahs currently stands at fewer than 20 000. Recent genetic analysis has found that the entire population exhibits very little genetic diversity. It appears that cheetahs may have narrowly escaped extinction at the end of the last ice age, about 10-20 000 years ago. If all modern cheetahs arose from a very limited genetic stock, this would explain their present lack of genetic diversity. The lack of genetic variation has resulted in a number of problems that threaten cheetah survival, including sperm abnormalities, decreased fecundity, high cub mortality, and sensitivity to disease.

Illinois prairie chicken: When Europeans first arrived in North America, there were millions of prairie chickens. As a result of hunting and habitat loss, the Illinois population of prairie chickens fell from about 100 million in 1900 to fewer than 50 in the 1990s. A comparison of the DNA from birds collected in the mid-twentieth century and DNA from the surviving population indicated that most of the genetic diversity has been lost.

Photo: Dept. of Natural Resources, Illinois

1. Endangered species are often subjected to genetic bottlenecks. Explain how genetic bottlenecks affect the ability of a population of an endangered species to recover from its plight:

_____

_____

_____

2. Why has the lack of genetic diversity in cheetahs increased their sensitivity to disease? _____

_____

_____

3. Describe the effect of a genetic bottleneck on the potential of a species to adapt to changes (i.e. its ability to evolve):

_____

_____

© 2016 **BIOZONE** International
ISBN: **978-1-927309-32-2**
Photocopying Prohibited

127 Selective Breeding in Animals

Key Idea: Selective breeding is the process of breeding together organisms with desirable qualities (e.g. high milk yield) so the trait is reliably passed on to the next generation. **Selective breeding** (or artificial selection) is the process by which humans select organisms with desirable traits and breed them together so the trait appears in the next generation. The process is repeated over many generations until the characteristic becomes common. Selective breeding often uses reproductive technologies, such as artificial insemination, so that the desirable characteristics of one male can be passed onto many offspring. This increases the rate at which the desirable trait is passed to progeny. There are problems associated with selective breeding. The gene pool becomes more constrained and some alleles may be lost. A reduction in genetic diversity decreases the ability of a species to adapt to changes in the environment.

The origins of domestic dogs

All breeds of dog are members of the same species, **_Canis familiaris_** and provide an excellent example of selective breeding. The dog was the first domesticated species and, over centuries, humans have selected for desirable traits, so extensively that there are now more than 400 breeds of dogs. Until very recently, the grey wolf was considered to the ancestor of the domestic dog. However, recent (2015) genetic studies provide strong evidence that domestic dogs and grey wolves are sister groups and shared a now extinct wolf-like common ancestor, which gave rise to the dog before the agricultural revolution 12 000 years ago. Based on genetic analysis, four major clusters of ancient dog breeds are recognised. Through selective breeding, all other breeds are thought to have descended from these clusters.

1: Older lineages
The oldest lineages, including Chinese breeds, basenji, huskies, and malamutes.

2: Mastiff-type
An older lineage that includes the mastiffs, bull terriers, boxers, and rottweilers.

3: Herding
Includes German shepherd, St Bernard, borzoi, collie, corgi, pug, and greyhound

4: Hunting
Most arose in Europe. Includes terriers, spaniels, poodles, and modern hounds.

Modern dog breeds exhibit a huge variety of physical and behavioural phenotypes. Selective breeding has produced breeds to meet the specific requirements of humans.

Problems with selective breeding

Selection for a desirable phenotype can lead to a consequential emphasis of undesirable traits, often because genes for particular characteristics are linked and selection for one inadvertently selects for the other. For example, the German shepherd is a working dog, originally bred for its athleticism and ability to track targets. However in German shepherds bred to meet the specific appearance criteria of show dogs, some traits have been exaggerated so much that it causes health issues. The body shape of the show German shepherd has been selected for a flowing trot and has a pronounced sloping back. This has resulted in leg, hip, and spinal problems. In addition, selective breeding has increased the incidence of some genetic diseases such as epilepsy and blood disorders.

Straight-backed German shepherd

Sloped-backed German shepherd

1. (a) What is selective breeding? _____

   _____

   (b) What are the advantages of selective breeding? _____

   _____

2. List the physical and behavioural traits that would be desirable (selected for) in the following uses of a dog:

   (a) Hunting large game (e.g. boar and deer): _____

   (b) Stock control (sheep/cattle dog): _____

   (c) Family pet (house dog): _____

   (d) Guard dog: _____

3. As a group, discuss the ethical considerations of using selective breeding to "improve" dog breeds. What would it take to change breed standards to avoid health issues? Summarise your arguments and attach the summary to this page.

© 2016 **BIOZONE** International
ISBN: **978-1-927309-32-2**
Photocopying Prohibited

128 Selection in Dairy Cows

Key Idea: Selective breeding is able to produce rapid change in the phenotypic characteristics of a population.

Humans may create the selection pressure for evolutionary change by choosing and breeding together individuals with particular traits. The example of milk yield in Holstein cows (below) illustrates how humans have directly influenced the genetic makeup of Holstein cattle with respect to milk production and fertility. Since the 1960s, the University of Minnesota has maintained a Holstein cattle herd that has not been subjected to any selection. They also maintain a herd that was subjected to selective breeding for increased milk production between 1965 and 1985. They compared the genetic merit of milk yield in these groups to that of the USA Holstein average.

Gain in genetic merit of milk yield

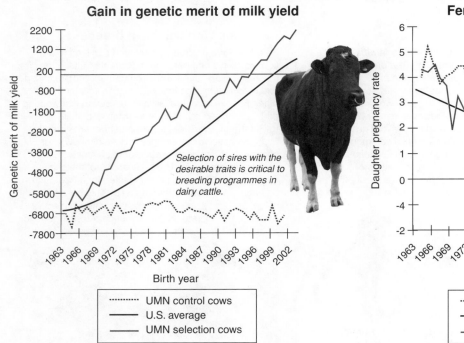

Selection of sires with the desirable traits is critical to breeding programmes in dairy cattle.

Birth year

.... UMN control cows
——— U.S. average
——— UMN selection cows

Fertility in holstein cows

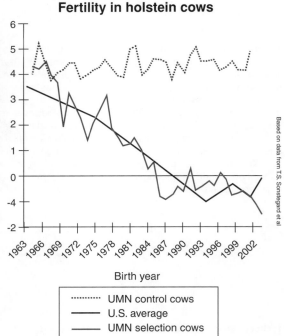

Birth year

.... UMN control cows
——— U.S. average
——— UMN selection cows

Based on data from T.S. Sonstegard et al

Milk production in the University of Minnesota (UMN) herd subjected to selective breeding increased in line with the U.S. average production. In real terms, milk production per cow per milking season increased by 3740 kg since 1964. The herd with no selection remained effectively constant for milk production.

Along with increased milk production there has been a distinct decrease in fertility. The fertility of the University of Minnesota (UMN) herd that was not subjected to selection remained constant while the fertility of the herd selected for milk production decreased with the U.S. fertility average.

1. (a) Describe the relationship between milk yield and fertility on Holstein cows: _____

_____

(b) What does this suggest about where the genes for milk production and fertility are carried? _____

_____

_____

2. What limits might this place on maximum milk yield? _____

_____

3. Why is sire selection important in selective breeding, even if the characters involved are expressed only in the female?

_____

4. Natural selection is the mechanism by which organisms with favourable traits become proportionally more common in the population. How does selective breeding mimic natural selection? How does the example of the Holstein cattle show that reproductive success is a compromise between many competing traits?

_____

_____

_____

_____

© 2016 **BIOZONE** International
ISBN: 978-1-927309-32-2
Photocopying Prohibited

129 Selective Breeding in Crop Plants

Key Idea: The genetic diversity within crop varieties provides options to develop new crop plants through selective breeding. For thousands of years, farmers have used the variation in wild and cultivated plants to develop crops. *Brassica oleracea* is a good example of the variety that can be produced by selectively growing plants with desirable traits. Not only are there six varieties of *Brassica oleracea*, but each of those has a number of sub-varieties as well. Although brassicas have been cultivated for several thousand years, cauliflower, broccoli, and brussels sprouts appeared only in the last 500 years.

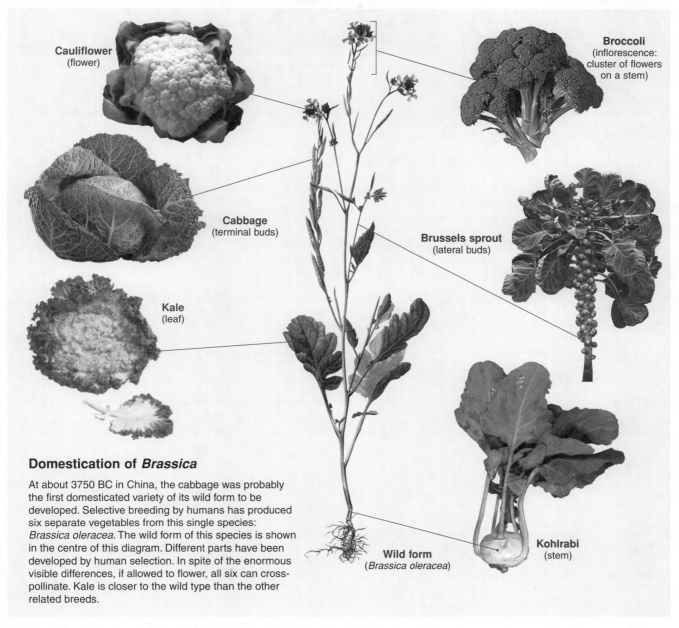

Cauliflower (flower)

Broccoli (inflorescence: cluster of flowers on a stem)

Cabbage (terminal buds)

Brussels sprout (lateral buds)

Kale (leaf)

Kohlrabi (stem)

Wild form (*Brassica oleracea*)

Domestication of *Brassica*

At about 3750 BC in China, the cabbage was probably the first domesticated variety of its wild form to be developed. Selective breeding by humans has produced six separate vegetables from this single species: *Brassica oleracea*. The wild form of this species is shown in the centre of this diagram. Different parts have been developed by human selection. In spite of the enormous visible differences, if allowed to flower, all six can cross-pollinate. Kale is closer to the wild type than the other related breeds.

1. Study the diagram above and identify which part of the plant has been selected for to produce each of the vegetables:

   (a) Cauliflower: _____   (d) Brussels sprout: _____

   (b) Kale: _____   (e) Cabbage: _____

   (c) Broccoli: _____   (f) Kohlrabi: _____

2. Describe the feature of these vegetables that suggests they are members of the same species: _____
   _____

3. What features of *Brassica oleracea* would humans have selected to produce broccoli? _____
   _____
   _____
   _____

172

Many varieties of dwarf plants (e.g. dwarf beans) and crops have been developed. They contain mutant alleles that do not produce gibberellin and so grow only short stems. This means that fewer of the plant's resources are put into growing tall and more are diverted to producing fruit or grain.

In 18th-century Ireland, potatoes were the main source of food for about 30% of the population, and farmers relied almost entirely on one very fertile and productive variety. That variety proved susceptible to the potato blight fungus which resulted in a widespread famine.

Hybrid corn varieties have been bred to minimise damage by insect pests such as corn rootworm (above). Hybrids are important because they recombine the genetic characteristics of parental lines and show increased heterozygosity and hybrid vigour.

4. (a) Describe a phenotypic characteristic that might be desirable in an apple tree: _____

(b) Outline how selective breeding could be used to establish this trait in the next generation: _____
_____
_____
_____

5. (a) Explain why genetic diversity might decline during selective breeding for particular characteristics: _____
_____
_____
_____

(b) With reference to an example, discuss why retaining genetic diversity in crop plants is important for food security:
_____
_____
_____
_____

6. Cultivated American cotton plants have a total of 52 chromosomes (2N = 52). In each cell there are 26 large chromosomes and 26 small chromosomes. Old World cotton plants have 26 chromosomes (2N = 26), all large. Wild American cotton plants have 26 chromosomes, all small. How might cultivated American cotton have originated from Old World cotton and wild American cotton:
_____
_____
_____

7. The Cavendish is the variety of banana most commonly sold in world supermarkets. It is seedless, sterile, and under threat of extinction by Panama disease Race 4. Explain why Cavendish banana crops are so endangered by this fungus:
_____
_____
_____

8. Why is it important to maintain the biodiversity of wild plants and ancient farm breeds? _____
_____
_____
_____

© 2016 BIOZONE International
ISBN: 978-1-927309-32-2
Photocopying Prohibited

130 Breeding Modern Wheat

Key Idea: Modern wheat evolved as a result of two natural hybridisation events and the doubling of its chromosomes.

Wheat has been cultivated for more than 9000 years and has undergone many genetic changes during its domestication. The evolution of modern bread wheat from its wild ancestors (below) involved two natural **hybridisation** events, accompanied by **polyploidy**. Once wheat became domesticated, selective breeding emphasised characteristics such as high protein (gluten) content, high yield, and pest and disease resistance. Hybrid vigour (improved characteristics)

in wheat cultivars is produced by crossing inbred lines and selecting for desirable traits in the progeny, which can now be identified using genetic techniques such as marker assisted selection. This is an indirect selection process where a trait of interest is selected on the basis of a marker linked to it. Increasingly, research is focused on enhancing the genetic diversity of wheat to provide for future crop development. With this in mind, there is renewed interest in some of the lower yielding, ancient wheat varieties, which possess alleles no longer present in modern inbred varieties.

The evolution and domestication of wheat

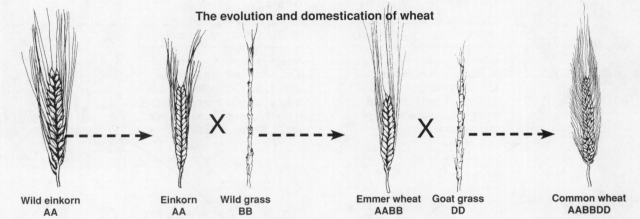

| Wild einkorn AA | → | Einkorn AA | X | Wild grass BB | → | Emmer wheat AABB | Goat grass DD | X | → | Common wheat AABBDD |

Wild einkorn becomes domesticated in the Middle East. There are slight changes to phenotype but not chromosome number.

A sterile hybrid between einkorn and wild grass undergoes a chromosome doubling to create fertile emmer wheat.

A sterile hybrid between emmer wheat and goat grass undergoes a chromosome doubling to create fertile common wheat.

Ancient cereal grasses had heads which shattered easily so that the seeds were widely scattered. In this more primitive morphology, the wheat ear breaks into spikelets when threshed, and milling or pounding is needed to remove the hulls and obtain the grain. Cultivation and repeated harvesting and sowing of the grains of wild grasses led to domestic strains with larger seeds and sturdier heads. Modern selection methods incorporate genetic techniques to identify and isolate beneficial genes, e.g. the RHt dwarfing gene, which gave rise to shorter stemmed modern wheat varieties.

Modern bread wheat has been selected for its non-shattering heads, high yield, and high gluten (protein) content. The grains are larger and the seeds (spikelets) remain attached to the ear by a toughened rachis during harvesting. On threshing, the chaff breaks up, releasing the grains. Selection for these traits by farmers might not necessarily have been deliberate, but occurred because these traits made it easier to gather the seeds. Such 'incidental' selection was an important part of crop domestication. **Hybrid vigour** in cultivars is generated by crossing inbred lines.

Stripe rust

Some of the most important characteristics selected for in wheat varieties are related to resistance to disease and to insect pests. Fungal diseases such as rusts and mildews can reduce crop yields. There are many different wheat varieties, which vary in their resistance to certain diseases. If a certain disease is more common in an area, e.g. stripe rust in cooler areas, then a wheat variety resistant to that disease in grown. Continual development of disease resistance in wheat (through selection) is necessary because of continual evolution of the plant pathogens.

1. Describe three phenotypic characteristics that would be desirable in a wheat plant:

   (a) _____

   (b) _____

   (c) _____

2. How have both natural events and selective breeding contributed to the high yielding modern wheat varieties?

   _____

   _____

LINK 139   LINK 129   WEB 130   KNOW

131 The Evidence for Evolution

Key Idea: Evidence for the fact that populations evolve comes from many fields of science.

Recall that evolution is simply the heritable genetic changes occurring in a population over time. There are two important points to take from this definition. The first is that evolution refers to populations, not individuals. The second is that the changes must be passed on to the next generation (i.e. be inherited). The evidence for evolution comes from many diverse branches of science and includes evidence from both past and present populations. Drawing on evidence from a number of scientific disciplines helps to build a robust explanation for the evolutionary history of taxa.

Comparative anatomy

Comparative anatomy examines the similarities and differences in the anatomy of different species. Similarities in anatomy (e.g. the bones forming the arms in humans and the wings in birds and bats) indicate descent from a common ancestor.

Geology

Geological strata (the layers of rock, soil, and other deposits such as volcanic ash) can be used to determine the relative order of past events and therefore the relative dates of fossils. Fossils in lower strata are older than fossils in higher (newer) strata, unless strata have been disturbed.

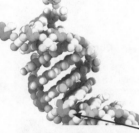

DNA comparisons

DNA can be used to determine how closely organisms are related to each other. The greater the similarities between the DNA sequences of species, the more closely related the species are.

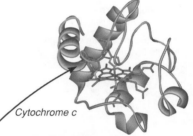

Cytochrome c

Protein evidence

Similarities (and differences) between proteins provides evidence for determining shared ancestry. Fewer differences in amino acid sequences reflects closer genetic relatedness.

EVOLUTION

Fossil record

Fossils, like this shark's tooth (left) are the remains of long-dead organisms. They provide a record of the appearance and extinction of organisms.

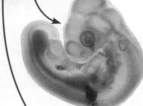

Developmental evidence

The study of developmental processes and the genes that control them gives insight into evolutionary processes. This field of study is called evolutionary developmental biology (evo-devo).

Biogeography

The geographical distribution of living and extinct organisms provides evidence of common ancestry and can be explained by speciation, extinction, and continental drift. The biogeography of islands, e.g the Galápagos Islands, provides evidence of how species evolve when separated from their ancestral population on the mainland.

Chronometric dating

Radiometric dating techniques (such as carbon dating) allow scientists to determine an absolute date for a fossil by dating it or the rocks around it. Absolute dating has been used to assign ages to strata, and construct the geological time scale.

REFER WEB 131 LINK 132 LINK 133 LINK 134

© 2016 **BIOZONE** International
ISBN: 978-1-927309-32-2
Photocopying Prohibited

132 Using Mitochondrial DNA

Key Idea: Mitochondrial DNA (mtDNA) can be used to determine relationships between closely related species. Mitochondrial DNA (mtDNA) is a single circular piece of DNA found in the mitochondria of eukaryotic organisms. mtDNA mutates at a much higher rate than nuclear DNA and it is inherited, without the usual genetic recombination*, only from the mother (except in extremely rare occurrences). Thus mtDNA mutations are passed on 100% of the time from mother to all her offspring. These two features make mtDNA useful for determining relationships between closely related species or individuals within a species, and for following maternal lineages through time.

The length of the mtDNA can vary between eukaryotes. The human mitochondrial genome contains about 16 kilobases. It encodes 37 genes, 22 of them being for mitochondrial tRNA. Genes that are commonly compared are the 16S rRNA gene and the control region of the mtDNA.

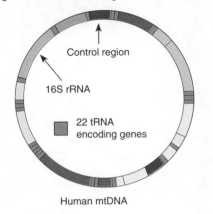

Control region

16S rRNA

22 tRNA encoding genes

Human mtDNA

Identifying species using mtDNA

Transatlantic mangrove oysters of the genus *Crassostrea* are important commercial oysters on the Atlantic shores of South America and Africa. mtDNA studies have found that the division of this genus into distinct South American and African species (the African *C. gasar* and the South American *C. rhizophorae*) may be incorrect.

A study sequenced a 570 base-pair length of mtDNA from the 16S rRNA gene of 18 individuals from nine locations along the African and South American coastline. The study found two distinct DNA sequences. Bases 1 - 60 are shown below:

```
A  TTGATTTTTAGTAGTACCTGCCCAGTGCG-TATTATCTTGTTAACGGCCGCCTT
B  · · · · · · · · · · · C· · · · · · · · · · · · · · · · ·A· · · · ·AG·C· ·C· · · · · · · · · · · ·
```

In was presumed that the mangrove oyster *Crassostrea gasar* was found only on the African side of the Atlantic while *Crassostrea rhizophorae* was found only in South America. All samples from the African coastline had the same sequence as A above. However the South American sample was found to have both A and B DNA sequences, showing that *Crassostrea gasar* is also present in South America.

C. gasar on mangrove roots

Using mtDNA to trace human ancestry

Because mtDNA is passed through the maternal line without the usual genetic recombination* it can be used to trace maternal lineage. This means that, barring new mutations, the mtDNA of any one person is the same as their direct maternal ancestor back many generations. In humans, this concept has been used to trace the most-recent common mitochondrial ancestor of all humans, a single female from Africa (dubbed Mitochondrial Eve or ME). The ME represents that woman whose mitochondrial DNA (with mutations) exists in all humans alive today. Mutations to the mtDNA provide the molecular clock that allows us to determine how much time has elapsed since the ME lived. The existence of a ME does not mean that no other women have left descendents; we have ancestors who are not via matrilineal descent (e.g. you have nuclear DNA from your both father's and mother's mother, but only mitochondrial DNA from your mother's mother). At some point, these other females must have produced no daughters themselves and so broke the mitochondrial line (right).

*Although mtDNA does recombine, it does so with copies of itself within the same mitochondrion.

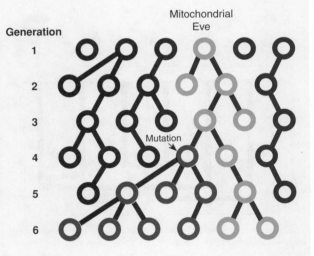

Generation

Mitochondrial Eve

1

2

3

Mutation

4

5

6

---

1. (a) How does mtDNA differ from nuclear DNA? _____

_____

(b) Why is mtDNA useful for following maternal lineages? _____

_____

_____

2. Why is mtDNA useful for determining relationships between closely related species: _____

_____

_____

_____

LINK
135
WEB
132 KNOW

133 Homologous DNA

Key Idea: The relatedness of species can be deduced from the differences in their DNA.

DNA-DNA hybridisation (below) provides a way to compare the genomes of different species by measuring the degree of genetic similarity between DNA sequences. More closely related species have fewer differences between their genomes than more distantly related species. This technique gives a measure of 'relatedness' and can be calibrated as a **molecular clock** against known fossil dates. It has been used to help determine the approximate date of human divergence from the apes, which has been estimated to be between 10 and 5 million years ago.

DNA hybridisation

1. DNA from the two species to be compared is extracted, purified and cut into short fragments (e.g. 600-800 base pairs).

2. The DNA of one species is mixed with the DNA of another.

3. The mixture is incubated to allow DNA strands to dissociate and reanneal, forming hybrid double-stranded DNA.

4. The hybridised sequences that are highly similar will bind more firmly. A measure of the heat energy required to separate the hybrid strands provides a measure of DNA relatedness.

DNA homologies today

DNA-DNA hybridisation has been criticised because duplicated sequences within a single genome make it unreliable comparing closely related species.

Today, DNA sequencing and computed comparisons are more widely used to compare genomes, although DNA-DNA hybridisation is still used to help identify bacteria.

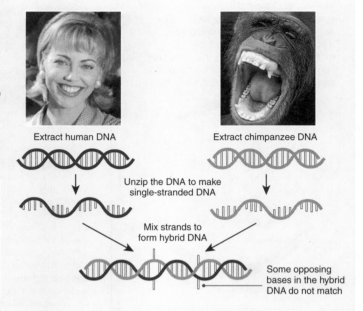

Extract human DNA   Extract chimpanzee DNA

Unzip the DNA to make single-stranded DNA

Mix strands to form hybrid DNA

Some opposing bases in the hybrid DNA do not match

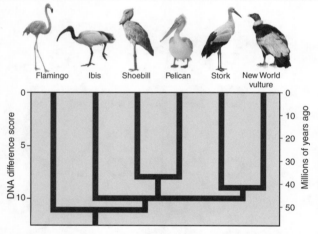

Flamingo   Ibis   Shoebill   Pelican   Stork   New World vulture

The relationships among the New World vultures and storks have been determined using DNA hybridisation. It has been possible to estimate how long ago various members of the group shared a common ancestor.

Similarity of human DNA to that of other primates

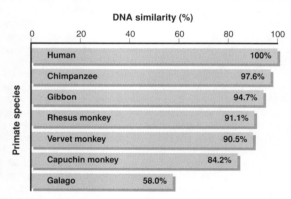

Primate species	DNA similarity (%)
Human	100%
Chimpanzee	97.6%
Gibbon	94.7%
Rhesus monkey	91.1%
Vervet monkey	90.5%
Capuchin monkey	84.2%
Galago	58.0%

The genetic relationships among the primates has been investigated using DNA hybridisation. Human DNA was compared with that of the other primates. It largely confirmed what was suspected from anatomical evidence.

1. Explain how **DNA hybridisation** can give a measure of genetic relatedness between species:

_____

_____

_____

2. Study the graph showing the results of a DNA hybridisation between human DNA and that of other primates.

(a) Which is the most closely related primate to humans? _____

(b) Which is the most distantly related primate to humans? _____

3. State the DNA difference score for: (a) Shoebills and pelicans:_____   (b) Storks and flamingos: _____

4. On the basis of DNA hybridisation, state how long ago the ibises and New World vultures shared a common ancestor:

_____

© 2016 **BIOZONE** International
ISBN: 978-1-927309-32-2
Photocopying Prohibited

134 Homologous Proteins

Key Idea: Proteins are the product of gene expression, so an analysis of the differences between the same protein in different taxa gives an indication of species relatedness.

Traditionally, phylogenies were based largely on anatomical traits, and biologists attempted to determine the relationships between taxa based on similarity or by tracing the appearance of key characteristics. With the advent of new molecular techniques, homologies (similarities resulting from shared ancestry) could be studied at the molecular level as well and the results compared to phylogenies established using other methods. Protein sequencing provides an excellent tool for establishing homologies. A protein has a specific number of amino acids arranged in a specific order. Any differences in the sequence reflect changes in the DNA sequence. Commonly studied proteins include blood proteins, such as haemoglobin, and the respiratory protein cytochrome c.

Amino acid differences in haemoglobin

Human beta chain	0
Chimpanzee	0
Gorilla	1
Gibbon	2
Rhesus monkey	8
Squirrel monkey	9
Dog	15
Horse, cow	25
Mouse	27
Grey kangaroo	38
Chicken	45
Frog	67

When the sequence of the **beta haemoglobin chain** (right), which is 146 amino acids long, is compared between humans, five other primates, and six other vertebrates, the results support the phylogenies established using other methods. The numbers in the table (left) represent the number of amino acid differences between the beta chain of humans and those of other species. In general, the number of amino acid differences between the haemoglobins of different vertebrates is inversely proportional to genetic relatedness.

Shading indicates (from top) primates, non-primate placental mammals, marsupials, and non-mammals.

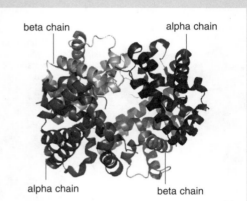
beta chain   alpha chain
alpha chain   beta chain

In most vertebrates, the oxygen-transporting blood protein haemoglobin is composed of four polypeptide chains, two alpha chains and two beta chains. Haemoglobin is derived from myoglobin, and ancestral species had just myoglobin for oxygen transport. When the amino acid sequences of myoglobin, the haemoglobin alpha chain, and the haemoglobin beta chain are compared, there are several amino acids that remain **conserved** between all three. These amino acid sequences must be essential for function because they have remained unchanged throughout evolution.

Using immunology to determine phylogeny

The immune system of one species will recognise the blood proteins of another species as foreign and form antibodies against them. This property can be used to determine the extent of relatedness between species. Blood proteins, such as albumins, are used to prepare **antiserum** in rabbits. The antiserum contains antibodies against the test blood proteins (e.g. human) and will react to those proteins in any blood sample they are mixed with. The extent of the reaction indicates how similar the proteins are; the greater the reaction, the more similar the proteins. This principle is illustrated (right) for antiserum produced to human blood and its reaction with the blood of other primates and a rat.

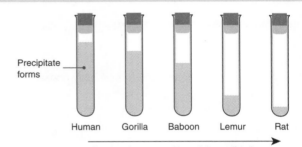
Precipitate forms

Human   Gorilla   Baboon   Lemur   Rat

Decreasing recognition of the antibodies against human blood proteins

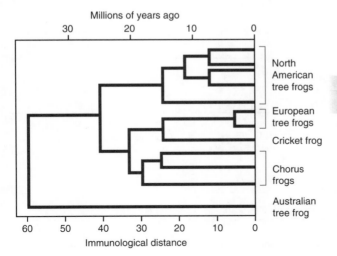

Millions of years ago
30   20   10   0

North American tree frogs
European tree frogs
Cricket frog
Chorus frogs
Australian tree frog

60   50   40   30   20   10   0
Immunological distance

The relationships among tree frogs have been established by immunological studies based on blood proteins such as immunoglobulins and albumins. The **immunological distance** is a measure of the number of amino acid substitutions between two groups. This, in turn, has been calibrated to provide a time scale showing when the various related groups diverged.

LINK LINK WEB
135 133 134 KNOW

Highly conserved proteins

Some proteins are common in many different species. These proteins are called **highly conserved proteins**, meaning they change (mutate) very little over time. This is because they have critical roles in the organism (e.g. in cellular respiration) and mutations are likely to prevent them from functioning correctly.

Evidence indicates that highly conserved proteins are homologous and have been derived from a common ancestor. Because they are highly conserved, changes in the amino acid sequence are likely to represent major divergences between groups during the course of evolution.

Cytochrome C (left) is a respiratory protein located in the electron transport chain in mitochondria.

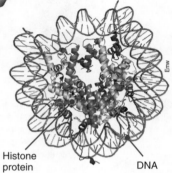

Histones (right) are a family of proteins that associate with DNA and organise it so that it can fit inside the cell nucleus.

Histone protein   DNA

The Pax-6 protein provides evidence for evolution

► The Pax-6 gene belongs to a family of genes that regulate the formation of a number of organs, including the eye, during embryonic development.

► The Pax-6 gene produces the Pax-6 protein, which acts as a transcription factor to control the expression of certain genes.

► Scientists know the role of Pax-6 in eye development because they created a knockout model in mice where the Pax-6 gene is not expressed. The knockout model is eyeless or has very underdeveloped eyes.

► The Pax-6 gene is so highly conserved that the gene from one species can be inserted into another species, and still produce a normal eye.

► This suggests the Pax-6 proteins are homologous, and the gene has been inherited from a common ancestor.

An experiment inserted mouse Pax-6 gene into fly DNA and turned it on in a fly's legs. The fly developed morphologically normal eyes on its legs!

1. Compare the differences in the haemoglobin sequence of humans, rhesus monkeys, and horses. What do these tell you about the relative relatedness of these organisms?

_____

_____

_____

2. (a) What is a highly conserved protein? _____

_____

(b) What type of proteins tend to be highly conserved? _____

_____

(c) Why are the proteins named in (b) highly conserved? _____

_____

(d) Why are highly conserved proteins good for constructing phylogenies? _____

_____

_____

3. (a) Describe the role of the Pax-6 gene: _____

_____

_____

(b) What evidence is there that the Pax-6 protein is highly conserved? _____

_____

_____

_____

135 The Molecular Clock Theory

Key Idea: The molecular clock hypothesis proposes that mutations occur at a steady rate and that changes in DNA sequences between species can determine phylogeny.
The molecular clock hypothesis states that mutations occur at a relatively constant rate for any given gene. The genetic difference between any two species can indicate when two species last shared a common ancestor and can be used to construct a phylogenetic tree. The molecular clock for each species, and each protein, may run at different rates, so molecular clock data is calibrated with other evidence (e.g. morphological) to confirm phylogeny. Molecular clock calculations are carried out on DNA or amino acid sequences.

In a theoretical example, the DNA sequence for a gene in two species (A & B, right) alive today differs by four bases. The mutation rate for the gene is approximately one base per 25 million years. Based on this rate, it can be determined that the common ancestor for these two species lived 50 mya.

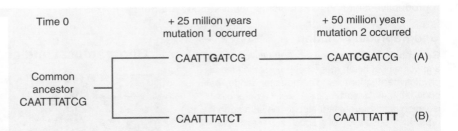

	Time 0	+ 25 million years mutation 1 occurred	+ 50 million years mutation 2 occurred
Common ancestor CAATTTATCG		CAATT**G**ATCG	CAAT**C**GATCG (A)
		CAATTTATC**T**	CAATTTAT**T** (B)

Cytochrome *c* and the molecular clock theory

		1	2	3	4	5	6	7	8	9	10	11	12	13	14	15	16	17	18	19	20	21	22
Human		Gly	Asp	Val	Glu	Lys	Gly	Lys	Lys	Ile	Phe	Ile	Met	Lys	Cys	Ser	Gln	Cys	His	Thr	Val	Glu	Lys
Pig												Val	Gln			Ala							
Chicken				Ile						Val		Val	Gln			Ala							
Dogfish										Val		Val	Gln			Ala							Asn
Drosophila	<<									Leu		Val	Gln	Arg		Ala							Ala
Wheat	<<		Asn	Pro	Asp	Ala		Ala				Lys	Thr	Arg		Ala						Asp	Ala
Yeast	<<		Ser	Ala	Lys			Ala	Thr	Leu		Lys	Thr	Arg		Glu	Leu						

This table shows the N-terminal 22 amino acid residues of human cytochrome *c*, with corresponding sequences from other organisms aligned beneath. Sequences are aligned to give the most position matches. A shaded square indicates no change. In every case, the cytochrome's heme group is attached to the Cys-14 and Cys-17. In *Drosophila*, wheat, and yeast, arrows indicate that several amino acids precede the sequence shown.

The sequence homology of cytochrome *c* (right), a respiratory protein, has been used to construct a phylogenetic tree for some species. Overall, the phylogeny aligns well to other evolutionary data, although the tree indicates that primates branched off before the marsupials diverged from other placental mammals, which is incorrect based on other evidence. Highly conserved proteins, such as cytochrome *c*, change very little over time and between species because they carry out important roles and if they changed too much they may no longer function properly.

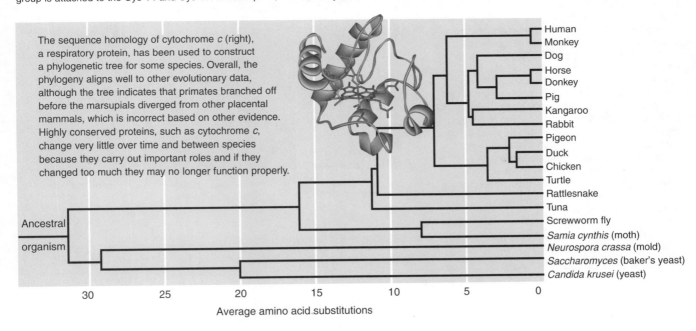

Average amino acid substitutions

1. Describe a limitation of using molecular clocks to establish phylogeny: _____

_____

_____

2. For cytochrome *c*, suggest why amino acids 14 and 17 are unchanged in all the organisms shown in the table: _____

_____

LINK 134   LINK 133   LINK 132   WEB 135   **KNOW**

136 Isolation and Species Formation

Key Idea: Ecological and geographical isolation are important in separating populations prior to reproductive isolation. Isolating mechanisms are barriers to successful interbreeding between species. **Reproductive isolation** is fundamental to the biological species concept, which defines a species by its inability to breed with other species to produce fertile offspring. **Geographical barriers** are not regarded as reproductive isolating mechanisms because they are not part of the species' biology, although they are often a necessary precursor to reproductive isolation in sexually reproducing populations. Ecological isolating mechanisms are those that isolate gene pools on the basis of ecological preferences, e.g. habitat selection. Although ecological and geographical isolation are sometimes confused, they are quite distinct, as ecological isolation involves a component of the species biology.

Geographical isolation

Geographical isolation describes the isolation of a species population (gene pool) by some kind of physical barrier, for example, mountain range, water body, isthmus, desert, or ice sheet. Geographical isolation is a frequent first step in the subsequent reproductive isolation of a species. For example, geological changes to the lake basins has been instrumental in the subsequent proliferation of cichlid fish species in the rift lakes of East Africa (right). Similarly, many Galapagos Island species (e.g. iguanas, finches) are now quite distinct from the Central and South American species from which they arose after isolation from the mainland.

Ecological (habitat) isolation

Ecological isolation describes the existence of a **prezygotic reproductive barrier** between two species (or sub-species) as a result of them occupying or breeding in different habitats within the same general geographical area. Ecological isolation includes small scale differences (e.g. ground or tree dwelling) and broad differences (e.g. desert vs grasslands). The red-browed and brown **treecreepers** (*Climacteris* spp.) are sympatric in south-eastern Australia and both species feed largely on ants. However the brown spends most of its time foraging on the ground or on fallen logs while the red-browed forages almost entirely in the trees. Ecological isolation often follows geographical isolation, but in many cases the geographical barriers may remain in part. For example, five species of **antelope squirrels** occupy different habitat ranges throughout the southwestern United States and northern Mexico, a region divided in part by the Grand Canyon. The white tailed antelope squirrel is widely distributed in desert areas to the north and south of the canyon, while the smaller, more specialised Harris' antelope squirrel has a much more limited range only to the south in southern Arizona. The Grand Canyon still functions as a barrier to dispersal but the species are now ecologically isolated as well.

Geographical and ecological isolation of species

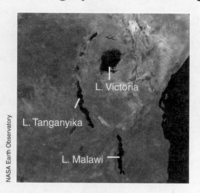

Malawi cichlid species

L. Victoria
L. Tanganyika
L. Malawi

NASA Earth Observatory

Red-browed treecreeper

Both photos: Aviceda

Brown treecreeper

White-tailed antelope squirrel

UtahCamera

The Grand Canyon - a massive rift in the Colorado Plateau

Harris' antelope squirrel

Photo: Allan and Elaine Wilson

istock

1. Describe the role of isolating mechanisms in maintaining the integrity of a species: _____

_____

_____

2. (a) Why is geographical isolation not regarded as a reproductive isolating mechanism? _____

_____

   (b) Explain why, despite this, it often precedes reproductive isolation: _____

_____

3. Distinguish between geographical and ecological isolation: _____

_____

WEB 136   LINK 137   LINK 138   LINK 139   KNOW

© 2016 **BIOZONE** International
ISBN: 978-1-927309-32-2
Photocopying Prohibited

137 Reproductive Isolation

Key Idea: Reproductive isolating mechanisms acting before and after fertilisation, prevent interbreeding between species. Reproductive isolation is a defining feature of biological species. Any mechanism that prevents two species from producing viable, fertile hybrids contributes to reproductive isolation. Single barriers to gene flow (such as geographical barriers) are usually insufficient to isolate a gene pool, so most species commonly have more than one type of barrier. Most reproductive isolating mechanisms (RIMs) are prezygotic and operate before fertilisation. Postzygotic RIMs, which act after fertilisation, are important in maintaining the integrity of closely related species.

Prezygotic isolating mechanisms

Temporal Isolation

Individuals from different species do not mate because they are active during different times of the day or in different seasons. Plants flower at different times of the year or at different times of the day to avoid hybridisation (e.g. species of the orchid genus *Dendrobium* occupy the same location but flower on different days). Closely related animal species may have different breeding seasons or periods of emergence. Species of **periodical cicadas** (*Magicicada*) in a particular region are developmentally synchronised, despite very long life cycles. Once their underground period of development (13 or 17 years depending on the species) is over, the entire population emerges at much the same time to breed.

Gamete Isolation

The gametes from different species are often incompatible, so even if they meet they do not survive. Where fertilisation is internal, the sperm may not survive in the reproductive tract of another species. If the sperm does survive and reach the ovum, chemical differences in the gametes prevent fertilisation. Gamete isolation is particularly important in aquatic environments where the gametes are released into the water and fertilised externally, such as in reproduction in frogs. Chemical recognition is also used by flowering plants to recognise pollen from the same species.

Behavioural isolation

Behavioural isolation operates through differences in species courtship behaviours. Courtship is a necessary prelude to mating in many species and courtship behaviours are species specific. Mates of the same species are attracted with distinctive dances, vocalisations, and body language. Courtship behaviours are not easily misinterpreted and will be unrecognised and ignored by individuals of another species. Birds exhibit a remarkable range of courtship displays. The use of song is widespread but ritualised movements, including nest building, are also common. For example, the elaborate courtship bowers of bowerbirds are well known, and Galápagos frigatebirds have an elaborate display in which they inflate a bright red gular pouch (right). Amongst insects, empid flies have some of the most elaborate of courtship displays. They are aggressive hunters so ritualised behaviour involving presentation of a prey item facilitates mating. The sexual organs of the flies are also like a lock-and-key, providing mechanical reproductive isolation as well (see below).

Mechanical (morphological) isolation

Structural differences (incompatibility) in the anatomy of reproductive organs prevents sperm transfer between individuals of different species. This is an important isolating mechanism preventing breeding between closely related species of arthropods. Many flowering plants have coevolved with their animal pollinators and have flowers structures to allow only that insect access. Structural differences in the flowers and pollen of different plant species prevents cross breeding because pollen transfer is restricted to specific pollinators and the pollen itself must be species compatible.

Temporal isolation: periodical cicadas

Cicada emergence

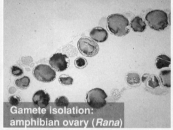
Gamete isolation: amphibian ovary (*Rana*)

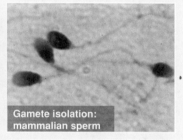
Gamete isolation: mammalian sperm

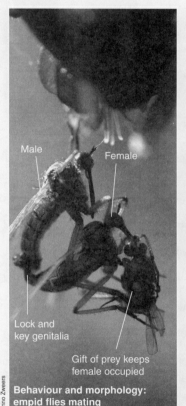
Male
Female
Lock and key genitalia
Gift of prey keeps female occupied
Behaviour and morphology: empid flies mating

Behaviour: male frigatebird display

Behaviour: male tree frog calling

Behaviour: wing beating in male sage grouse

Mechanical: Damselflies mating

Mechanical: flower shape in orchids

LINK 140 LINK 139 LINK 138 LINK 136 KNOW

Postzygotic isolating mechanisms

Hybrid sterility

Even if two species mate and produce hybrid offspring that are vigorous, the species are still reproductively isolated if the hybrids are sterile (genes cannot flow from one species' gene pool to the other). Such cases are common among the horse family (such as the zebra and donkey shown on the right). One cause of this sterility is the failure of meiosis to produce normal gametes in the hybrid. This can occur if the chromosomes of the two parents are different in number or structure (see the "**zebronkey**" karyotype on the right). The **mule**, a cross between a donkey stallion and a horse mare, is also an example of **hybrid vigour** (they are robust) as well as **hybrid sterility**. Female mules sometimes produce viable eggs but males are infertile.

Hybrid inviability

Mating between individuals of two species may produce a zygote, but genetic incompatibility may stop development of the zygote. Fertilised eggs often fail to divide because of mis-matched chromosome numbers from each gamete. Very occasionally, the hybrid zygote will complete embryonic development but will not survive for long. For example, although sheep and goats seem similar and can be mated together, they belong to different genera. Any offspring of a sheep-goat pairing is generally stillborn.

Hybrid breakdown

Hybrid breakdown is common feature of some plant hybrids. The first generation (F_1) may be fertile, but the second generation (F_2) are infertile or inviable. Examples include hybrids between cotton species (near right), species within the genus *Populus*, and strains of the cultivated rice *Oryza* (far right)

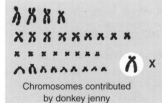

Zebra stallion (2N = 44) **X** Donkey jenny (2N = 62)

Karyotype of 'Zebronkey' offspring (2N = 53)

Chromosomes contributed by zebra stallion

Chromosomes contributed by donkey jenny

Sheep (*Ovis*) 54 chromosomes

Goat (*Capra*) 60 chromosomes

1. In the following examples, classify the reproductive isolating mechanism as either **prezygotic** or **postzygotic** and describe the mechanisms by which the isolation is achieved (e.g. structrual isolation, hybrid sterility etc.):

   (a) Some different cotton species can produce fertile hybrids, but breakdown of the hybrid occurs in the next generation when the offspring of the hybrid die in their seeds or grow into defective plants:

   Prezygotic / postzygotic (delete one)   Mechanism of isolation: _____

   (b) Many plants have unique arrangements of their floral parts that stops transfer of pollen between plants:

   Prezygotic / postzygotic (delete one)   Mechanism of isolation: _____

   (c) Two skunk species do not mate despite having habitats that overlap because they mate at different times of the year:

   Prezygotic / postzygotic (delete one)   Mechanism of isolation: _____

   (d) Several species of the frog genus *Rana*, live in the same regions and habitats, where they may occasionally hybridise. The hybrids generally do not complete development, and those that do are weak and do not survive long:

   Prezygotic / postzygotic (delete one)   Mechanism of isolation: _____

2. Postzygotic isolating mechanisms are said to reinforce prezygotic ones. Explain why this is the case:

   _____

   _____

   _____

   _____

   _____

138 Allopatric Speciation

Key Idea: Allopatric speciation is the genetic divergence of a population after it becomes subdivided and isolated.

Allopatric speciation refers to the genetic divergence of a species after a population becomes split and then isolated geographically. It is probably the most common mechanism by which new species arise and has certainly been important in regions where there have been cycles of geographical fragmentation, e.g. as a result of ice expansion and retreat (and accompanying sea level changes) during glacial and interglacial periods.

Stage 1: Moving into new environments

There are times when the range of a species expands for a variety of different reasons. A single population in a relatively homogeneous environment will move into new regions of their environment when they are subjected to intense competition (whether it is interspecific or intraspecific). The most severe form of competition is between members of the same species since they are competing for identical resources in the habitat. In the diagram on the right there is a 'parent population' of a single species with a common gene pool with regular 'gene flow' (theoretically any individual has access to all members of the opposite sex for mating purposes).

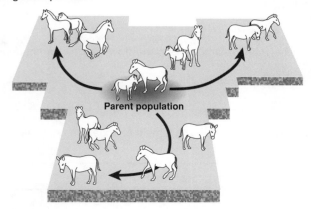

Parent population

Stage 2: Geographical isolation

Isolation of parts of the population may occur due to the formation of **physical barriers**, such as mountains, deserts, or stretches of water. These barriers may cut off those parts of the population that are at the extremes of the range and gene flow is prevented or rare. The rise and fall of the sea level has been particularly important in functioning as an isolating mechanism. Climatic change can leave 'islands' of habitat separated by large inhospitable zones that the species cannot traverse.

Example: In mountainous regions, alpine species can populate extensive areas of habitat during cool climatic periods. During warmer periods, they may become isolated because their habitat is reduced to 'islands' of high ground surrounded by inhospitable lowland habitat.

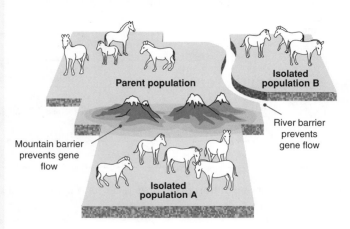

Parent population

Isolated population B

River barrier prevents gene flow

Mountain barrier prevents gene flow

Isolated population A

Stage 3: Different selection pressures

The isolated populations (A and B) may be subjected to quite different selection pressures. These will favour individuals with traits that suit each particular environment. For example, population A will be subjected to selection pressures that relate to drier conditions. This will favour those individuals with phenotypes (and therefore genotypes) that are better suited to dry conditions. They may for instance have a better ability to conserve water. This would result in improved health, allowing better disease resistance and greater reproductive performance (i.e. more of their offspring survive). Finally, as allele frequencies for certain genes change, the population takes on the status of a subspecies. Reproductive isolation is not yet established but the **subspecies** are significantly different genetically from other related populations.

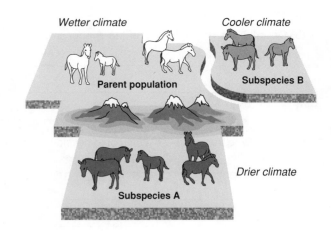

Wetter climate

Cooler climate

Parent population

Subspecies B

Subspecies A

Drier climate

Stage 4: Reproductive isolation

The separated populations (isolated subspecies) undergo genetic and behavioural changes. These ensure that the gene pool of each population remains isolated and 'undiluted' by genes from other populations, even if the two populations should be able to remix (due to the removal of the geographical barrier). Gene flow does not occur. The arrows (diagram, right) indicate the zone of overlap between two species after Species B has moved back into the range inhabited by the parent population. Closely-related species whose distribution overlaps are said to be **sympatric species**. Those that remain geographically isolated are called **allopatric species**.

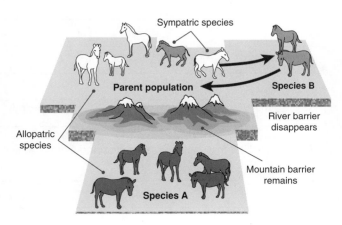

Sympatric species

Parent population

Species B

River barrier disappears

Allopatric species

Mountain barrier remains

Species A

© 2016 **BIOZONE** International
ISBN: 978-1-927309-32-2
Photocopying Prohibited

LINK 140 LINK 139 LINK 136 WEB 138 KNOW

1. Why do some animals, given the opportunity, move into new environments? _____

_____

_____

2. Plants are unable to move. How might plants disperse to new environments? _____

_____

3. Describe the amount of **gene flow** within a parent population prior to and during the expansion of a species' range:

_____

_____

4. Explain how cycles of climate change can cause large changes in **sea level** (up to 200 m): _____

_____

_____

5. (a) What kinds of **physical barriers** could isolate different parts of the same population? _____

_____

_____

_____

(b) How might emigration achieve the same effect as geographical isolation? _____

_____

_____

6. (a) How might **selection pressures** differ for a population that becomes isolated from the parent population?

_____

_____

(b) Describe the general effect of the change in selection pressures on the **allele frequencies** of the isolated gene pool:

_____

_____

_____

7. Explain how reproductive isolation could develop in geographically separated populations (see previous pages):

_____

_____

_____

_____

_____

_____

_____

_____

_____

8. What is the difference between allopatric and sympatric species? _____

_____

_____

© 2016 **BIOZONE** International
ISBN: 978-1-927309-32-2
Photocopying Prohibited

139 Stages in Species Formation

Key Idea: Speciation may occur in stages marked by increasing isolation of diverging gene pools. Physical separation is followed by increasing reproductive isolation.

The diagram below shows a possible sequence of events in the origin of two new species from an ancestral population. Over time, the genetic differences between two populations increase and the populations become increasingly isolated from each other. The isolation of the two gene pools may begin with a geographical barrier. This may be followed by progressively greater reduction in gene flow between the populations until the two gene pools are isolated and they each attain species status.

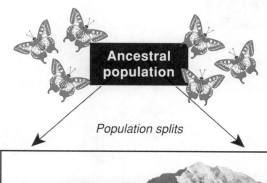

Ancestral population

Population splits

A species of butterfly lives on a plateau. The plateau is covered with grassland strewn with boulders. During colder weather, some butterflies sit on the sun-heated boulders to absorb the heat, while others retreat to the lower altitude grassland to avoid the cold.

Evolutionary development or time

 Population A

 Population B

Gene flow common

Continued mountain building raises the altitude of the plateau, separating two populations of butterflies, one in the highlands the other in the lowlands.

  Race A

 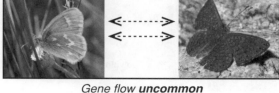

 Race B

Gene flow uncommon

In the highlands, boulder-sitting butterflies (BSBs) do better than grass-sitting butterflies (GSBs). In the lowlands, the opposite is true. BSBs only mate on boulders with other BSBs. Darker BSBs have greater fitness than light BSBs. (they can absorb more heat from the boulders). In the lowlands, light GSBs blend in with the grass and survive better than darker butterflies.

 Subspecies A

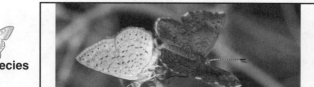

 Subspecies B

Gene flow very rare

Over time, only boulder-sitting butterflies are found in the highlands and grass-sitting butterflies in the lowlands. Occasionally wind brings members of the two groups together, but if they mate, the offspring are usually not viable or have a much lowered fitness.

Species A

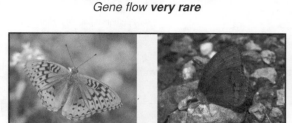

 Species B

Separate species

Eventually gene flow between separated populations ceases as variation between the populations increases. They fail to recognise each other as members of the same species.

1. Identify the variation in behaviour in the original butterfly population: _____

_____

2. What were the selection pressures acting on BSBs in the highlands and GSBs in the lowlands respectively?

_____

_____

_____

LINK 138 LINK 136 **KNOW**

140 Sympatric Speciation

Key Idea: Sympatric speciation is speciation occurring in the absence of physical barriers between gene pools.

Sympatric speciation refers to the formation of new species within the same place (sympatry). Sympatric speciation is rarer than allopatric speciation because it is difficult to prevent gene flow. However, it is not uncommon in plants that form **polyploids** (organisms with extra complete sets of chromosomes). Sympatric speciation can occur through niche differentiation in areas of sympatry, or by instant speciation through polyploidy.

Speciation through niche differentiation

Niche isolation

In a heterogeneous environment (one that is not the same everywhere), a population exists within a diverse collection of **microhabitats**. Some organisms prefer to occupy one particular type of 'microhabitat' most of the time, only rarely coming in contact with fellow organisms that prefer other microhabitats. Some organisms become so dependent on the resources offered by their particular microhabitat that they never meet up with their counterparts in different microhabitats.

Reproductive isolation

Finally, the individual groups have remained genetically isolated for so long because of their microhabitat preferences, that they have become reproductively isolated. They have become new species that have developed subtle differences in behaviour, structure, or physiology. Gene flow (via sexual reproduction) is limited to organisms that share a similar microhabitat preference (as shown in the diagram on the right).

Example: Some beetles prefer to find plants identical to the species they grew up on, when it is time for them to lay eggs. Individual beetles of the same species have different preferences.

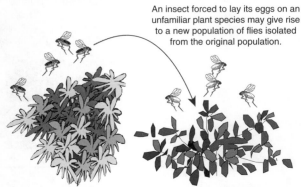

An insect forced to lay its eggs on an unfamiliar plant species may give rise to a new population of flies isolated from the original population.

Original host plant species   **New host plant species**

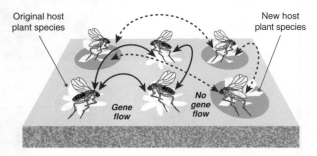

Original host plant species

New host plant species

Gene flow

No gene flow

Instant speciation by polyploidy

Polyploidy (duplication of chromosome sets) may result in the formation of a new species without physical isolation from the parent species. Polyploidy produces sudden reproductive isolation for the new group. Polyploids in animals are rarely viable. Many plants, on the other hand, are able to reproduce vegetatively, or carry out self pollination. This ability to reproduce on their own enables such polyploid plants to produce a breeding population.

Polyploidy in a hybrid between two different species can often make the hybrid fertile. This occurred in modern wheat. Swedes are also a polyploid species formed from a hybrid between a type of cabbage and a type of turnip.

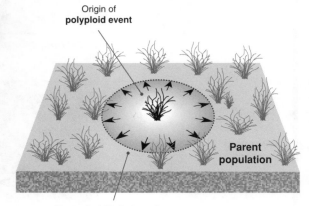

Origin of **polyploid event**

Parent population

New polyploid plant species spreads outwards through the existing parent population

1. Explain what is meant by **sympatric speciation** (do not confuse this with sympatric species):

_____

_____

2. Explain how **polyploidy** can result in the formation of a new species: _____

_____

_____

3. Identify an example of a species that has been formed by polyploidy: _____

4. Explain how **niche differentiation** can result in the formation of a new species: _____

_____

_____

© 2016 **BIOZONE** International
ISBN: 978-1-927309-32-2
Photocopying Prohibited

141 Extinction

Key Idea: Extinction is a natural process. Mass extinctions involve the extinction of large numbers of species and genera in a geologically short period of time.

Most species that have ever lived are now extinct. Extinction (loss of all the members of a species or other taxonomic group) is an important process in evolution as it provides opportunities, in the form of vacant niches, for new species to arise. The background extinction rate is the steady rate of species turnover in a taxonomic group. Superimposed on this are catastrophic events (called mass extinctions) that wipe out large numbers of species within a geologically brief period of time. In the past 500 years, human activity has resulted in a rapid rise in natural extinction rates with over 750 extinctions recorded since 1500 AD and probably many more unrecorded. Some of the causes of extinction, both past and present, are summarised below.

Climate change: Species are adapted to particular environments, e.g. the polar bears and emperor penguins are adapted to polar conditions. If the environment changes too rapidly, species may not be able to adapt quickly enough to survive the change. They may become extinct (e.g. many of the large woolly megafauna of the ice age died out when global temperatures rose) or evolve into a new species, in which case the parent species becomes extinct.

Global catastrophe: The Earth has had many global catastrophic events that have led to mass extinctions. There are five recognised past mass extinction events, excluding the current sixth extinction event. The most important was the Permian event in which 90% of all marine life and many terrestrial species died out. The Cretaceous extinction 65 million years ago saw the end of the dinosaurs and many large terrestrial and marine reptiles.

Humans: Humans are the greatest predator the Earth has ever produced. Our ability to kill organisms both intentionally and unintentionally is unmatched by any other organism. Many organisms have been intentionally exterminated by humans, e.g. the passenger pigeon (globally extinct) and the gray wolf (locally extinct in many parts of the world). Others have been brought to the brink of extinction before being saved, e.g. the American bison and Przewalski's horse.

Genetic pollution: A particular problem for isolated species is the prospect of genetic pollution when closely related species are introduced. For example, in New Zealand, the introduced mallard duck hybridises with the native subspecies of grey duck (above). The grey duck is now critically endangered in New Zealand as it is thought there are very few pure bred grey ducks left.

Competition: Competition is an important factor in extinction, especially of threatened species. Species that cannot compete successfully for resources are forced out of the environment or become extinct if there is nowhere to go. If the species adopts a new niche and becomes sufficiently isolated, the parent species effectively becomes extinct (by way of sequential evolution).

Habitat loss: Habitat loss can come about in two main ways. Either the climate changes and the habitat changes with it, or humans remove or significantly modify a habitat entirely, e.g. through deforestation or pollution. In either case, organisms dependent on a particular habitat may become extinct as a result of losing the resources required for their survival and reproduction.

1. Explain what is meant by extinction: _____

_____

2. Describe how each of the following contribute to or cause extinction:

   (a) Climate change: _____

   _____

   (b) Competition: _____

   _____

   (c) Human activity: _____

   _____

   _____

KNOW

142 Chapter Review

Summarise what you know about this topic under the headings and sub-headings provided. You can draw diagrams or mind maps, or write short notes to organise your thoughts. Use the images and hints to help you and refer back to the introduction to check the points covered:

Gene pools

HINT: How do gene pools change over time? What is the Hardy-Weinberg principle and how is it applied to the study of evolving populations.

Speciation

HINT: Describe speciation in allopatric and sympatric populations and explain the role of reproductive isolating mechanisms in the formation of species.

Natural selection

HINT: Define natural selection and include examples of types of natural selection.

Selective breeding

HINT: Explain the process of selective breeding. Why is it important to maintain genetic diversity?

REVISE

143 KEY TERMS AND IDEAS: Did You Get?

1. Match each term to its definition, as identified by its preceding letter code.

allopatric speciation

allele frequency

founder effect

gene flow

gene pool

genetic bottleneck

genetic drift

Hardy-Weinberg principle

natural selection

polyploidy

mate choice

selective breeding

sympatric speciation

A The process by which heritable traits become more or less common in a population through differential survival and reproduction.

B An evolutionary event in which a significant proportion of the alleles in a population are lost.

C The sum total of all genes of all breeding individuals in a population at any one time.

D The process by which particular phenotypes are favoured through human intervention.

E A type of intersexual selection. Typically the female selects the male she will mate with.

F Speciation as a result of reproductive isolation without any physical separation of the populations, i.e. populations remain within the same range.

G The movement of alleles between populations as a result of migration.

H Speciation in which the populations are physically separated.

I The loss of genetic variation when a new colony is formed by a very small number of individuals from a larger population.

J The principle of genetic equilibrium that describes the constancy of population allele frequencies in the absence of evolutionary influences.

K The proportion of an allele of a gene within a population relative to other alleles of the same gene.

L The change in allele frequency in a population as a result of random sampling. The effect is proportionally larger in small populations.

M The heritable condition of having more than two complete chromosome sets. Rare in animals but important in the speciation events of many plants.

2. Using examples, contrast the characteristics of directional and stabilising selection and their effects:

_____

_____

_____

_____

3. Within a population of butterflies, brown colour (B) is dominant over white (b) and 40% of butterflies are white. Calculate:

(a) The percentage of butterflies that are heterozygous: _____

_____

(b) The frequency of homozygous dominant individuals: _____

_____

4. Blood samples of 1000 individuals were typed for the MN blood group, which can be detected because the alleles are codominant. Using the results (right) calculate the frequency of each allele in the population:

(a) Frequency of M: _____

_____

(b) Frequency of N: _____

_____

Blood type	Genotype	No. of individuals	Frequency
M	MM	490	0.49
MN	MN	420	0.42
N	NN	90	0.09

TEST

Topic 18

Biodiversity, classification, and conservation

Key terms

abiotic factor
abundance
alien species
belt transect
biodiversity
biotic factor
class
conservation
contraception
correlation
diversity index
domain
ecosystem
embryo transfer
endangered species
ex-situ conservation
family
genetic diversity
genus
habitat diversity
in-situ conservation
IVF
kingdom
Lincoln index
line transect
mark-release-recapture
niche
order
phylum
quadrat
species
species diversity
species evenness
species richness
taxon
taxonomic category

18.1 Biodiversity

Learning outcomes

Activity number

☐ 1 Define the terms species, ecosystem, and niche. — 144

☐ 2 Explain how we can consider biodiversity at three levels: habitat diversity, species diversity (species richness and species evenness or relative abundance), and genetic diversity (genetic diversity within each species) — 145

☐ 3 Explain why random sampling is important in the determination of biodiversity. — 146 147

☐ 4 Use suitable methods, such as frame quadrats, line transects, belt transects, and mark-release-recapture, to assess the distribution and abundance of organisms in a local area. — 147 148 150-157

☐ 5 Use Spearman's rank correlation and Pearson's linear correlation to analyse the relationships between distribution and abundance of species and abiotic (e.g. temperature) or biotic factors (e.g. competition). Understand that appropriate use of these tests depends on knowing the distribution of the data. — 160-162

☐ 6 Extension: Understand that the chi-squared test for independence can also be used to analyse distribution and abundance in relation to biotic or abiotic factors. — 158 159

☐ 7 Use Simpson's Index of Diversity (D) to calculate the biodiversity of a habitat. Explain the significance of different values of D. — 149 150

18.2 Classification

Learning outcomes

Activity number

☐ 8 Describe the classification of species in the taxonomic hierarchy of domain, kingdom, phylum, class, order, family, genus, and species. — 163

☐ 9 Outline the characteristic features of the domains Archaea, Bacteria, and Eukarya and the kingdoms Protoctista, Fungi, Plantae, and Animalia. — 164-166

☐ 10 Explain why viruses are not included in the three domain classification and outline how they are classified on the basis of their nucleic acid (DNA/RNA/SS/DS). — 167

18.3 Conservation

Learning outcomes

Activity number

☐ 11 Discuss the threats to aquatic and terrestrial biodiversity (refer to #2 above). — 168 169

☐ 12 Discuss the reasons for maintaining biodiversity (economic, ecological aesthetic). — 170

☐ 13 Discuss *in-situ* and *ex-situ* methods of protecting endangered species. — 171-173

☐ 14 Discuss methods of assisted reproduction used in the conservation of endangered mammals, with reference to IVF, embryo transfer, and surrogacy. — 174

☐ 15 Discuss the use of culling and contraception as population control measures. — 175

☐ 16 Using examples, explain why alien species require controlling. — 176

☐ 17 Discuss the role of NGOs, e.g. WWF and CITES, in local and global conservation. — 177

☐ 18 Using examples, outline methods for the restoration of degraded habitats. — 172

144 Components of an Ecosystem

Key Idea: An ecosystem consists of all the organisms living in a particular area and their physical environment.

An **ecosystem** is a community of living organisms and the physical (non-living) components of their environment. The community (living component of the ecosystem) is in turn made up of a number of **populations**, these being organisms of the same species living in the same geographical area. The structure and function of an ecosystem is determined by the physical (abiotic) and the living (biotic) factors, which determine species distribution and survival.

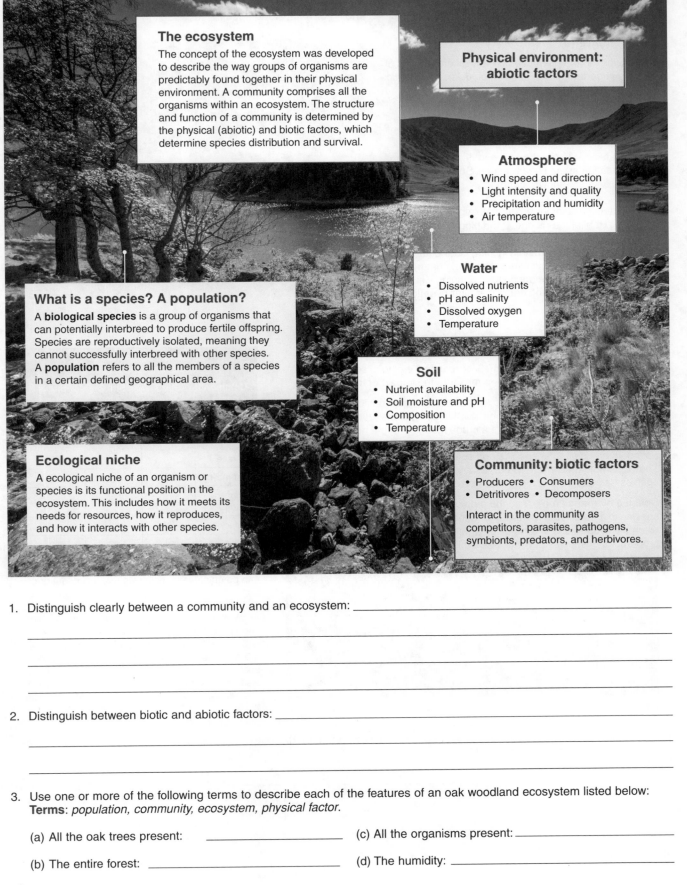

The ecosystem

The concept of the ecosystem was developed to describe the way groups of organisms are predictably found together in their physical environment. A community comprises all the organisms within an ecosystem. The structure and function of a community is determined by the physical (abiotic) and biotic factors, which determine species distribution and survival.

Physical environment: abiotic factors

Atmosphere
- Wind speed and direction
- Light intensity and quality
- Precipitation and humidity
- Air temperature

Water
- Dissolved nutrients
- pH and salinity
- Dissolved oxygen
- Temperature

What is a species? A population?

A **biological species** is a group of organisms that can potentially interbreed to produce fertile offspring. Species are reproductively isolated, meaning they cannot successfully interbreed with other species. A **population** refers to all the members of a species in a certain defined geographical area.

Soil
- Nutrient availability
- Soil moisture and pH
- Composition
- Temperature

Ecological niche

A ecological niche of an organism or species is its functional position in the ecosystem. This includes how it meets its needs for resources, how it reproduces, and how it interacts with other species.

Community: biotic factors
- Producers • Consumers
- Detritivores • Decomposers

Interact in the community as competitors, parasites, pathogens, symbionts, predators, and herbivores.

1. Distinguish clearly between a community and an ecosystem: _____

_____

_____

_____

2. Distinguish between biotic and abiotic factors: _____

_____

_____

3. Use one or more of the following terms to describe each of the features of an oak woodland ecosystem listed below:
   Terms: *population, community, ecosystem, physical factor.*

   (a) All the oak trees present: _____   (c) All the organisms present: _____

   (b) The entire forest: _____   (d) The humidity: _____

LINK 145   WEB 144   **KNOW**

145 What is Biodiversity?

Key Idea: Biodiversity is the sum of all biotic variation from the level of genes to ecosystems. All organisms within an ecosystem contribute to its functioning, but keystone species have a disproportionate effect on ecosystem functioning.

Biodiversity is defined as the sum of all biotic variation from the level of genes to ecosystems. Species diversity describes species richness (the number of species), genetic diversity is the diversity of genes within a species, and ecosystem diversity (of which habitat diversity is a part) refers to the diversity at the ecosystem level. Total biodiversity is threatened by the loss of just one of these components. While every species plays a role in ecosystem function, **keystone species** have a disproportionate effect on ecosystem stability because of their pivotal role in some aspect of ecosystem functioning, e.g. as predators or in nutrient cycling. The loss of a keystone species can result in rapid ecosystem change.

Habitat diversity

Habitat diversity (the presence of many different types of habitat) is important for maintaining biodiversity. Specific habitats are occupied by different organisms and, in general, the greater the number of habitats, the greater the species diversity. Within habitats, microhabitats (smaller areas with specific characteristics) further increase biodiversity. For example, in a stream habitat, microhabitats exist under the rocks, in riffles, in pools, and in vegetation at the stream edges. Some common English habitats are shown (right).

Habitat protection is important to maintain species biodiversity. Habitat loss is one of the biggest threats to biodiversity and is the most common cause of extinction. Examples of habitat destruction include clear cutting forests for logging and agriculture, ploughing natural meadows to make way for agriculture, draining wetland and peatlands, and creating dams that alter river flows.

Coastal sand dunes, Wales

Stream, Peak district

Bluebell woodland

Meadow, Yorkshire

Measuring biodiversity

Biodiversity is quantified for a variety of reasons, e.g. to assess the success of conservation work or to measure the impact of human activity.

One measure of biodiversity is to simply count all the species present (the **species richness**). Species richness (S) is directly related to the number of species in a sampled area. It is a crude measure of the homogeneity of a community but it does not give any information about the relative abundance of particular species and so is relatively meaningless by itself. Thus a sample area with 500 daisies and 3 dandelions has the same species richness as a sample area with 200 daisies and 300 dandelions.

Species evenness measures the proportion of individuals of each species in an area (the relative abundance). Species evenness is highest when the proportions of all species are the same and decreases as the proportions of species become less similar.

Sample of freshwater invertebrates in a stream			
Common name	Site 1 / $n\,m^{-2}$	Site 2 / $n\,m^{-2}$	Site 3 / $n\,m^{-2}$
Freshwater shrimp	67	20	5
Freshwater mite	4	15	1
Flat mayfly	23	21	0
Bighead stonefly	12	18	2
Blackfly	78	40	100
Bloodworm	21	22	43

Data for species richness and species evenness can be obtained by sampling, e.g. using quadrats. In the example above, three sites in a stream were sampled using quadrats and the species and number of individuals per m² recorded for each site. Using Site 1 as an example, species richness is 6, since $S = n$. Measures of species evenness are an integral component of biodiversity indices, such as Simpson's Index of biodiversity, but can also be estimated from the numbers of individuals of each species. In terms of species evenness, site 2 > site 1 > site 3.

High species richness

Low species richness

1. Distinguish between species diversity, genetic diversity, and habitat diversity and explain the importance of each of these to our definition of total ecological diversity:

_____

_____

_____

_____

© 2016 **BIOZONE** International
ISBN: 978-1-927309-32-2
Photocopying Prohibited

146 Types of Sampling

Key Idea: A population's characteristics may be inferred from data collected by sampling. Random sampling methods are preferred as they provide unbiased data.

In most ecological studies, it is not possible to measure or count all the members of a population. Instead, information is obtained through sampling in a manner that provides a fair (unbiased) representation of the organisms present and their distribution. This is usually achieved through **random**

sampling, a technique in which each individual has the same probability of being selected at any stage during the sampling process. Sometimes researchers collect information by **non-random sampling**, a process that does not give all the individuals in the population an equal chance of being selected. While faster and cheaper to carry out than random sampling, non-random sampling may not give a true representation of the population.

Sampling strategies

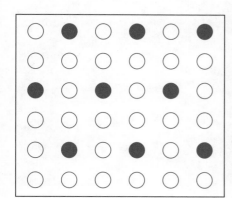

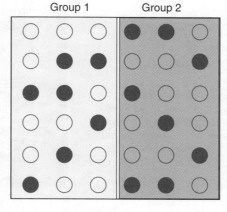
Group 1   Group 2

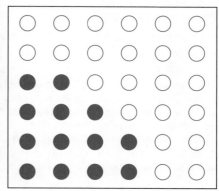

Systematic sampling

Samples from a larger population are selected according to a random starting point and a fixed, periodic sampling interval. For the example above, the sampling period is every fourth individual. Systematic sampling is a random sampling method, provided the periodic interval is determined beforehand and the starting point is random.

Example: Selecting individuals from a patient list.

Stratified sampling

Stratified sampling divides the population into subgroups before sampling. The strata should be mutually exclusive, and individuals must be assigned to only one stratum. Stratified sampling is used to highlight a specific subgroup within the population. Individuals are then randomly sampled from the strata to study.

Example: Dividing the population into males and females.

Opportunistic sampling

A non-random sampling technique in which subjects are selected because of they are easily accessible to the researcher. Opportunistic sampling excludes a large proportion of the population and is usually not representative of the population. It is sometimes used in pilot studies to gather data quickly and with little cost.

Example: Selecting 13 people at a cafe where you are having lunch.

1. Why do we sample populations? _____

_____

_____

2. Why is random sampling preferable to non-random sampling? _____

_____

3. (a) Why can stratified sampling be considered a random sampling method? _____

_____

   (b) Describe a situation where its use might be appropriate? _____

_____

4. A student wants to investigate the incidence of asthma in their school. Describe how they might select samples from the school population using:

   (a) Systematic sampling: _____

_____

   (b) Stratified sampling: _____

_____

   (c) Opportunistic sampling: _____

_____

147 Measuring Distribution and Abundance

Key Idea: Random sampling using an appropriate technique provides unbiased information about the distribution and abundance of species in a community.

Most practical exercises in ecology involve collecting data about the distribution and abundance of one or more species in a community. Most studies also measure the physical factors in the environment as these may help to explain the patterns of distribution and abundance observed. The use of random sampling methods, in which every possible sample of a given size the same chance of selection, provides unbiased data. As long as the sample size is large enough and the sampling technique is appropriate to the community being studied, sample data enables us to make inferences about aspects of the whole population.

Distribution and abundance

Ecological sampling collects data about where organisms are found and how they are distributed in the environment. This information can be used to determine the health and viability of a population and its ecosystem. When investigating populations it is useful to monitor:

▶ Species **distribution** (where the species are located)

▶ Species **abundance** (how many of a species there are)

The methods used to sample communities and their constituent populations must be appropriate to the ecosystem being investigated. Communities in which the populations are at low density and have a random or clumped distribution will require a different sampling strategy to those where the populations are uniformly distributed and at higher density. There are many sampling options (below), each with advantages and drawbacks for particular communities.

Sampling designs and techniques

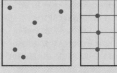

Random   Systematic (grid)

Point sampling
Individual points are chosen (using a grid reference or random numbers applied to a map grid) and the organisms are sampled at those points. Point sampling is most often used to collect data about vegetation distribution. It is time efficient and good for determining species abundance and community composition, however, organisms in low abundance may be missed.

Area sampling using quadrats
A quadrat is a sampling tool that provides a known unit area of sample (e.g. 0.5 m²). Quadrats are placed randomly or in a grid pattern on the sample area. The presence and abundance of organisms in these squares is noted. Quadrat sampling is appropriate for plants and slow moving animals and can be used to evaluate community composition.

Line transects
A tape or rope marks the line. The species occurring on the line are recorded (all along the line or at regular points). Lines can be chosen randomly (left) or may follow an environmental gradient. Line transects have little impact on the environment and are good for assessing the presence/absence of plant species. However, rare species may be missed.

Belt transects
A measured strip is located across the study area and quadrats are used to sample the plants or animals at regular intervals along the belt. Belt transects provide information on abundance and distribution as well as presence/absence. Depending on the width of the belt and length of the transect, they can be time consuming.

0.5 m

Environmental gradient

First sample: marked   Second sample: proportion recapture

Mark and recapture sampling
Animals are captured, marked, and released. After a suitable time, the population is resampled. The number of marked animals recaptured in a second sample is recorded as a proportion of the total. Mark and recapture is useful for highly mobile species which are otherwise difficult to record. However, it is time consuming to do well.

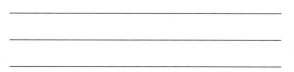

1. Distinguish between distribution and abundance:

_____

_____

_____

_____

2. Name a sampling technique that would be appropriate for determining:

   (a) Percentage cover of a plant species in pasture:

   _____

   _____

   (b) Change in community composition from low to high altitude on a mountain:

   _____

   _____

   (c) Association of plant species with particular soil types in a nature reserve:

   _____

   _____

3. Why is it common practice to also collect information about the physical environment when sampling populations?

_____

_____

_____

_____

_____

© 2016 **BIOZONE** International
ISBN: 978-1-927309-32-2
Photocopying Prohibited

148 Interpreting Samples

Key Idea: If sample data are collected without bias and in sufficient quantity, even a simple analysis can provide useful information about the composition of a community and the possible physical factors influencing this.

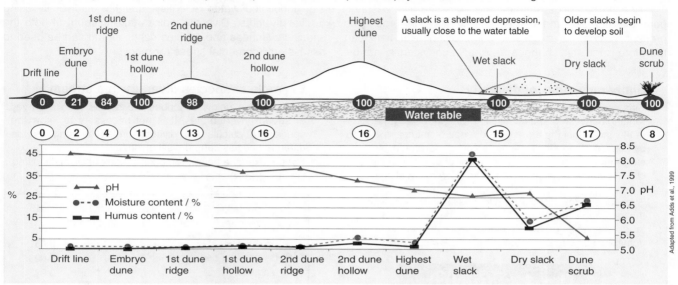

1. The beach dune profile (top) shows transect sampling points at fixed morphological features (e.g. dune ridges). The blue ovals on the dune profile represent the percentage vegetation cover at each sampling point. The white ovals record the number of plant species. Some physical data for each sampling site are presented in the graph below the profile.

   (a) What is the trend in pH from drift line to dune scrub? _____

   (b) Suggest why moisture and humus content increase along the transect? _____

   _____

   _____

   _____

2. The figure below shows changes in vegetation cover along a 2 m vertical transect up the trunk of an oak tree. Changes in the physical factors light, humidity, and temperature along the same transect were also recorded.

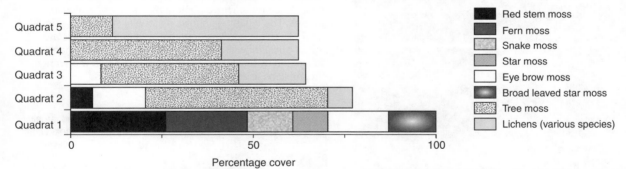

Legend:
- Red stem moss
- Fern moss
- Snake moss
- Star moss
- Eye brow moss
- Broad leaved star moss
- Tree moss
- Lichens (various species)

QUADRAT	1	2	3	4	5
Height / m	0.4	0.8	1.2	1.6	2.0
Light / arbitrary units	40	56	68	72	72
Humidity / percent	99	88	80	76	78
Temperature / °C	12.1	12.2	13	14.3	14.2

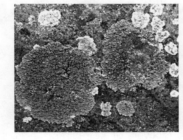

   (a) At which height were mosses most diverse and abundant? _____

   (b) What plant type predominates at 2.0 m height? _____

   (c) What can you deduce about the habitat preferences of most mosses and lichens from this study? _____

   _____

LINK
150 DATA

149 Diversity Indices

Key Idea: Diversity indices quantify the biodiversity in an area and can be used to measure ecosystem health.

The health of an ecosystem can be assessed by measuring both the number and relative abundances of organisms present. A change in species composition over time can therefore indicate changes in that ecosystem's status.

Certain **indicator species** are also useful in this respect as they are associated with habitats of a particular status, e.g. unpolluted water. Scientists quantify biodiversity using a diversity index. Diversity indices take account of both the species evenness and species richness and can be used to assess environmental stress (or recovery).

Simpson's index of diversity

Simpson's Index of Diversity (below) produces values ranging between 0 and almost 1. There are other variants of this index, but the more limited range of values provided by this calculation makes it more easily interpreted. No single index offers the "best" measure of diversity; each is chosen on the basis of suitability to different situations.

Simpson's Index of Diversity (D) is easily calculated using the following simple formula. Communities with a wide range of species produce a higher score than communities dominated by larger numbers of only a few species.

$$D = 1 - (\Sigma(n/N)^2)$$

D = Diversity index
N = Total number of individuals (of all species) in the sample
n = Number of individuals of each species in the sample

Example of species diversity in a stream

The example below describes the results from a survey of stream invertebrates. It is not necessary to know the species to calculate a diversity index as long as the different species can be distinguished.

For the example below, Simpson's Index of Diversity using $D = 1 - (\Sigma(n/N)^2)$ is:

Species	n	n/N	(n/N)²
A (backswimmer)	12	0.300	0.090
B (stonefly larva)	7	0.175	0.031
C (silver water beetle)	2	0.050	0.003
D (caddisfly larva)	6	0.150	0.023
E (water spider)	5	0.125	0.016
F (mayfly larva)	8	0.20	0.040
	$\Sigma n = 40$		$\Sigma(n/N)^2 = 0.201$

$$D = 1 - 0.201 = 0.799$$

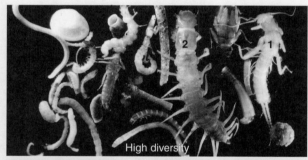
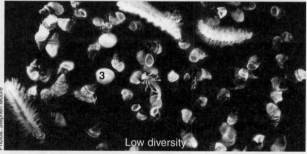

High diversity

Low diversity

Photos: Stephen Moore

Using diversity indices and the role of indicator species

To be properly interpreted, indices are usually evaluated with reference to earlier measurement or a standard ecosystem measure. The photographs left show samples from two stream communities, a high diversity community with a large number of macroinvertebrate species (top) and a low diversity community (lower photograph) with fewer species in large numbers. These photographs also show indicator species. The top image shows a stonefly (1) and an alderfly larva (2). These species (together with mayfly larvae) are typical of clean, well oxygenated water. The lower image is dominated by snails (3), which are tolerant of a wide range of conditions, included degraded environments.

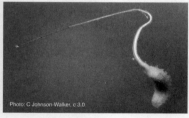

Photo: C Johnson-Walker, c 3.0

The aptly named rat-tail maggot is the larva of the drone fly. This species is an indicator of gross pollution. Its prominent feature is a long snorkel-like breathing siphon.

1. Why might it be useful to have baseline data (prior knowledge of a system) before interpreting a diversity index?

_____

_____

2. (a) How might you monitor the recovery of a stream ecosystem following an ecological restoration project? _____

_____

_____

(b) What role could indicator species play in the monitoring programme? _____

_____

© 2016 **BIOZONE** International
ISBN: 978-1-927309-32-2
Photocopying Prohibited

150 Investigating Biodiversity

Key Idea: Sampling must be carefully planned in order to obtain meaningful results.

Careful planning is needed before sampling to ensure sound, unbiased data are obtained. If your sampling technique, assumptions, sample size, or sample unit are inadequate, your results will not provide a true representation of the community under study. The Simpson's index of diversity can be used to compare species diversity at two different sites.

Observation

Walking through a conifer plantation, a student observed that there seemed to be only a few different invertebrate species in the forest leaf litter. She wondered if more invertebrate species would be found in a nearby oak woodland.

Hypothesis

The oak woodland has a more varied leaf litter composition than the conifer plantation, so will support a wider variety of invertebrate species.

The **null hypothesis** is that there is no difference between the diversity of invertebrate species in oak woodland and coniferous plantation litter.

Oak woodland   Conifer plantation

Sampling programme

The student designed a sampling programme to test the prediction that there would be a greater diversity of invertebrates in the leaf litter of oak woodlands than in coniferous plantation.

Equipment and procedure

Sites: For each of the two forest types, an area 20 x 8 m was chosen and marked out in 2 x 2 m grids. Eight sampling sites were selected, evenly spaced along the grid as shown (right).

- The two general sampling areas for the study (oak and conifer) were **randomly selected**.
- Eight sites were chosen as the largest number feasible to collect and analyse in the time available.
- The two areas were sampled on sequential days.

Capture of invertebrates: At each site, a 0.4 x 0.4 m quadrat was placed on the forest floor and the leaf litter within the quadrat was collected. Leaf litter invertebrates were captured using a simple gauze lined funnel containing the leaf litter from within the quadrat. A lamp was positioned over each funnel for two hours and the invertebrates in the litter moved down and were trapped in the collecting jar.

- After two hours, each jar was labelled with the site number and returned to the lab for analysis.
- The litter in each funnel was bagged, labeled with the site number and returned to the lab for weighing.
- The number of each invertebrate species at each site was recorded.
- After counting and analysis of the samples, all the collected invertebrates were returned to the sites.

Assumptions

- The areas chosen in each forest were representative in terms of invertebrate abundance.
- Eight sites were sufficient to adequately sample the invertebrate populations in each forest.
- A quadrat size of 0.4 x 0.4 m contained enough leaf litter to adequately sample the invertebrates at each sample site.
- The invertebrates did not prey on each other once captured in the collecting jar.
- All the invertebrates within the quadrat were captured.
- Invertebrates moving away from the light are effectively captured by the funnel apparatus and cannot escape.
- Two hours was long enough for the invertebrates to move down through the litter and fall into the trap.

Note that these last two assumptions could be tested by examining the bagged leaf litter for invertebrates after returning to the lab.

Oak woodland or coniferous plantation

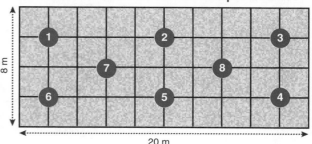

1   Sampling sites numbered 1-8 at evenly spaced intervals on a 2 x 2 m grid within an area of 20 m x 8 m.

Sampling equipment: leaf litter light trap

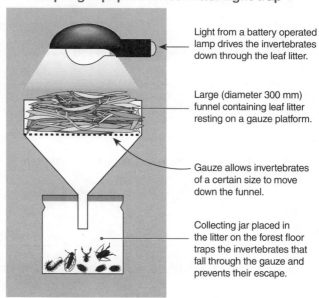

Light from a battery operated lamp drives the invertebrates down through the leaf litter.

Large (diameter 300 mm) funnel containing leaf litter resting on a gauze platform.

Gauze allows invertebrates of a certain size to move down the funnel.

Collecting jar placed in the litter on the forest floor traps the invertebrates that fall through the gauze and prevents their escape.

The importance of sample size

In any field study, two of the most important considerations are the **sample size** (the number of samples you will take) and the size of the **sampling unit** (e.g. quadrat size). An appropriate choice will enable you to collect sufficient, unbiased data to confidently test your hypothesis. The number of samples you take will be determined largely by the resources and time that you have available to collect and analyse your data (your **sampling effort**).

LINK
149 DATA

Results

The results from the student's study are presented in the tables and images below. The invertebrates are not drawn to scale.

Site 1: Oak woodland

Species	Number of animals / n	n/N	(n/N)²
Species 1	35		
Species 2	14		
Species 3	13		
Species 4	12		
Species 5	8		
Species 6	6		
Species 7	6		
Species 8	4		
	$\sum n = 98$		$\sum (n/N)^2 =$

Site 2: Conifer plantation

Species	Number of animals / n	n/N	(n/N)²
Species 1	74		
Species 2	20		
Species 3	3		
Species 4	3		
Species 5	1		
Species 6	0		
Species 7	0		
Species 8	0		
	$\sum n = 101$		$\sum (n/N)^2 =$

Species 1	Species 2	Species 3	Species 4	Species 5	Species 6	Species 7	Species 8
Mite	Ant	Earwig	Woodlice	Centipede	Longhorn beetle	Small beetle	Pseudoscorpion

1. What type of sampling design is used in this study? _____

2. Explain the importance of each of the following in field studies:

   (a) Appropriately sized sampling unit: _____

   _____

   (b) Recognising any assumptions that you are making: _____

   _____

   (c) Appropriate consideration of the environment: _____

   _____

   (d) Return of organisms to the same place after removal: _____

   _____

   (e) Appropriate size of total sampling area within which the sites are located: _____

   _____

3. (a) Complete the two tables above by calculating the values for n/N and (n/N)² for the student's two sampling sites:

   (b) Calculate the Simpson's Index of Diversity for site 1: _____

   (c) Calculate the Simpson's Index of Diversity for site 2: _____

   (d) Compare the diversity of the two sites and suggest any reasons for it: _____

   _____

   _____

   _____

151 Quadrat Sampling

Key Idea: Quadrat sampling involves a series of random placements of a frame of known size over an area of habitat to assess the abundance or diversity of organisms.

Quadrat sampling is a method by which organisms in a certain proportion (sample) of the habitat are counted directly. It is used when the organisms are too numerous to count in total. It can be used to estimate population **abundance** (number), **density, frequency of occurrence**, and **distribution**. Quadrats may be used without a transect when studying a relatively uniform habitat. In this case, the quadrat positions are chosen randomly using a random number table.

The general procedure is to count all the individuals (or estimate their percentage cover) in a number of quadrats of known size and to use this information to work out the abundance or percentage cover value for the whole area.

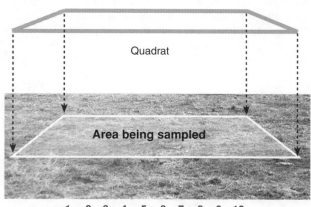

Quadrat

Area being sampled

$$\text{Estimated average density} = \frac{\text{Total number of individuals counted}}{\text{Number of quadrats} \ \text{X} \ \text{area of each quadrat}}$$

Guidelines for quadrat use:

1. The **area of each quadrat** must be known. Quadrats should be the same shape, but not necessarily square.

2. **Enough quadrat samples** must be taken to provide results that are representative of the total population.

3. The **population of each quadrat** must be known. Species must be distinguishable from each other, even if they have to be identified at a later date. It has to be decided beforehand what the count procedure will be and how organisms over the quadrat boundary will be counted.

4. The size of the quadrat should be appropriate to the organisms and habitat, e.g. a large size quadrat for trees.

5. The quadrats must be **representative of the whole area.** This is usually achieved by **random sampling** (right).

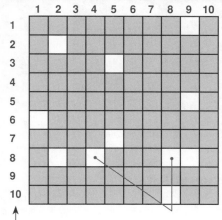

The area to be sampled is divided up into a grid pattern with indexed coordinates

Quadrats are applied to the predetermined grid on a random basis. This can be achieved by using a random number table.

Sampling a centipede population

A researcher by the name of Lloyd (1967) sampled centipedes in Wytham Woods, near Oxford in England. A total of 37 hexagon–shaped quadrats were used, each with a diameter of 30 cm (see diagram on right). These were arranged in a pattern so that they were all touching each other. Use the data in the diagram to answer the following questions.

1. Determine the average number of centipedes captured per quadrat:

   _____

2. Calculate the estimated average density of centipedes per square metre (remember that each quadrat is 0.08 square metres in area):

   _____

3. Looking at the data for individual quadrats, describe in general terms the distribution of the centipedes in the sample area:

   _____

   _____

4. Describe one factor that might account for the distribution pattern:

   _____

   _____

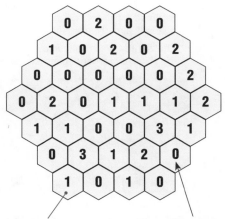

Each quadrat was a hexagon with a diameter of 30 cm and an area of 0.08 square meters.

The number in each hexagon indicates how many centipedes were caught in that quadrat.

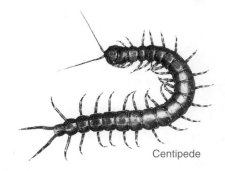

Centipede

LINK LINK WEB
153 152 151 DATA

152 Quadrat-Based Estimates

Key Idea: The size and number of quadrats used to sample a community must be sufficient to be representative of that community without taking an excessively long time to use.
The simplest description of a community is a list of the species present. This does not provide information about the relative abundance of the species, although this can be estimated using abundance scales (e.g. ACFOR). Quadrats can provide quantitative information about a community. The size of the quadrat and the number of samples taken must represent the community as fairly as possible.

What size quadrat?

Quadrats are usually square, and cover 0.25 m^2 (0.5 m x 0.5 m) or 1 m^2, but they can be of any size or shape, even a single point. The quadrats used to sample plant communities are often 0.25 m^2. This size is ideal for low-growing vegetation, but quadrat size needs to be adjusted to habitat type. The quadrat must be large enough to be representative of the community, but not so large as to take a very long time to use.

A quadrat covering an area of 0.25 m^2 is suitable for most low growing plant communities, such as this alpine meadow, fields, and grasslands.

Larger quadrats (e.g.1m^2) are needed for communities with shrubs and trees. Quadrats as large as 4 m x 4 m may be needed in woodlands.

Small quadrats (0.01 m^2 or 100 mm x 100 mm) are appropriate for lichens and mosses on rock faces and tree trunks.

How many quadrats?

As well as deciding on a suitable quadrat size, the other consideration is how many quadrats to take (the sample size). In species-poor or very homogeneous habitats, a small number of quadrats will be sufficient. In species-rich or heterogeneous habitats, more quadrats will be needed to ensure that all species are represented adequately.

Determining the number of quadrats needed

- Plot the cumulative number of species recorded (on the y axis) against the number of quadrats already taken (on the x axis).

- The point at which the curve levels off indicates the suitable number of quadrats required.

Fewer quadrats are needed in species-poor or very uniform habitats, such as this bluebell woodland.

Describing vegetation

Density (number of individuals per unit area) is a useful measure of abundance for animal populations, but can be problematic in plant communities where it can be difficult to determine where one plant ends and another begins. For this reason, plant abundance is often assessed using **percentage cover**. Here, the percentage of each quadrat covered by each species is recorded, either as a numerical value or using an abundance scale such as the ACFOR scale.

The ACFOR Abundance Scale

A = Abundant (30% +)

C = Common (20-29%)

F = Frequent (10-19%)

O = Occasional (5-9%)

R = Rare (1-4%)

The ACFOR scale could be used to assess the abundance of species in this wildflower meadow. Abundance scales are subjective, but it is not difficult to determine which abundance category each species falls into.

1. Describe one difference between the methods used to assess species abundance in plant and in animal communities:

   _____

2. What is the main consideration when determining appropriate quadrat size? _____

3. What is the main consideration when determining number of quadrats? _____

4. Explain two main disadvantages of using the ACFOR abundance scale to record information about a plant community:

   (a) _____

   (b) _____

© 2016 **BIOZONE** International
ISBN: 978-1-927309-32-2
Photocopying Prohibited

153 Sampling a Rocky Shore Community

Key Idea: The estimates of a population gained from using quadrat sampling may vary depending on where the quadrats are placed. Larger samples can account for variation. The diagram (next page) represents an area of seashore with its resident organisms. The distribution of coralline algae and four animal species are shown. This exercise is designed to prepare you for planning and carrying out a similar procedure to practically investigate a natural community.

1. **Decide on the sampling method**
   For the purpose of this exercise, it has been decided that the populations to be investigated are too large to be counted directly and a quadrat sampling method is to be used to estimate the average density of the four animal species as well as that of the algae.

2. **Mark out a grid pattern**
   Use a ruler to mark out 3 cm intervals along each side of the sampling area (area of quadrat = 0.03 x 0.03 m). **Draw lines** between these marks to create a 6 x 6 grid pattern (total area = 0.18 x 0.18 m). This will provide a total of 36 quadrats that can be investigated.

3. **Number the axes of the grid**
   Only a small proportion of the possible quadrat positions will be sampled. It is necessary to select the quadrats in a random manner. It is not sufficient to simply guess or choose your own on a 'gut feeling'. The best way to choose the quadrats randomly is to create a numbering system for the grid pattern and then select the quadrats from a random number table. Starting at the *top left hand corner*, **number the columns** and **rows** from 1 to 6 on each axis.

4. **Choose quadrats randomly**
   To select the required number of quadrats randomly, use random numbers from a random number table. The random numbers are used as an index to the grid coordinates. Choose 6 quadrats from the total of 36 using table of random numbers provided for you at the bottom of the next page. Make a note of which column of random numbers you choose. Each member of your group should choose a different set of random numbers (i.e. different column: A–D) so that you can compare the effectiveness of the sampling method.

   Column of random numbers chosen: _____

   NOTE: Highlight the boundary of each selected quadrat with coloured pen/highlighter.

5. **Decide on the counting criteria**
   Before the counting of the individuals for each species is carried out, the criteria for counting need to be established.

There may be some problems here. You must decide before sampling begins as to what to do about individuals that are only partly inside the quadrat. Possible answers include:

(a) Only counting individuals that are completely inside the quadrat.
(b) Only counting individuals with a clearly defined part of their body inside the quadrat (such as the head).
(c) Allowing for 'half individuals' (e.g. 3.5 barnacles).
(d) Counting an individual that is inside the quadrat by half or more as one complete individual.

Discuss the merits and problems of the suggestions above with other members of the class (or group). You may even have counting criteria of your own. Think about other factors that could cause problems with your counting.

6. **Carry out the sampling**
   Carefully examine each selected quadrat and **count the number of individuals** of each species present. Record your data in the spaces provided on the next page.

7. **Calculate the population density**
   Use the combined data TOTALS for the sampled quadrats to estimate the average density for each species by using the formula:

$$\text{Density} = \frac{\text{Total number in all quadrats sampled}}{\text{Number of quadrats sampled} \times \text{area of a quadrat}}$$

Remember that a total of 6 quadrats are sampled and each has an area of 0.0009 m². The density should be expressed as the number of individuals *per square metre* (no. m^{-2}).

Plicate barnacle: [ ] Snakeskin chiton: [ ]

Oyster borer: [ ] Coralline algae: [ ]

Limpet: [ ]

8. (a) In this example the animals are not moving. Describe the problems associated with sampling moving organisms. Explain how you would cope with sampling these same animals if they were really alive and very active:

   _____

   _____

   _____

(b) Carry out a direct count of all 4 animal species and the algae for the whole sample area (all 36 quadrats). Apply the data from your direct count to the equation given in (7) above to calculate the actual population density (remember that the number of quadrats in this case = 36):

   Barnacle: [ ]   Oyster borer: [ ]   Chiton: [ ]   Limpet: [ ]   Algae: [ ]

   Compare your estimated population density to the actual population density for each species:

   _____

   _____

   _____

LINK
151 PRAC

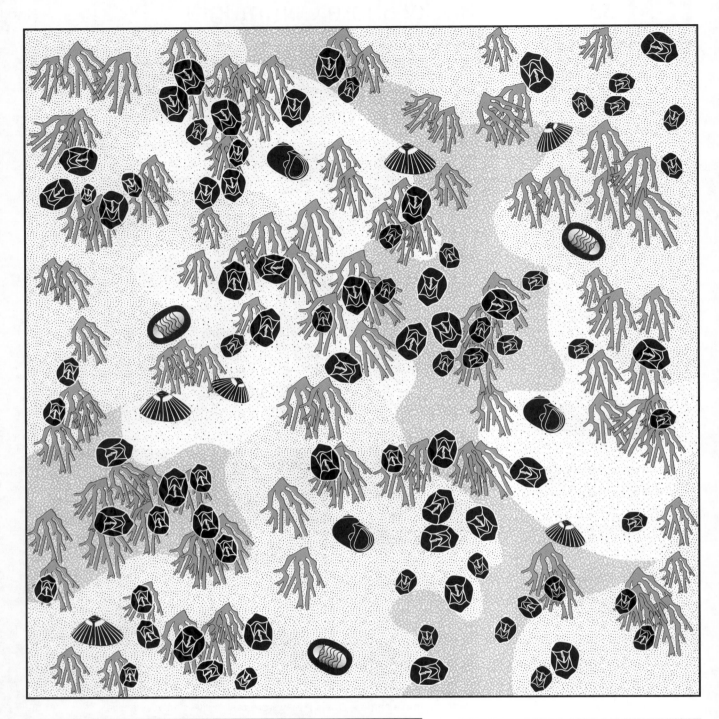

Coordinates for each quadrat	Plicate barnacle	Oyster borer	Snakeskin chiton	Limpet	Coralline algae
1:					
2:					
3:					
4:					
5:					
6:					
TOTAL					

Table of random numbers

A	B	C	D
2 2	3 1	6 2	2 2
3 2	1 5	6 3	4 3
3 1	5 6	3 6	6 4
4 6	3 6	1 3	4 5
4 3	4 2	4 5	3 5
5 6	1 4	3 1	1 4

The table above has been adapted from a table of random numbers from a statistics book. Use this table to select quadrats randomly from the grid above. Choose one of the columns (A to D) and use the numbers in that column as an index to the grid. The first digit refers to the row number and the second digit refers to the column number. To locate each of the 6 quadrats, find where the row and column intersect, as shown below:

Example: [5 2] refers to the 5th row and the 2nd column

© 2016 **BIOZONE** International
ISBN: 978-1-927309-32-2
Photocopying Prohibited

154 Transect Sampling

Key Idea: Transect sampling is useful for providing information on species distribution along an environmental gradient.

A **transect** is a line placed across a community of organisms. Transects provide information on the distribution of species in the community. They are particularly valuable when the transect records community composition along an **environmental gradient** (e.g. up a mountain or across a seashore). The usual practice for small transects is to stretch a string between two markers. The string is marked off in measured distance intervals and the species at each marked point are noted. The sampling points along the transect may also be used for the siting of quadrats, so that changes in density and community composition can be recorded. Belt transects are essentially a form of continuous quadrat sampling. They provide more information on community composition but can be difficult to carry out. Some transects provide information on the vertical, as well as horizontal, distribution of species (e.g. tree canopies in a forest).

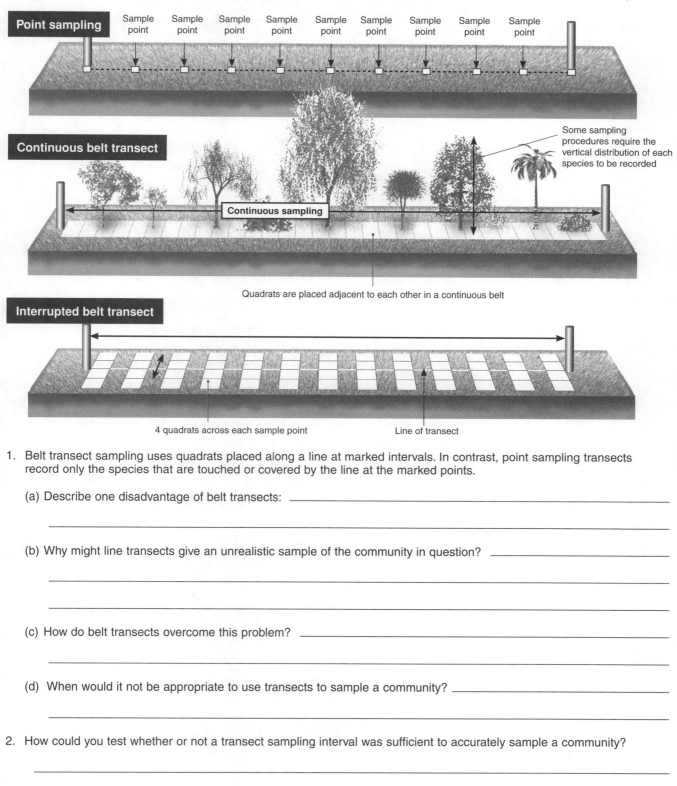

Point sampling — Sample point (×9)

Continuous belt transect — Continuous sampling

Some sampling procedures require the vertical distribution of each species to be recorded

Quadrats are placed adjacent to each other in a continuous belt

Interrupted belt transect

4 quadrats across each sample point   Line of transect

1. Belt transect sampling uses quadrats placed along a line at marked intervals. In contrast, point sampling transects record only the species that are touched or covered by the line at the marked points.

   (a) Describe one disadvantage of belt transects: _____

   _____

   (b) Why might line transects give an unrealistic sample of the community in question? _____

   _____

   _____

   (c) How do belt transects overcome this problem? _____

   _____

   (d) When would it not be appropriate to use transects to sample a community? _____

   _____

2. How could you test whether or not a transect sampling interval was sufficient to accurately sample a community?

   _____

   _____

   _____

A **kite graph** is a good way to show the distribution of organisms sampled using a belt transect. Data may be expressed as abundance or percentage cover along an environmental gradient. Several species can be shown together on the same plot so that the distributions can be easily compared.

3. The data on the right were collected from a rocky shore field trip. Four common species of barnacle were sampled in a continuous belt transect from the low water mark, to a height of 10 m above that level. The number of each of the four species in a 1 m² quadrat was recorded.

Plot a **kite graph** of the data for all four species on the grid below. Be sure to choose a scale that takes account of the maximum number found at any one point and allows you to include all the species on the one plot. Include the scale on the diagram so that the number at each point on the kite can be calculated.

An example of a kite graph

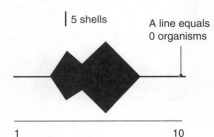

5 shells

A line equals 0 organisms

1   10
Distance above water line (m)

Field data notebook

Numbers of barnacles (4 common species) showing distribution on a rocky shore

Height above low water (m)	Barnacle species			
	Plicate barnacle	Columnar barnacle	Brown barnacle	Sheet barnacle
0	0	0	0	65
1	10	0	0	12
2	32	0	0	0
3	55	0	0	0
4	100	18	0	0
5	50	124	0	0
6	30	69	2	0
7	0	40	11	0
8	0	0	47	0
9	0	0	59	0
10	0	0	65	0

© 2016 **BIOZONE** International
ISBN: 978-1-927309-32-2
Photocopying Prohibited

155 Qualitative Practical Work: Seaweed Zonation

Key Idea: Qualitative and quantitative data can be used to explain patterns of zonation in seashore communities.

Three species of brown algae (genus *Fucus*), together with the brown alga *Ascophyllum nodosum*, form the dominant seaweeds on rocky shores in Britain, where they form distinct zones along the shore. Zonation is a characteristic feature of many seashore communities where species' distribution is governed by tolerances to particular physical conditions (e.g. time of exposure to air). When collecting data on the distribution and abundance of *Fucus* species, it is useful to also make qualitative observations about the size, vigour, and degree of desiccation of specimens at different points on the shore. These observations provide biological information which can help to explain the observed patterns.

Spiral wrack (*Fucus spiralis*)

Andreas Trepte

Fucus is a genus of marine brown algae, commonly called wracks, which are found in the midlittoral zone of rocky seashores (i.e. the zone between the low and high levels). A group of students made a study of a rocky shore dominated by three species of *Fucus*: spiral wrack, bladder wrack, and serrated wrack. Their aim was to investigate the distribution of three *Fucus* species in the midlittoral zone and relate this to the size and vigour (V) of the seaweeds and the degree of desiccation (D) evident.

Bladder wrack (*F. vesiculosus*)

Thalli

Stemonitis

Serrated wrack (*F. serratus*)

Stemonitis

Procedure

Three 50 cm³ quadrats were positioned from the LTL to the HTL at two sites on the shore as shown in the diagram (far right). An estimate of **percentage cover** (C) of each species of *Fucus* was made for each sample. Information on vigour and degree of desiccation was collected at the same time.

Qualitative data were collected as simple scores:
- + = vigorous with large thalli
  no evidence of desiccation
- 0 = less vigorous with smaller thalli
  some evidence of desiccation
- − = small, poorly grown thalli
  obvious signs of desiccation

(Diagram, right:) Site 1 | Site 2 — Covered at high tide only — HTL — 50 cm³ — Upper midlittoral — Equally covered and exposed — MTL — Lower midlittoral — Exposed at low tide only — LTL — Lower littoral

1. (a) Describe the quantitative component of this study:

_____

_____

   (b) Describe the qualitative component of this study:

_____

	SITE 1									SITE 2								
	HTL			MTL			LTL			HTL			MTL			LTL		
Species	C	D	V	C	D	V	C	D	V	C	D	V	C	D	V	C	D	V
Spiral wrack	50	0	+	0	na	na	0	na	na	30	+	0	0	na	na	0	na	na
Bladder wrack	15	−	−	80	+	+	20	+	0	50	0	−	70	+	+	0	na	na
Serrated wrack	0	na	na	0	na	na	75	+	+	0	na	na	10	−	−	80	+	+

2. The results of the quadrat survey are tabulated above. On a separate sheet, plot a column graph of the percentage coverage of each species at each position on the shore and at sites 1 and 2. Staple it to this page.

3. Relate the distribution pattern to the changes in degree of desiccation and in size and vigour of the seaweed thalli:

_____

_____

_____

_____

4. Suggest why the position of the quadrats was staggered for the two sites and describe a disadvantage of this design:

_____

_____

LINK
151 KNOW

156 Field Study of a Rocky Shore

Key Idea: Field studies collect physical and biological data that measure aspects of community structure or function. Many biological investigations require the collection of data from natural communities. Biotic data may include the density or distribution of organisms at a site. Recording physical (abiotic) data of the site allows the site to be compared with others. The investigation below looks at the populations of animals found on an exposed and a sheltered rocky shore.

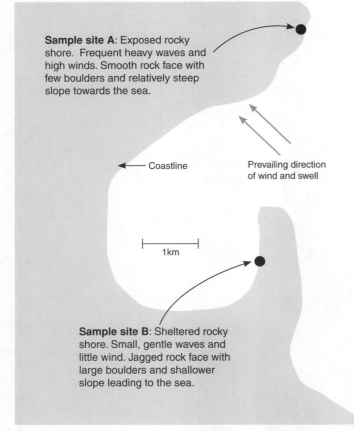

Sample site A: Exposed rocky shore. Frequent heavy waves and high winds. Smooth rock face with few boulders and relatively steep slope towards the sea.

Coastline

Prevailing direction of wind and swell

1km

Sample site B: Sheltered rocky shore. Small, gentle waves and little wind. Jagged rock face with large boulders and shallower slope leading to the sea.

The aim

To investigate the differences in the abundance of intertidal animals on an exposed rocky shore and a sheltered rocky shore.

Background

The composition of rocky shore communities is strongly influenced by the shore's physical environment. Animals that cling to rocks must keep their hold on the substrate while being subjected to intense wave action and currents. However, the constant wave action brings high levels of nutrients and oxygen. Communities on sheltered rocky shores, although encountering less physical stress, may face lower nutrient and oxygen levels.

To investigate differences in the abundance of intertidal animals, students laid out 1 m^2 quadrats at regular intervals along one tidal zone at two separate but nearby sites: a rocky shore exposed to wind and heavy wave action and a rocky shore with very little heavy wave action. The animals were counted and their numbers in each quadrat recorded.

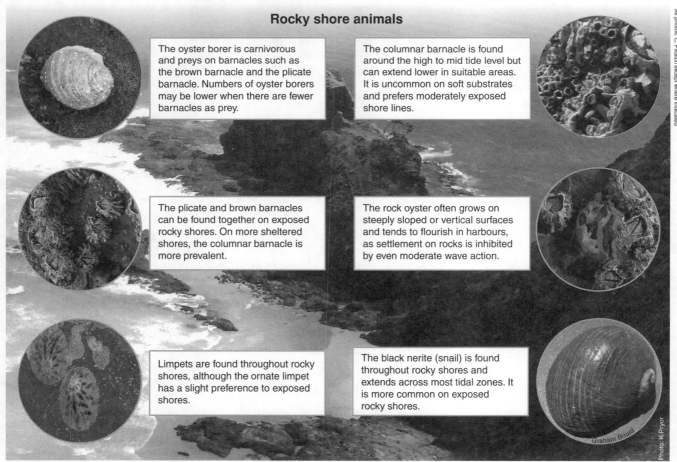

Rocky shore animals

The oyster borer is carnivorous and preys on barnacles such as the brown barnacle and the plicate barnacle. Numbers of oyster borers may be lower when there are fewer barnacles as prey.

The columnar barnacle is found around the high to mid tide level but can extend lower in suitable areas. It is uncommon on soft substrates and prefers moderately exposed shore lines.

The plicate and brown barnacles can be found together on exposed rocky shores. On more sheltered shores, the columnar barnacle is more prevalent.

The rock oyster often grows on steeply sloped or vertical surfaces and tends to flourish in harbours, as settlement on rocks is inhibited by even moderate wave action.

Limpets are found throughout rocky shores, although the ornate limpet has a slight preference to exposed shores.

The black nerite (snail) is found throughout rocky shores and extends across most tidal zones. It is more common on exposed rocky shores.

Graham Bould

Photo: K.Pryor

LINK LINK LINK
DATA 104 105 151

© 2016 **BIOZONE** International
ISBN: 978-1-927309-32-2
Photocopying Prohibited

1. Underline an appropriate hypothesis for this field study from the four possible hypotheses below:

   (a) Rocky shore communities differ because of differences in wave action.

   (b) Rocky shore communities differ because of the topography of the coastline.

   (c) The physical conditions of exposed rocky shores and sheltered rocky shores are very different and so the intertidal communities will also be different.

   (d) Rocky shore communities differ because of differences in water temperature.

2. During the field study, students counted the number of animals in each quadrat and recorded them in a note book. Complete the table with the total number of each species at each site, the mean number of animals per quadrat, and the median and mode for each set of samples per species. Remember, in this case, there can be no 'part animals' so you will need to round your values to the nearest whole number:

Field data notebook
Count per quadrat. Quadrats 1 m²

Site A	1	2	3	4	5	6	7	8
Brown barnacle	39	38	37	21	40	56	36	41
Oyster borer	6	7	4	3	7	8	9	2
Columnar barnacle	6	8	14	10	9	12	8	11
Plicate barnacle	50	52	46	45	56	15	68	54
Ornate limpet	9	7	8	10	6	7	6	10
Radiate limpet	5	6	4	8	6	7	5	6
Black nerite	7	7	6	8	4	6	8	9
Site B								
Brown barnacle	7	6	7	5	8	5	7	7
Oyster borer	2	3	1	3	2	2	1	1
Columnar barnacle	56	57	58	55	60	47	58	36
Plicate barnacle	11	11	13	10	14	9	9	8
Rock oyster	7	8	8	6	2	4	8	6
Ornate limpet	7	8	5	6	5	7	9	3
Radiate limpet	13	14	11	10	14	12	9	13
Black nerite	6	5	3	1	4	5	2	3

		Brown barnacle	Oyster borer	Columnar barnacle	Plicate barnacle	Rock oyster	Ornate limpet	Radiate limpet	Black nerite
Site A	Total number of animals								
	Mean number of animals per m²								
	Median value								
	Modal value								
Site B	Total number of animals								
	Mean number of animals per m²								
	Median value								
	Modal value								

3. Use the grid below to draw a column graph of the mean number of species per 1 m² at each sample site. Remember to include a title, correctly labelled axes, and a key.

4. (a) Compare the mean, median, and modal values obtained for the samples at each site: _____

_____

(b) What does this tell you about the distribution of the data: _____

_____

5. (a) Which species was entirely absent from site A? _____

(b) Suggest why this might be the case: _____

_____

6. (a) Explain why more brown barnacles and plicate barnacles were found at site A: _____

_____

_____

(b) Explain why more oyster borers were found at site A: _____

_____

_____

7. (a) Comment on the numbers of limpets at each site: _____

_____

(b) What does this suggest to you about their biology: _____

_____

© 2016 BIOZONE International
ISBN: 978-1-927309-32-2
Photocopying Prohibited

157 Mark and Recapture Sampling

Key Idea: Mark and recapture sampling allows the population size of highly mobile organisms to be estimated.

The mark and recapture method of estimating population size is used in the study of animal populations in which the individuals are highly mobile. It is of no value where animals do not move or move very little. The number of animals caught in each sample must be large enough to be valid. The technique is outlined in the diagram below.

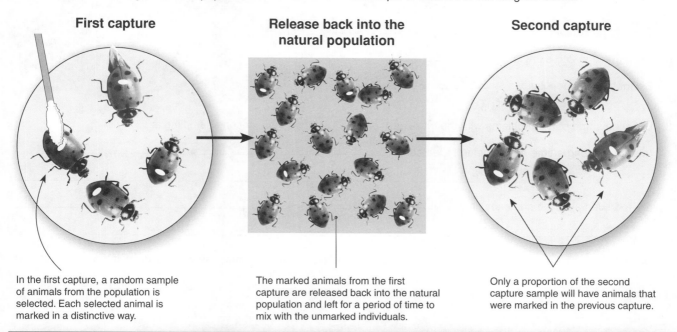

First capture

Release back into the natural population

Second capture

In the first capture, a random sample of animals from the population is selected. Each selected animal is marked in a distinctive way.

The marked animals from the first capture are released back into the natural population and left for a period of time to mix with the unmarked individuals.

Only a proportion of the second capture sample will have animals that were marked in the previous capture.

The Lincoln Index

Total population = (No. of animals in 1st sample (all marked) X Total no. of animals in 2nd sample) / (Number of marked animals in the second sample (recaptured))

The mark and recapture technique comprises a number of simple steps:

1. The population is sampled by capturing as many of the individuals as possible and practical.

2. Each animal is marked in a way to distinguish it from unmarked animals (unique mark for each individual not required).

3. Return the animals to their habitat and leave them for a long enough period for complete mixing with the rest of the population to take place

4. Take another sample of the population (this does not need to be the same sample size as the first sample, but it does have to be large enough to be valid).

5. Determine the numbers of marked to unmarked animals in this second sample. Use the equation above to estimate the size of the overall population.

1. For this exercise you will need several boxes of matches and a pen. Work in a group of 2-3 students to 'sample' the population of matches in the full box by using the mark and recapture method. Each match will represent one animal.

(a) Take out 10 matches from the box and mark them on 4 sides with a pen so that you will be able to recognise them from the other unmarked matches later.
(b) Return the marked matches to the box and shake the box to mix the matches.
(c) Take a sample of 20 matches from the same box and record the number of marked matches and unmarked matches.
(d) Determine the total population size by using the equation above.
(e) Repeat the sampling 4 more times (steps b–d above) and record your results:

	Sample 1	Sample 2	Sample 3	Sample 4	Sample 5
Estimated population					

(f) Count the actual number of matches in the matchbox : _____

(g) Compare the actual number to your estimates and state by how much it differs: _____

© 2016 **BIOZONE** International
ISBN: 978-1-927309-32-2
Photocopying Prohibited

LINK 147 WEB 157 **DATA**

2. In 1919 a researcher by the name of Dahl wanted to estimate the number of trout in a Norwegian lake. The trout were subject to fishing so it was important to know how big the population was in order to manage the fish stock. He captured and marked 109 trout in his first sample. A few days later, he caught 177 trout in his second sample, of which 57 were marked. Use the **Lincoln index** (on the previous page) to estimate the total population size:

Size of 1st sample: _____

Size of 2nd sample: _____

No. marked in 2nd sample: _____

Estimated total population: _____

3. Describe some of the problems with the mark and recapture method if the second sampling is:

(a) Left too long a time before being repeated: _____

_____

(b) Too soon after the first sampling: _____

4. Describe two important assumptions in this method of sampling that would cause the method to fail if they were not true:

(a) _____

_____

_____

(b) _____

_____

_____

5. Some types of animal would be unsuitable for this method of population estimation (i.e. would not work).

(a) Name an animal for which this method of sampling would not be effective: _____

(b) Explain your answer above: _____

_____

_____

6. Describe three methods for marking animals for mark and recapture sampling. Take into account the possibility of animals shedding their skin, or being difficult to get close to again:

(a) _____

(b) _____

(c) _____

7. Scientists in the UK and Canada have, at various times since the 1950s, been involved in computerised tagging programs for Northern cod (a species once abundant in Northern Hemisphere waters but now severely depleted). Describe the type of information that could be obtained through such tagging programs:

_____

_____

_____

_____

_____

_____

158 Chi-squared Test for Independence

Key Idea: The chi-squared test is used to compare sets of categorical data and evaluate if differences between them are statistically significant or due to chance.

The chi-squared test (χ^2) is used to determine differences between categorical data sets when working with frequencies (counts). For the test to be valid, the data recorded for each categorical variable (e.g. species) must be raw counts (not measurements or derived data). The chi-squared test is used for two types of comparison: test for goodness of fit and tests of independence (i.e. association or not). A test for goodness of fit is used to compare an experimental result with an expected theoretical outcome. You will perform this test later to compare the outcome of genetic crosses to an expected theoretical ratio. A test for independence evaluates whether two variables are associated. The chi-squared test is not valid when sample sizes are small (<20). Like all statistical tests, it aims to test the null hypothesis; the hypothesis of no difference (or no association) between groups of data. The worked example below uses the chi-squared test for independence in a study of habitat preference in mudfish.

Using the Chi-squared test for independence

The black mudfish is a small fish species native to New Zealand and found in wetlands and swampy streams. Researchers were interested in finding environmental indicators of favourable mudfish habitat. They sampled 80 wetland sites for the presence or absence of mudfish and recorded if there was emergent vegetation present or absent. Emergent vegetation, defined as vegetation rooted in water but emerging above the water surface, is an indicator of a relatively undisturbed environment. A chi-squared for independence was used to test if mudfish were found more often at sites with emergent vegetation than by chance alone. The null hypothesis was that there is no association (distribution is independent of vegetation). The worked example is below. The table of observed values records the number of sites with or without mudfish and with or without emergent vegetation.

Photo and data: Rhys Barrier, University of Waikato

Black mudfish (*Neochanna diversus*) can air-breathe and so can survive seasonal drying of their wetland habitat.

Step 1: Enter the observed values (O) in a contingency table
A χ^2 test for independence requires that the data (counts or frequencies) are entered in a **contingency table** (a matrix format to analyse and record the relationship between two or more categorical variables). Marginal totals are calculated for each row and column and a grand total is recorded in the bottom right hand corner (right).

	Mudfish absent (0)	Mudfish present (1)	Total
Emergent vegetation absent (0)	15	0	15
Emergent vegetation present (1)	26	39	65
Total	41	39	80

Step 2: Calculate the expected values (E)
Calculating the expected values for a contingency table is simple. For each category, divide the row total by the grand total and multiply by the column total. You can enter these in a separate table or as separate columns next to the observed values (right).

	Mudfish absent (0)	Mudfish present (1)	Total
Emergent vegetation absent (0)	7.69	7.31	15
Emergent vegetation present (1)	33.31	31.69	65
Total	41	39	80

Step 3: Calculate the value of chi-squared (χ^2) of $(O - E)^2 \div (E)$
The difference between the observed (O) and expected (E) values is calculated as a measure of the deviation from a predicted result. Since some deviations are negative, they are all squared to give positive values. This step is best done as a tabulation to obtain a value for $(O - E)^2 \div (E)$ for each category. The sum of all these values is the value of chi squared (blue table right).

$$\chi^2 = \sum \frac{(O - E)^2}{E}$$

Where: O = the observed result
E = the expected result
Σ = sum of

Category	O	E	O–E	$(O–E)^2$	$\dfrac{(O–E)^2}{E}$
Mudfish 0/EmVeg 0	15	7.69	7.31	53.44	6.95
Mudfish 1/EmVeg 0	0	7.31	-7.31	53.44	7.31
Mudfish 0/EmVeg 1	26	33.31	-7.31	53.44	1.60
Mudfish 1/EmVeg 1	39	31.69	7.31	53.44	1.69

Total = 80 $\chi^2 \longrightarrow \Sigma = 17.55$

Step 4: Calculate the degrees of freedom (df)
The degrees of freedom for a contingency table is given by the formula: (rows-1) x (columns-1). For this example, degrees of freedom (df) is therefore (2-1) x (2-1) = 1.

Critical values of χ^2 at different levels of probability. By convention, the critical probability for rejecting the null hypothesis (H_0) is 5%. If the test statistic is greater than the tabulated value for P = 0.05 we reject H_0 in favour of the alternative hypothesis.

Step 5: Using the chi squared table
On the χ^2 table (relevant part reproduced in the table right) with 1 degree of freedom, the calculated value for χ^2 of 17.55 corresponds to a probability of less than 0.001 (see arrow). *This means that by chance alone a χ^2 value of 17.55 could be expected less than 0.1% of the time.* This probability is much lower than the 0.05 value which is generally regarded as significant. The null hypothesis can be rejected and we have reason to believe that black mudfish are associated with sites with emergent vegetation more than expected by chance alone.

	Level of Probability (P)				
df	0.05	0.025	0.01	0.005	0.001
1	3.84	5.02	6.63	7.88	(10.83)
2	5.99	7.38	9.21	10.60	13.82
3	7.81	9.35	11.34	12.84	16.27

159 Using the Chi-Squared Test for Independence

Key Idea: Chi-squared can be used to determine if an association between two species is statistically significant.

In ecological studies, it is often found that two or more species are found in association. This is usually because of similar environmental requirements or because one species depends on the other. The following hypothetical example outlines a study in which the presence or absence of two plant species was recorded in a marked area. The two species are sometimes, but not always, found together. The chi squared test is used to test the significance of the association.

Using chi square to test species associations in a successional marsh-meadow community

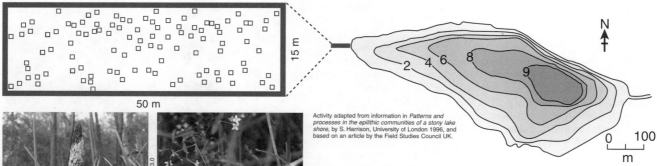

50 m   15 m

N

0   100 m

Activity adapted from information in *Patterns and processes in the epilithic communities of a stony lake shore*, by S. Harrison, University of London 1996, and based on an article by the Field Studies Council UK.

Lesser pond sedge (*Carex acutiformis*) is a swamp plant

Marsh bedstraw (*Galium palustre*) grows in ditches and wet meadows

Lake Crosemere (above) is a one of a series of kettle hole lakes in England, formed by glacial retreat at the end of the last glacial period. In a natural process of succession, the lake is gradually infilling from its western edge, and wet meadow and marsh species are replacing the species of the open water. Students investigated the association between two plants previously recorded in studies of the area: the lesser pond sedge (LPS) and marsh bedstraw (MBS). They recorded species presence or absence in 100 quadrats (0.5 m²) placed in an area 15 X 50 m using coordinates generated using a random number function on a spreadsheet. The results are summarised in table 1 below. Follow the steps to complete the analysis.

1. State the null hypothesis (H₀) for this investigation:

   _____

   _____

2. In words, summarise the observed results in table 1:

   _____

   _____

   _____

   _____

3. Calculate the expected values for presence/absence of LPS and MBS. Enter the figures in table 2:

4. Complete the table to calculate the χ² value: _____

5. Calculate the degrees of freedom: _____

6. Using the χ², state the *P* value corresponding to your calculated χ² value (use the χ² table opposite):

   _____

7. State whether or not you reject your null hypothesis:

   reject H₀ / do not reject H₀   (*circle one*)

8. What could you conclude about this plant community:

   _____

   _____

   _____

   _____

	LPS present (1)	LPS absent (0)	Total
MBS present (1)	11	3	14
MBS absent (0)	31	55	86
Total	42	58	100

Table 1: Observed results for presence/absence of lesser pond-sedge (LPS) and marsh bedstraw (MBS).

	LPS present (1)	LPS absent (0)	Total
MBS present (1)			
MBS absent (0)			
Total			

Table 2: Expected results for presence/absence of lesser pond-sedge (LPS) and marsh bedstraw (MBS).

Category	O	E	O–E	(O–E)²	$\frac{(O–E)^2}{E}$
LPS 1/MBS 1					
LPS 0/MBS 1					
LPS 1/MBS 0					
LPS 0/MBS 0					
Total = 100					Σ =

160 Correlation or Causation

Key Idea: A correlation is a mutual relationship or association between two or more variables. A correlation between two variables does not imply that one causes change in the other. Researchers often want to know if two variables have any **correlation** (relationship) to each other. This can be achieved by plotting the data as a scatter graph and drawing a line of best fit through the data, or by testing for correlation using a statistical test. The strength of a correlation is indicated by the correlation coefficient (r), which varies between 1 and -1. A value of 1 indicates a perfect (1:1) relationship between the variables. A value of -1 indicates a 1:1 negative relationship and 0 indicates no relationship between the variables.

Correlation does not imply causation

You may come across the phrase "correlation does not necessarily imply causation". This means that even when there is a strong correlation between variables (they vary together in a predictable way), you cannot assume that change in one variable caused change in the other.

Example: When data from the organic food association and the office of special education programmes is plotted (below), there is a strong correlation between the increase in organic food and rates of diagnosed autism. However it is unlikely that eating organic food causes autism, so we can not assume a causative effect here.

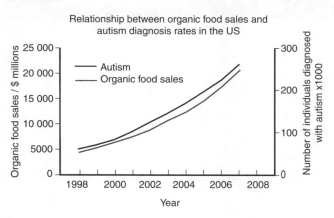

Drawing the line of best fit

Some simple guidelines need to be followed when drawing a line of best fit on your scatter plot.

► Your line should follow the trend of the data points.

► Roughly half of your data points should be above the line of best fit, and half below.

► The line of best fit does not necessarily pass through any particular point.

► The line of best fit should pivot around the point which represents the mean of the x and the mean of the y variables.

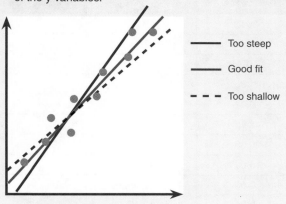

1. What does the phrase "correlation does not imply causation" mean? _____

_____

_____

2. A student measured the hand span and foot length measurements of 21 adults and plotted the data as a scatter graph (right).

   (a) Draw a line of best fit through the data:

   (b) Describe the results: _____

   _____

   _____

   _____

   _____

   (c) Using your line of best fit as a guide, comment on the correlation between handspan and foot length:

   _____

   _____

   _____

   _____

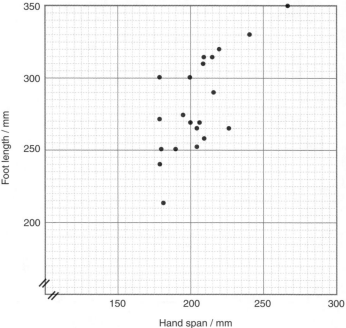

DATA

161 Pearson's Linear Correlation

Key Idea: Pearson's linear correlation measures the correlation of two normally distributed variables.

Pearson's linear correlation or Pearson's product-moment correlation coefficient is a measure of the linear correlation between two variables, each of which has a normal distribution. It ranges from +1 to -1 inclusive. +1 represents the strongest positive correlation, while -1 represents the strongest negative correlation. 0 indicates no correlation.

Pearson's product-moment correlation can be calculated using the formula:

$$r = \frac{\Sigma xy - n\bar{x}\bar{y}}{ns_x s_y}$$

s_x = standard deviation of x
s_y = standard deviation of y

To find s_x and s_y use the population standard deviation:

$$s = \sqrt{\frac{\Sigma(x - \bar{x})^2}{n}}$$

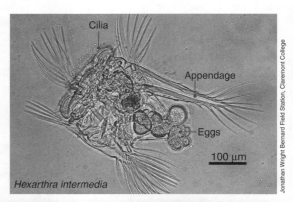

Cilia

Appendage

Eggs

100 μm

Hexarthra intermedia

Jonathan Wright Bernard Field Station, Claremont College

Hexarthra intermedia (right) is a species of rotifer. Rotifers are small ciliated animals found in fresh water ponds. Most feed on small algae. A study was carried out in order to understand how changes in their abundance might be related to seasonal changes in environmental factors. The data below records abundance per litre of pond water against pond temperature at the time that sample was taken. Note that the *Hexarthra* counts are not in whole numbers because number per litre was calculated from a larger, filtered sample volume.

Hexarthra no. (x) / L	Temperature (y) / °C	$(x - \bar{x})^2$	$(y - \bar{y})^2$	xy
36.21	19.75			
33.76	17.53			
10.83	15.05			
1.88	14.40			
0.33	11.73			
2.40	11.05			
0.35	9.23			
0.08	8.75			
0.00	12.35			
0.04	13.13			
0.00	14.15			
0.21	14.63			
0.29	15.98			
5.72	19.63			
4.39	18.00			
7.42	19.80			
72.87	23.33			
443.38	23.30			
34.38	22.30			
147.58	25.88			
947.64	24.58			
573.47	22.90			
444.63	20.95			
338.25	21.10			
34.33	18.90			
$\bar{x}=$	$\bar{y}=$	$\Sigma(x - \bar{x})^2 =$	$\Sigma(y - \bar{y})^2 =$	$\Sigma xy =$
Standard deviation x =		Standard deviation y =	$r =$	

1. Complete the table above to calculate *r*.

2. What does *r* tell you about the relationship between *Hexarthra* numbers and temperature? _____

_____

_____

KNOW

162 Spearman Rank Correlation

Key Idea: The Spearman rank correlation is a test used to determine if there is a statistical dependence (correlation) between two variables.

The Spearman rank correlation is appropriate for data that have a non-normal distribution (or where the distribution is not known) and assesses the degree of association between the X and Y variables (if they are correlated). For the test to work, the values used must be monotonic i.e. the values must increase or decrease together or one increases while the other decreases. A value of 1 indicates a perfect correlation; a value of 0 indicates no correlation between the variables. The example below examines the relationship between precipitation and the number of plant species in southern Africa.

Spearman's rank data for number of plant species and precipitation

Site	No. plant species	Rank (R_1)	Annual precipitation / mm	Rank (R_2)	Difference (D) (R_1-R_2)	D^2	Working space
1	60		60				
2	30		150				
3	40		240				
4	70		330				
5	120		410				
6	50		450				
7	160		550				
8	280		500				
9	150		610				
10	320		520				
11	340		750				
12	140		910				
13	400		400				
14	550		550				
15	570	1	500	7.5			r_s value
					Σ(Sum) D^2=		

Data based on Global patterns in biodiversity Nature Vol 405, 11 May 2000

Step one: Rank the data for each variable. For each variable, the numbers are ranked in descending order, e.g. for the variable, volume, the highest value 570 species is given the rank of 1 while its corresponding frequency value is given the rank of 7.5. Fill in the rank columns in the table above in the same way. If two numbers have the same rank value, then use the mean rank of the two values (e.g. 1+2 = 3. 3/2= 1.5).

Step two: Calculate the difference (D) between each pair of ranks (R_1-R_2) and enter the value in the table (as a check, the sum of all differences should be 0).

Step three: Square the differences and enter them into the table above (this removes any negative values).

Step four: Sum all the D^2 values and enter the total into the table.

Analysing the data

Step five: Use the formula below to calculate the Spearman Rank Correlation Coefficient (r_s). Enter the r_s value in the box above.

$$r_s = 1 - \left(\frac{6\Sigma D^2}{n^3-n} \right)$$

Spearman rank correlation coefficient

Step six: Compare the r_s value to the table of critical values (right) for the appropriate number of pairs. If the r_s value (ignoring sign) is greater than or equal to the critical value then there is a significant correlation. If r_s is positive then there is a positive correlation. If r_s is negative then there is a negative value correlation.

Number of pairs of measurements	Critical value
5	1.00
6	0.89
7	0.79
8	0.74
9	0.68
10	0.65
12	0.59
15	0.521
20	0.45
25	0.398
30	0.362

1. State the null hypothesis (H_o) for the data set: _____

   _____

2. (a) Identify the critical value for the plant-precipitation data: _____

   (b) State if the correlation is positive or negative: _____

   (c) State whether the correlation is significant: _____

KNOW

163 Classification Systems

Key Idea: Organisms can be placed into groups based on their shared characteristics.

Taxonomy is the science of grouping organisms based on shared characteristics. Smaller, more precise groups can be grouped together into larger less precise groups, forming a hierarchy of taxonomic ranks. There are various ways in which organisms can be classified, but not all fairly represent their evolutionary relationships. For example, the traditional group reptiles excludes the birds, which are more closely related to the crocodiles than the crocodiles are to lizards and snakes. In modern classification, distinction of taxa is not so much based on morphological similarities but on evolutionary relationships (phyletics). Classification is also now more commonly based on molecular studies, including genetic and protein analyses. Both morphological and molecular studies should provide evidence that is not contradictory.

Taxonomic ranks

Traditionally, living organisms are classified into a hierarchy of seven main **taxonomic ranks** (although commonly today the rank of "domain" is often included above kingdom as the most encompassing group, making eight major taxonomic ranks). The taxonomic ranks in descending order are: domain, kingdom, phylum, class, order, family, genus, species. Other ranks such as subclass, may also be included. There are also some differences between naming conventions depending on the organism, e.g. animal phyla are equivalent to plant divisions.

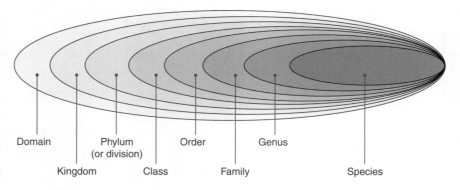

Domain
Phylum (or division)
Order
Genus
Kingdom
Class
Family
Species

The example below shows how as we move through the taxanomic ranks, the organisms we are grouping become more exclusive based on the characteristics of the group. In this case, we are looking at the classification of the grey wolf *Canis lupus*.

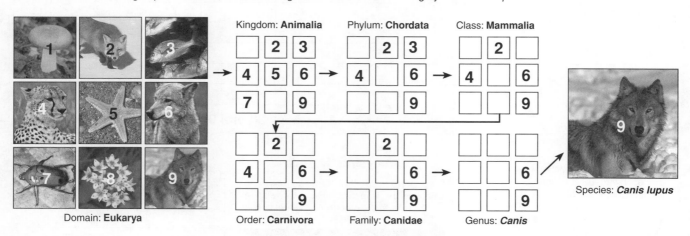

Domain: **Eukarya**

Kingdom: **Animalia** Phylum: **Chordata** Class: **Mammalia**

Order: **Carnivora** Family: **Canidae** Genus: *Canis*

Species: *Canis lupus*

1. The table below shows part of the classification for humans using the eight major levels of classification. For this question, use the example of the classification of the grey wolf, above as a guide.

   (a) Complete the list of the taxonomic ranks on the left hand side of the table below:

   (b) Complete the classification for humans (*Homo sapiens*) on the table below.

	Taxonomic rank	Human classification
1.	_____	_____
2.	_____	_____
3.	_____	_____
4.	_____	_____
5.	_____	_____
6.	Family	Hominidae
7.	_____	_____
8.	_____	_____

WEB 163 LINK 164 LINK 165

© 2016 **BIOZONE** International
ISBN: 978-1-927309-32-2
Photocopying Prohibited

Why are birds dinosaurs?

Defining groups of organisms and evaluating their ancestry using morphological features alone can be problematic because similarities in structure may not necessarily be the result of shared ancestry. This problem can be overcome by only considering the shared derived characteristics, i.e. the characteristics of two of more taxa that are present in their most recent common ancestor but not in older ancestors. Tracing the evolution of derived character states can more accurately identify the evolutionary history of a taxon. The ancestry of birds below illustrates this. Although birds are commonly regarded as a single taxon (and in modern terms they are) birds are simply the last in the lineage of the dinosaurs. Recent analysis of the protein structure of fossil collagen from Tyrannosaur fossils puts birds and dinosaurs in the same taxon.

Features shared by birds and dinosaurs

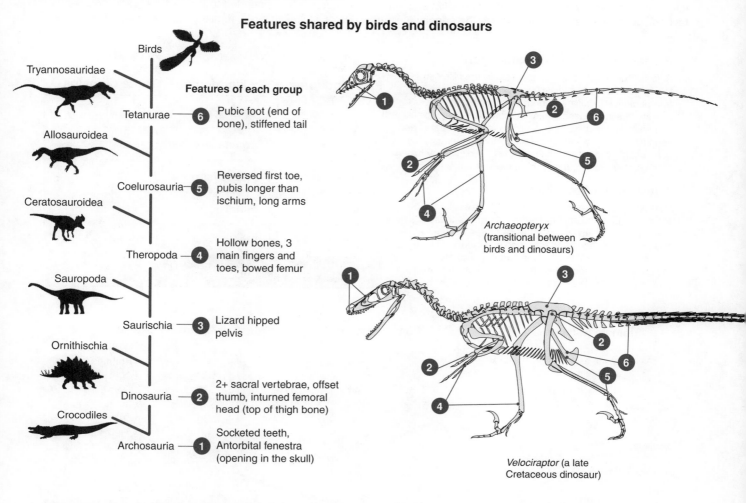

Features of each group

6 — Pubic foot (end of bone), stiffened tail

5 — Reversed first toe, pubis longer than ischium, long arms

4 — Hollow bones, 3 main fingers and toes, bowed femur

3 — Lizard hipped pelvis

2 — 2+ sacral vertebrae, offset thumb, inturned femoral head (top of thigh bone)

1 — Socketed teeth, Antorbital fenestra (opening in the skull)

Archaeopteryx (transitional between birds and dinosaurs)

Velociraptor (a late Cretaceous dinosaur)

2. Construct an acronym or mnemonic to help you remember the principal taxonomic ranks (DKPCOFGS):

_____

3. Classification has traditionally been based on similarities in morphology, but new biochemical methods are now widely used to determine species relatedness. What contribution are these techniques making to the science of classification?

_____
_____
_____
_____

4. Explain why defining the boundaries between specific taxa can be problematic: _____

_____
_____

5. Explain how grouping organisms based on shared derived characteristics can help explain their evolutionary history:

_____
_____
_____

164 The New Tree of Life

Key Idea: The classification of biodiversity into groups, or taxa, is constantly being updated in light of new information. The variety of life on Earth is called biodiversity and its classification into formal groups is called taxonomy. Taxonomy, as with all science, is constantly changing as new information is discovered. With the advent of DNA sequencing technology, scientists began to analyse the genetic make-up of many bacteria. In 1996, these analyses confirmed that life comprises three major lineages (domains), not two as was the convention. The recognised lineages are the Bacteria, the Eukarya, and the Archaea. The new classification better reflects the evolutionary history of life on Earth. Molecular evidence has since led to the reclassification of many other taxa, including birds, reptiles, many plants, and primates.

A changing view of classification

Before DNA sequencing, taxonomists divided life into five kingdoms based mainly on visible characteristics (morphology). The five kingdom system places all prokaryotes in one kingdom, with protoctists, fungi, plants, and animals being the other four. This system is dated and seriously at odds with molecular evidence. In particular, it does not fairly represent the diversity or evolutionary history of the prokaryotic organisms or unicellular eukaryotes.

A new view of the world

In 1996, scientists deciphered the full DNA sequence of the thermophilic bacterium *Methanococcus jannaschii*. The data supported the hypothesis of three major evolutionary lineages and gave rise to a modified six kingdom classification. This was further revised to the current three domain system (below), which more properly represents the phylogeny of life on Earth.

Whittaker 1969 **Five kingdoms**	Woese *et al.* 1977 **Six kingdoms**	Woese *et al.* 1990 **Three domains**
Monera	Eubacteria	Bacteria
	Archaebacteria	Archaea
Protoctista	Protoctista	Eukarya
Fungi	Fungi	
Plantae	Plantae	
Animalia	Animalia	

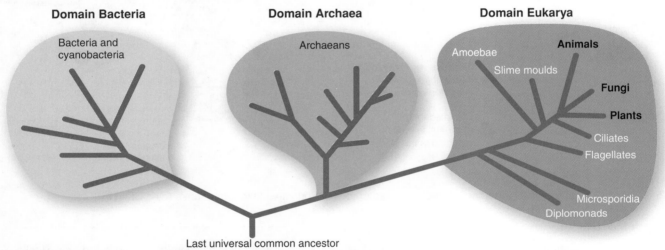

Domain Bacteria — Bacteria and cyanobacteria

Domain Archaea — Archaeans

Domain Eukarya — Amoebae, Slime moulds, **Animals**, **Fungi**, **Plants**, Ciliates, Flagellates, Microsporidia, Diplomonads

Last universal common ancestor

Domain Bacteria

Lack a distinct nucleus and cell organelles. Present in most of Earth's habitats and vital to its ecology. Includes well-known pathogens, many harmless and beneficial species, and the cyanobacteria (photosynthetic bacteria containing the pigments chlorophyll a and phycocyanin).

Domain Archaea

Methanococcus jannaschii was the first archaean genome to be sequenced. The sequencing identified many genes unique to Archaea and provided strong evidence for three evolutionary lineages. Although archaeans may resemble bacteria (e.g. they lack a nucleus), they posses several metabolic pathways that are similar to eukaryotes. Other aspects of their structure and metabolism, such their membrane lipids and respiratory pathways, are unique. Although once regarded as organisms of extreme environments, such as volcanic springs, archaeans are now known to be widespread in soil and water.

Domain Eukarya

Complex cell structure with organelles and nucleus. The three domain classification recognises the diversity and different evolutionary paths of the unicellular eukaryotes (formerly Protista), which have little in common with each other. The fungi, animals, and plants form the remaining lineages.

1. Describe one feature of the three domain system that is very different from the five kingdom classification:

_____

_____

2. List the distinguishing features of each of the three domains of life:

(a) _____

(b) _____

(c) _____

WEB LINK

165 Features of Taxonomic Groups

Key Idea: Organisms are identified and classified on the basis of their distinguishing features.

Taxonomy is the science of classifying organisms. It relies on identifying and describing characteristics that clearly distinguish organisms from each other (distinguishing features). Although the three domain classification system most accurately reflects the true diversity of life, the eukaryotic taxa are still commonly described under a more traditional scheme. The distinguishing features of some major **taxa**, including the kingdoms Protoctista, Fungi, Plantae, and Animalia, are provided in the following pages. Examples give an indication of the diversity within each taxon.

DOMAIN ARCHAEA

- The most ancient lineage of prokaryotes.
- Like the Bacteria, lack nuclei and have smaller 70S ribosomes.
- Live in extreme environments, such as deep sea vents (far right) and geothermal springs, but also widespread in oceans and soil.

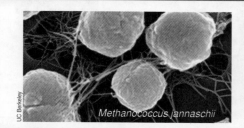
Methanococcus jannaschii

M. jannaschii was isolated from a deep sea hydrothermal vent.

DOMAIN BACTERIA

- Distinguished from Archaea by differences in cell wall composition, nucleotide structure, and ribosome shape.
- Diverse in nutrition and metabolism. Includes heterotrophic, photosynthetic, and chemosynthetic species. A relatively small proportion cause diseases in plants and animals.
- The **gram stain** distinguishes two broad groups of bacteria. It relies on the presence of peptidoglycan in the cell wall. The stain is easily washed from the thin peptidoglycan layer of gram negative walls but is retained by the thick peptidoglycan of gram positive cells, staining them violet.

Gram positive bacteria

The walls of gram positive bacteria consist of many layers of peptidoglycan forming a thick, single-layered structure that holds the gram stain.

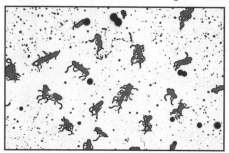

Bacillus alvei: a gram positive, flagellated bacterium. Note how the cells appear dark.

Gram negative bacteria

The cell walls of gram negative bacteria contain only a small proportion of peptidoglycan, so the dark violet stain is not retained by the organisms.

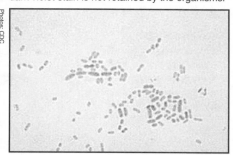

Alcaligenes odorans: a gram negative bacterium. Note how the cells appear pale.

DOMAIN: EUKARYA
Kingdom: FUNGI

- Heterotrophic.
- Rigid cell wall made of chitin.
- Vary from single celled to large multicellular organisms.
- Mostly saprotrophic (ie. feeding on dead or decaying material).
- Terrestrial and immobile.

Examples:
Mushrooms/toadstools, yeasts, truffles, morels, molds, and lichens.

Species diversity: 80 000 +

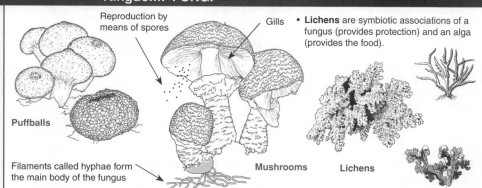

Reproduction by means of spores

Gills

- **Lichens** are symbiotic associations of a fungus (provides protection) and an alga (provides the food).

Puffballs

Filaments called hyphae form the main body of the fungus

Mushrooms

Lichens

Kingdom: PROTOCTISTA

- A diverse group of organisms. They are polyphyletic and so better represented in the 3 domain system.
- Unicellular or simple multicellular.
- Widespread in moist or aquatic environments.

Examples of algae: green, red, and brown algae, dinoflagellates, diatoms.

Examples of protozoa: amoebas, foraminiferans, radiolarians, ciliates.

Species diversity: 55 000 +

Algae 'plant-like' protoctists

- Autotrophic (photosynthesis)
- Characterised by the type of chlorophyll present

Cell walls of cellulose, sometimes with silica

Diatom

Protozoa 'animal-like' protoctists

- Heterotrophic nutrition and feed via ingestion
- Most are microscopic (5 μm - 250 μm)

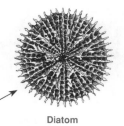

Move via projections called pseudopodia

Lack cell walls

Amoeba

REFER

Kingdom: PLANTAE

- Multicellular organisms (the majority are photosynthetic and contain chlorophyll).
- Cell walls made of cellulose; food is stored as starch.
- Subdivided into two major divisions based on tissue structure: **Bryophytes** (non-vascular plants) and **Tracheophytes** (vascular plants).

Non-Vascular Plants:

- Non-vascular, lacking transport tissues (no xylem or phloem).
- Small and restricted to moist, terrestrial environments.
- Do not possess 'true' roots, stems, or leaves.

Phylum Bryophyta: Mosses, liverworts, and hornworts.

Species diversity: 18 600 +

Phylum: Bryophyta

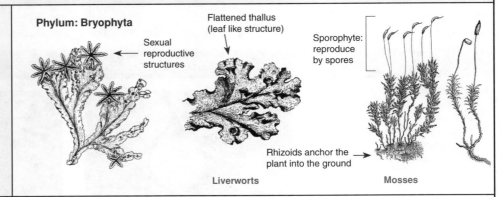

Sexual reproductive structures

Flattened thallus (leaf like structure)

Sporophyte: reproduce by spores

Rhizoids anchor the plant into the ground

Liverworts

Mosses

Vascular Plants:

- Vascular: possess transport tissues.
- Possess true roots, stems, and leaves, as well as stomata.
- Reproduce via spores, not seeds.
- Clearly defined alternation of sporophyte and gametophyte generations.

Seedless Plants:

Spore producing plants, includes:
Phylum Filicinophyta: Ferns
Phylum Sphenophyta: Horsetails
Phylum Lycophyta: Club mosses
Species diversity: 13 000 +

Phylum: Lycophyta

Leaves

Club moss

Phylum: Sphenophyta

Leaves

Horsetail

Phylum: Filicinophyta

Large dividing leaves called fronds

Reproduce via spores on the underside of leaf

Rhizome

Adventitious roots

Fern

Seed Plants:

Also called Spermatophyta. Produce seeds housing an embryo. Includes:

Gymnosperms

- Lack enclosed chambers in which seeds develop.
- Produce seeds in cones which are exposed to the environment.

Phylum Cycadophyta: Cycads
Phylum Ginkgophyta: Ginkgoes
Phylum Coniferophyta: Conifers
Species diversity: 730 +

Phylum: Cycadophyta

Palm-like leaves

Cone

Cycad

Phylum: Ginkgophyta

Flat leaves

Ginkgo

Phylum: Coniferophyta

Needle-like leaves

Male cones

Woody stems

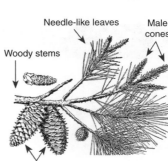

Female cones

Conifer

Angiosperms

Phylum: Angiospermophyta

- Seeds in specialised reproductive structures called flowers.
- Female reproductive ovary develops into a fruit.
- Pollination usually via wind or animals.

Species diversity: 260 000 +

The phylum Angiospermophyta may be subdivided into two classes:

Class Monocotyledoneae (Monocots)
Class Dicotyledoneae (Dicots)

Angiosperms: **Monocotyledons**

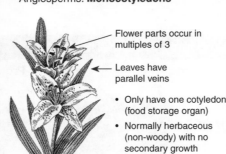

Flower parts occur in multiples of 3

Leaves have parallel veins

- Only have one cotyledon (food storage organ)
- Normally herbaceous (non-woody) with no secondary growth

Lily

Examples: cereals, lilies, daffodils, palms, grasses.

Angiosperms: **Dicotyledons**

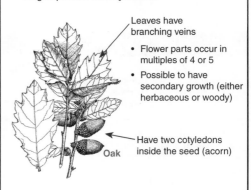

Leaves have branching veins

- Flower parts occur in multiples of 4 or 5
- Possible to have secondary growth (either herbaceous or woody)

Have two cotyledons inside the seed (acorn)

Oak

Examples: many annual plants, trees and shrubs.

Kingdom: ANIMALIA

- Over 800 000 species described in 33 existing phyla.
- Multicellular, heterotrophic organisms.
- Animal cells lack cell walls.

- Further subdivided into major phyla on the basis of body symmetry, development of the coelom (protostome or deuterostome), and external and internal structures.

Phylum: Porifera

- Lack organs.
- All are aquatic (mostly marine).
- Asexual reproduction by budding.
- Lack a nervous system.

Examples: sponges.
Species diversity: 8000 +

Body wall perforated by pores through which water enters

Water leaves by a larger opening - the osculum

Sponge

- Capable of regeneration (the replacement of lost parts)
- Possess spicules (needle-like internal structures) for support and protection

Tube sponge

Sessile (attach to ocean floor)

Phylum: Cnidaria

- Diploblastic with two basic body forms:
  Medusa: umbrella shaped and free swimming by pulsating bell.
  Polyp: cylindrical, some are sedentary, others can glide, or somersault or use tentacles as legs.
- Some species have a life cycle that alternates between a polyp stage and a medusa stage.
- All are aquatic (most are marine).

Examples: Jellyfish, sea anemones, hydras, and corals.
Species diversity: 11 000 +

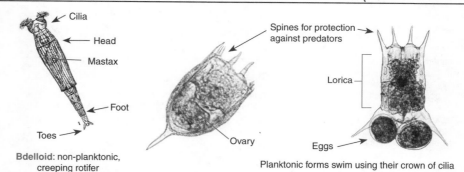

Some have air-filled floats

Single opening acts as mouth and anus

Polyps may aggregate in colonies

Nematocysts (stinging cells)

Polyps stick to seabed

Brain coral

Jellyfish (Portuguese man-of-war)

Sea anemone

Colonial poly

Contraction of the bell propels the free swimming medusa

Phylum: Rotifera

- A diverse group of small, pseudocoelomates with sessile, colonial, and planktonic forms.
- Most freshwater, a few marine.
- Typically reproduce via cyclic parthenogenesis.
- Characterised by a wheel of cilia on the head used for feeding and locomotion, a large muscular pharynx (mastax) with jaw like trophi, and a foot with sticky toes.

Species diversity: 1500 +

Cilia

Head

Mastax

Foot

Toes

Bdelloid: non-planktonic, creeping rotifer

Spines for protection against predators

Lorica

Ovary

Eggs

Planktonic forms swim using their crown of cilia

Phylum: Platyhelminthes

- Unsegmented. Coelom has been lost.
- Flattened body shape.
- Mouth, but no anus.
- Many are parasitic.

Examples: Tapeworms, planarians, flukes.
Species diversity: 20 000 +

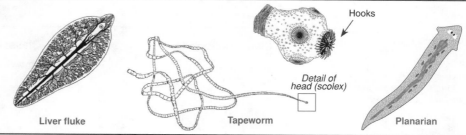

Hooks

Detail of head (scolex)

Liver fluke

Tapeworm

Planarian

Phylum: Nematoda

- Tiny, unsegmented roundworms.
- Many are plant/animal parasites

Examples: Hookworms, stomach worms, lung worms, filarial worms
Species diversity: 80 000 - 1 million

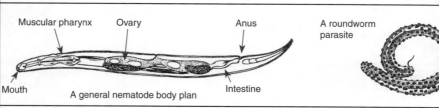

Muscular pharynx

Ovary

Anus

A roundworm parasite

Mouth

A general nematode body plan

Intestine

Phylum: Annelida

- Cylindrical, segmented body with chaetae (bristles).
- Move using hydrostatic skeleton and/or parapodia (appendages).

Examples: Earthworms, leeches, polychaetes (including tubeworms).
Species diversity: 15 000 +

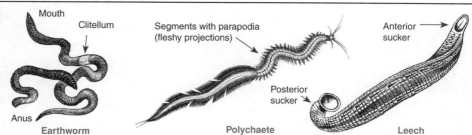

Mouth

Clitellum

Segments with parapodia (fleshy projections)

Anterior sucker

Posterior sucker

Anus

Earthworm

Polychaete

Leech

Kingdom: ANIMALIA (continued)

Phylum: Mollusca

- Soft bodied and unsegmented.
- Body comprises head, muscular foot, and visceral mass (organs).
- Most have radula (rasping tongue).
- Aquatic and terrestrial species.
- Aquatic species possess gills.

Examples: Snails, mussels, squid.
Species diversity: 110 000 +

Class: Bivalvia

- Radula lost in bivalves
- Mantle secretes shell
- Scallop
- Two shells hinged together

Class: Gastropoda

- Mantle secretes shell
- Tentacles with eyes
- Head
- Muscular foot for locomotion
- Land snail

Class: Cephalopoda

- Well developed eyes
- Squid
- Foot divided into tentacles

Phylum: Arthropoda

- Exoskeleton made of chitin.
- Grow in stages after moulting (ecdysis).
- Jointed appendages.
- Segmented bodies.
- Heart found on dorsal side of body.
- Open circulation system.
- Most have compound eyes.

Species diversity: 1 million +
Make up 75% of all living animals.
Arthropods are subdivided into the following classes:

Class: Crustacea (crustaceans)
- Mainly marine.
- Exoskeleton impregnated with mineral salts.
- Gills often present.
- Includes: Lobsters, crabs, barnacles, prawns, shrimps, isopods, amphipods
- **Species diversity:** 35 000 +

Class: Arachnida (chelicerates)
- Almost all are terrestrial.
- 2 body parts: cephalothorax and abdomen (except horseshoe crabs).
- Includes: spiders, scorpions, ticks, mites, horseshoe crabs.
- **Species diversity:** 57 000 +

Class: Insecta (insects)
- Mostly terrestrial.
- Most are capable of flight.
- 3 body parts: head, thorax, abdomen.
- Include: Locusts, dragonflies, cockroaches, butterflies, bees, ants, beetles, bugs, flies, and more
- **Species diversity:** 800 000 +

Myriapods (=many legs)
Class Diplopoda (millipedes)
- Terrestrial.
- Have a rounded body.
- Eat dead or living plants.
- **Species diversity:** 2000 +

Class Chilopoda (centipedes)
- Terrestrial.
- Have a flattened body.
- Poison claws for catching prey.
- Feed on insects, worms, and snails.
- **Species diversity:** 7000 +

Class: Crustacea

- 2 pairs of antennae
- Cephalothorax (fusion of head and thorax)
- Abdomen
- Crab
- 3 pairs of mouthparts
- Cheliped (first leg)
- Shrimp
- Walking legs
- Swimmerets
- Amphipod

Class: Arachnida

- 4 pairs of walking legs
- Abdomen
- Simple eyes
- Scorpion
- Tick
- Abdomen
- No antennae
- 2 pairs of feeding appendages
- Cephalothorax
- Spider
- Carapace
- Telson (tail)
- Horseshoe crab (exception to group: has 3 body parts)

Class: Insecta

- 1 pair of antennae
- 1 pair of compound eyes
- Locust
- Butterfly
- Head
- Thorax
- Abdomen
- 2 pairs of wings
- 3 pairs of legs
- Honey bee
- Beetles are the largest group within the animal kingdom with more than 300,000 species.
- Beetle

Class: Diplopoda

- Body with many similar segments
- Clearly defined head
- 1 pair of antennae
- Each segment has 2 pairs of legs
- 1 pair of mouthparts

Class: Chilopoda

- Body with many similar segments
- 1 pair of large antennae
- Clearly defined head
- 1 pair of mouthparts
- Each segment has 1 pair of legs

Phylum: Echinodermata

- Rigid body wall, internal skeleton made of calcareous plates.
- Many possess spines.
- Ventral mouth, dorsal anus.
- External fertilisation.
- Unsegmented, marine organisms.
- Tube feet for locomotion.
- Water vascular system.

Examples: Starfish, brittlestars, feather stars, sea urchins, sea lilies.
Species diversity: 6000 +

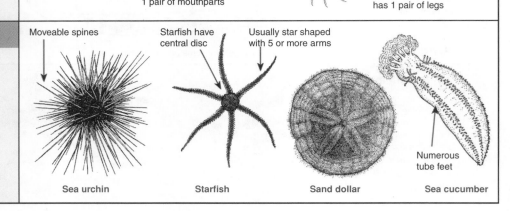

- Moveable spines
- Starfish have central disc
- Usually star shaped with 5 or more arms
- Sea urchin
- Starfish
- Sand dollar
- Numerous tube feet
- Sea cucumber

© 2016 **BIOZONE** International
ISBN: 978-1-927309-32-2
Photocopying Prohibited

Kingdom: ANIMALIA (continued)

Phylum: Chordata

- Dorsal notochord (flexible, supporting rod) present at some stage in the life history.
- Post-anal tail present at some stage in their development.
- Dorsal, tubular nerve cord.
- Pharyngeal slits present.
- Circulation system closed in most.
- Heart positioned on ventral side.

Species diversity: 48 000 +

- A very diverse group with several sub-phyla:
  - Urochordata (sea squirts, salps)
  - Cephalochordata (lancelet)
  - Craniata (vertebrates)

Sub-Phylum Craniata (vertebrates)
- Internal skeleton of cartilage or bone.
- Well developed nervous system.
- Vertebral column replaces notochord.
- Two pairs of appendages (fins or limbs) attached to girdles.

Further subdivided into:

Class: Chondrichthyes (cartilaginous fish)
- Skeleton of cartilage (not bone).
- No swim bladder.
- All aquatic (mostly marine).
- Include: Sharks, rays, and skates.

Species diversity: 850 +

Class: Osteichthyes (bony fish)
- Swim bladder present.
- All aquatic (marine and fresh water).

Species diversity: 21 000 +

Class: Amphibia (amphibians)
- Lungs in adult, juveniles may have gills (retained in some adults).
- Gas exchange also through skin.
- Aquatic and terrestrial (limited to damp environments).
- Include: Frogs, toads, salamanders, and newts.

Species diversity: 3900 +

Class Reptilia (reptiles)
- Ectotherms with no larval stages.
- Teeth are all the same type.
- Eggs with soft leathery shell.
- Mostly terrestrial.
- Include: Snakes, lizards, crocodiles, turtles, and tortoises.

Species diversity: 7000 +

Class: Aves (birds)
- Terrestrial endotherms.
- Eggs with hard, calcareous shell.
- Strong, light skeleton.
- High metabolic rate.
- Gas exchange assisted by air sacs.

Species diversity: 8600 +

Class: Mammalia (mammals)
- Endotherms with hair or fur.
- Mammary glands produce milk.
- Glandular skin with hair or fur.
- External ear present.
- Teeth are of different types.
- Diaphragm between thorax/abdomen.

Species diversity: 4500 +
Subdivided into three subclasses:
Monotremes, marsupials, placentals.

Class: Chondrichthyes (cartilaginous fish)

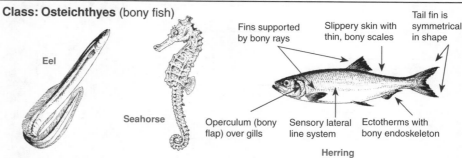

Lateral line sense organ

Asymmetrical tail fin provides lift

Skin with toothlike scales

Ectotherms with endoskeleton made of cartilage

Pelvic fin

Pectoral fin

Hammerhead shark

No operculum (bony flap) over gills

Stingray

Class: Osteichthyes (bony fish)

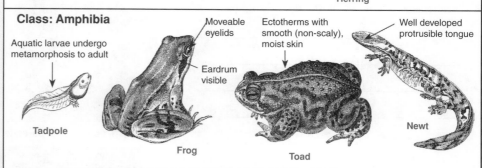

Eel

Seahorse

Fins supported by bony rays

Slippery skin with thin, bony scales

Tail fin is symmetrical in shape

Operculum (bony flap) over gills

Sensory lateral line system

Ectotherms with bony endoskeleton

Herring

Class: Amphibia

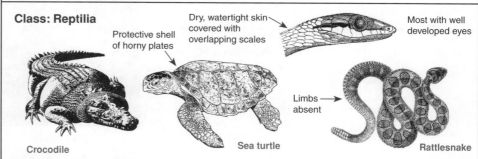

Aquatic larvae undergo metamorphosis to adult

Moveable eyelids

Ectotherms with smooth (non-scaly), moist skin

Well developed protrusible tongue

Eardrum visible

Tadpole

Frog

Toad

Newt

Class: Reptilia

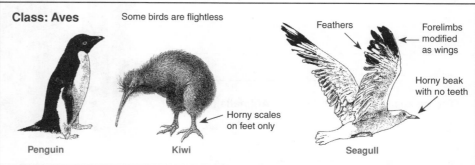

Protective shell of horny plates

Dry, watertight skin covered with overlapping scales

Most with well developed eyes

Limbs absent

Crocodile

Sea turtle

Rattlesnake

Class: Aves

Some birds are flightless

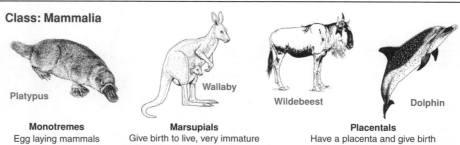

Feathers

Forelimbs modified as wings

Horny beak with no teeth

Horny scales on feet only

Penguin

Kiwi

Seagull

Class: Mammalia

Platypus

Wallaby

Wildebeest

Dolphin

Monotremes
Egg laying mammals

Marsupials
Give birth to live, very immature young, which then develop in a pouch

Placentals
Have a placenta and give birth to live, well developed young

166 Features of the Eukaryotic Kingdoms

Key Idea: The four kingdoms of eukaryotes can be classified on the basis of their distinguishing features. The classification of organisms is based on how they are related in an evolutionary sense. Organisms that are closely related will have more features in common than more distantly related organisms. Those features that definitively distinguish one taxon from another are called distinguishing features. Alone, or sometimes collectively, they should define the group. In this activity, you will summarise the distinguishing features of each of the four kingdoms of eukaryotes.

1. Distinguishing features of Kingdom **Protoctista** (A-D):

_____

_____

_____

_____

_____

_____

_____

2. Distinguishing features of Kingdom **Fungi** (E-F):

_____

_____

_____

_____

_____

_____

_____

3. Distinguishing features of Kingdom **Plantae** (G-H):

_____

_____

_____

_____

_____

_____

_____

4. Distinguishing features of Kingdom **Animalia** (I-J):

_____

_____

_____

_____

_____

_____

_____

_____

A: *Euglena* species

B: Dog vomit slime mould

Red blood cell

C: *Trypanosoma* parasite

D: *Amoeba*

E: Mushrooms

F: Yeast cells in solution

G: Moss

H: Pea plants

I: Cicada moulting

J: Gibbon

© 2016 **BIOZONE** International
ISBN: 978-1-927309-32-2
Photocopying Prohibited

167 What about Viruses?

Key Idea: Viruses can be classified based on the particular characteristics of their genetic material.

Viruses are not classified as living organisms as they do not exhibit all the characteristics of living things. Importantly viruses are not able to reproduce by themselves. They must use the cellular machinery of living organisms to reproduce new copies of themselves. Viruses are classified apart from living organisms, although they are an important component of biological interactions on Earth. They can be classified by the disease they cause, their morphology, and the type of genetic material they carry. There are two main classification schemes for viruses: the International Committee on Taxonomy of Viruses (ICTV) system and the Baltimore classification system (below). The Baltimore classification, proposed in 1971, classifies viruses into seven groups based on characteristics of the genetic material.

The Baltimore classification classifies viruses into seven groups, given the Roman numerals I - VII. Viruses may have DNA or RNA based genomes. The majority of viruses are RNA based. Both DNA and RNA may be double stranded (ds) or single stranded (ss).

Genome	Class			Examples
DNA	I. Double stranded DNA (dsDNA)		Class I viruses usually replicate their DNA inside the host cell's nucleus using viral enzymes. Proteins are synthesised using enzymes from the host cell.	Adenoviruses, Herpesviruses, Poxviruses
	II. Single stranded DNA (ssDNA)		The single stranded DNA is copied into a double strand by the host's cellular machinery. The dsDNA is then used as a template for making RNA and viral proteins.	Parvoviruses
	VII. Double stranded DNA with reverse transcriptase (dsDNA-RT)		Class VII viruses replicate by copying DNA in mRNA. The RNA is then used to produce proteins as well as being a template to produce more DNA using the viral enzyme reverse transcriptase.	Hepadnaviruses e.g. hepatitis B virus
RNA	III. Double stranded RNA (dsRNA)		Viral mRNA is produced in the cytoplasm where it is used to synthesise more viral proteins. One of the proteins acts as a RNA-dependent RNA polymerase to produce more RNA.	Reoviruses
	IV. Single stranded RNA +ve sense (+)ssRNA		The +ve strand RNA is used to produce proteins and as a template to produce –ve strand RNA which is then used to produce more +ve strand RNA.	Picornaviruses, e.g. common cold, Togaviruses
	V. Single stranded RNA –ve sense (-)ssRNA		The –ve strand RNA must be transcribed into mRNA before being used to produce proteins. The mRNA also serves as a template for producing more viral RNA.	Orthomyxoviruses, Rhabdoviruses
	VI. Single stranded RNA with reverse transcriptase (ssRNA-RT)		Class VI viruses replicate through a DNA intermediate. Commonly known as retroviruses, they use reverse transcriptase to copy the RNA into DNA. The DNA is then used as the template for producing proteins and more viral RNA.	Retroviruses (e.g. HIV)

1. Explain why viruses are classified separately from living things: _____

_____

2. (a) Which classes of viruses are DNA viruses? _____

(b) Which classes of virus are RNA viruses? _____

3. How do retroviruses differ from other RNA viruses? _____

_____

KNOW

168 Factors Affecting Biodiversity

Key Idea: A high level of diversity is needed for most ecosystems to function correctly. This includes both the number of species and the genetic diversity of those species. As the human population grows, demand on natural resources increases. As a consequence, pressure on habitats and their natural populations increases and biodiversity declines. A reduction in biodiversity reduces both the stability of ecosystems (so they begin to change in character) and also their ability to withstand disturbances. This can further accelerate the decline of biodiversity. As a population declines, genetic information is lost, reducing the capacity of the species to adapt to changing environments and increasing the risk of inbreeding. These factors further reduce the species viability and put them at risk of extinction.

The different species of Heliconius butterflies are difficult to distinguish because they mimic each other

As the human population increases, cities expand, fragmenting or destroying the natural ecosystems surrounding them. Careful management of urban development and resource use will be needed to prevent local extinctions and loss of biodiversity.

As the amount of suitable habitat declines, so too do the population numbers of species living there. The Chatham Island black robin suffered a massive population crash in the 1970s. All 200 current birds are related to one female. There is virtually no genetic difference between them.

The true loss of biodiversity is unknown, partly because many species remain undiscovered or unrecognised because they cannot be distinguished from related species (above). *In-situ* conservation of ecosystems has a vital role in conserving species like these.

Coral reefs provide a huge number of habitats for marine animals. They cover just 0.1% of the Earth's surface but support 25% of marine species. The coral is the base of a large food web supporting huge numbers of fish. Pollution and climate change, including fall in ocean pH, threaten both coral survival and the biodiversity of the reef.

Tropical rainforests are home to 80% of Earth's documented species. These rainforests are being destroyed rapidly as land is cleared for agriculture or cattle ranching, to supply logs, for mining, or to build dams. Deforestation places a majority of the Earth's biodiversity at risk and threatens and stability of important ecosystems.

Demand for food increases as the population grows. Modern farming techniques favour **monocultures** to maximise yield and profit. However monocultures, in which a single crop type is grown year after year, are low diversity systems and food supplies are vulnerable if the crop fails. The UN estimates that 12 plant species provide 75% of our total food supply.

1. Identify three factors that can threaten the biodiversity of ecosystems and explain the threat:

(a) _____

_____

_____

(b) _____

_____

_____

(c) _____

_____

_____

WEB   LINK   LINK

KNOW 168 165 169

© 2016 **BIOZONE** International
ISBN: 978-1-927309-32-2
Photocopying Prohibited

Loss of biodiversity

Insects make up 80% of all known animal species. There are an estimated 6-10 million insect species on Earth, but only 900 000 have been identified. Some 44 000 species may have become extinct over the last 600 years. The Duke of Burgundy butterfly (*Hamearis lucina*), right, is an endangered British species.

About 5% of the 8225 reptile species are at risk. These include the two tuatara species (right) from New Zealand, which are the only living members of the order Sphenodontia, and the critically endangered blue iguana. Only about 200 blue iguanas remain, all in the Grand Caymans.

	Total number of species*	Number of IUCN listed species
Plants	310 000 - 422 000	8474
Insects	6 -10 million	622
Fish	28 000	126
Amphibians	5743	1809
Reptiles	8225	423
Birds	10 000	1133
Mammals	5400	1027

* Estimated numbers

The giant panda (above), is one of many critically endangered terrestrial mammals, with fewer than 2000 surviving in the wild. Amongst the 120 species of marine mammals, approximately 25% (including the humpback whale and Hector's dolphin) are on the ICUN's red list.

Prior to the impact of human activity on the environment, one bird species became extinct every 100 years. Today, the rate is one every year, and may increase to 10 species every year by the end of the century. Some at risk birds, such as the Hawaiian crow (right), are now found only in captivity.

Current estimates suggest as many as 47% of plant species may be endangered. Some, such as the South African cycad *Encephalartos woodii* (above), is one of the rarest plants in the world. It is extinct in the wild and all remaining specimens are clones.

2. (a) Comment on the actual extinction rate compared with the estimated background extinction rate: _____

_____

_____

(b) What factor is attributed to this difference? _____

3. The International Union for Conservation (IUCN) has established a Red List Index (RLI) for four taxonomic groups: reef forming corals, amphibians, birds, and mammals. This index focusses on the genuine status of changes. An RLI of 1.0 equates to all species qualifying as Least Concern (unlikely to become extinct in the near future). An RLI of 0 means that all species have become extinct. The figure right shows the trends in risk for the four taxonomic groups currently completed.

(a) Which taxon is moving most rapidly towards extinction risk?

_____

(b) Which taxon is, on average, the most threatened?

_____

(c) Why would an index like this be useful and how could it help to highlight environmental issues of concern?

_____

_____

_____

Graph: IUCN Red List Index of species survival (y-axis, 0.70 to 1.00) vs Year (x-axis, 1980 to 2010) showing trends for Corals, Birds, Mammals, and Amphibians. Adapted from IUCN Red List of Endangered Species: www.iucnredlist.org/

4. Explain why conservation efforts are focussed on coral reefs and tropical rainforests: _____

_____

_____

_____

169 Agriculture and Biodiversity

Key Idea: Agricultural systems generally have lower biodiversity than natural ecosystems.

Throughout the world, the intensification of agriculture has been associated with a decline in biodiversity. After the native vegetation has been cleared, soil tillage and burning reduces microbial biomass in the soil, altering soil structure and processes such as decomposition and nutrient cycling. When habitats shrink, populations decline and small isolated populations may not be viable. Habitat fragmentation also

disrupts the activity patterns of mobile species, especially those that will not move over open agricultural land. Modern farming practices, such as dependence on mechanisation and a move away from mixed farming operations, have greatly accelerated the decline in biodiversity. In the UK, steps to conserve the countryside, such as hedgerow legislation, policies to increase woodland cover, and schemes to promote environmentally sensitive farming practices are designed to reduce loss of biodiversity.

Soil microbial diversity is decreased due to altered conditions

Habitat loss occurs when grasslands and forests are cleared for agriculture and wetlands are drained

The use of **GE crops** and a **monoculture** regime reduces biodiversity

Fertilisers and pesticide run-off contaminates water bodies and kills aquatic life

Large fields lacking hedgerows create an impoverished habitat and cause the isolation of remaining wooded areas

Livestock and wild fauna can be harmed by **bioaccumulation** of pesticides in the food chain. Bioaccumulation can even be fatal to top consumers.

Pesticide use causes a reduction in species diversity, particularly in invertebrates. Their loss from the food chain can affect other animals.

Wild predators are killed to protect livestock

Natural grasslands are diverse and productive ecosystems. Ancient meadows may have contained 80-100 plant species, in contrast to currently cultivated grasslands, which may contain as few as three species. Unfortunately, many of the management practices that promote grassland species diversity conflict with modern farming methods. For example, the extensive use of fertilisers and selective herbicides on pastures favours aggressive species, such as nettles and docks, which out-compete ecologically important species such as orchids and cowslips. Appropriate management can help to conserve grassland ecosystems while maintaining their viability for agriculture.

Wildflower meadow in Britain

1. One solution to the conflicting needs of conserving biodiversity and productivity is to intensively farm designated areas, leaving other areas for conservation. From the farmer's perspective, outline two advantages of this approach:

   (a) _____

   _____

   (b) _____

   _____

   (c) Describe a disadvantage of this management approach: _____

   _____

   _____

© 2016 **BIOZONE** International
ISBN: 978-1-927309-32-2
Photocopying Prohibited

An increase in urban sprawl and the pressure on farmers to increase productivity are having a dramatic impact on the once common flowering plants of Britain's grasslands. Diversity can be maintained only through careful management and conservation of existing ecosystems.

Grassland conservation is not only important for maintaining plant diversity, many animals rely on these ecosystems for food and shelter. A reduction in the diversity of grassland plant species translates to a reduction in the diversity of other species.

This woodland in Yorkshire, England, is home to numerous species of organisms. Clearing land for agriculture reduces both biodiversity and the ability of the community to adapt to changing environmental conditions. Natural ecosystem stability is decreased as a result.

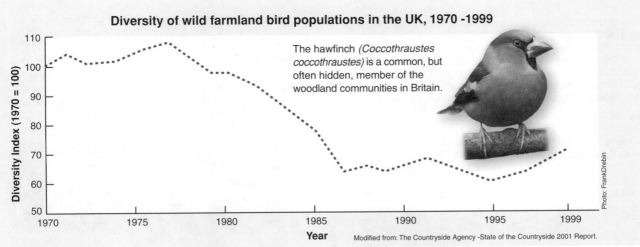

Diversity of wild farmland bird populations in the UK, 1970 -1999

The hawfinch (Coccothraustes coccothraustes) is a common, but often hidden, member of the woodland communities in Britain.

Photo: FrankDrebin

Modified from: The Countryside Agency -State of the Countryside 2001 Report.

2. Populations of wild farmland bird species, because of their wide distribution and position near the top of the food chain, provide good indicators of the state of other wildlife species and of environmental health in general. Over the last 25 years, there has been a marked net decline in the diversity of farmland bird populations (above). However, since 1986, diversity has ceased to decline further and, in recent years, has actually showed an increase.

Suggest two possible reasons for this decline in the diversity of farmland birds (also see the activity on hedgerows):

(a) _____

(b) _____

3. (a) Describe three initiatives local and national government have implemented in an attempt to reverse this decline:

_____

_____

_____

(b) Discuss the role of environmental impact assessments and biodiversity estimates when planning such initiatives:

_____

_____

_____

4. Provide an argument for retaining areas of uncultivated meadow alongside more intensively managed pasture:

_____

_____

_____

_____

170 Why is Biodiversity Important?

Key Idea: Maintaining biodiversity enhances ecosystem stability and functioning and also provides economic and aesthetic benefits to humans.

Ecosystems provide both material and non-material benefits to humans. These benefits, or ecosystem services, are best provided by healthy, diverse systems. As a general rule, high diversity ecosystems are ecologically more stable (constant in character over time) and resistant to disturbance (**resilient**) than systems with low diversity. Maintaining diversity therefore has economic benefits to humans through their use of ecosystem resources and through the generation of income from tourism to ecologically significant areas. Although often discussed as individual benefits, the ecological, aesthetic, and economic reasons for maintaining biodiversity overlap.

Ecological reasons for maintaining biodiversity

Evidence from both experimental and natural systems indicates that the most diverse ecosystems are generally the most stable, most probably because the complex network of species interactions has a buffering effect against change. Maintaining biodiversity is therefore critical to maintaining key ecological functions such as nutrient cycling and water purification.

Ecosystems include many interdependent species (e.g. flowering plants and their pollinators, hosts and parasites). The loss of even one species can detrimentally alter ecosystem dynamics, especially if the species is a keystone species. For example, in the Caledonian forest in Scotland, the Scots pine is key to the survival of many of the species present there. Its loss would affect the survival of those species and compromise the stability of the ecosystem.

Genetic diversity is an important component of ecosystem stability and resilience. A loss of genetic diversity is associated with an increased risk of extinction and a greater chance that an ecosystem will become impoverished and degraded. Genetic diversity effectively represents genetic resources, i.e. those genes in living organisms that may have benefits to humans (e.g. medicinal plants). Once an organism is extinct, those genetic resources are also lost.

Rainforest

Monoculture of soy beans

Rainforests represent the highest diversity systems on Earth. Whilst they are generally resistant to disturbance (resilient), once degraded (e.g. by deforestation), they have little ability to recover. Monocultures, which provide the majority of the world's food supply, represent very low diversity systems and are particularly susceptible to diseases, pests, and disturbance.

Aesthetic reasons for maintaining biodiversity

Many people enjoy looking at, or spending time in areas of natural beauty. Viewing aesthetically pleasing landscapes provides satisfaction and enjoyment to the individual. Nature can also provide inspiration for artists, photographers, and writers, as well as economic benefits from tourism. As countries become more populated and development increases, it becomes more important to maintain and protect natural landscapes as areas of natural beauty. The UK has several programmes designed to protect habitat and landscape for a variety of reasons, including aesthetics.

The images below show two coral reefs. Reef A has high biodiversity, many different species are represented and it is full of colour and life. Reef B is an area of coral bleaching and supports far fewer species. Imagine you were a tourist paying to visit the reef. Which would you rather visit?

A

B

1. What is the most likely reason for high diversity ecosystems being more stable than ecosystems with low biodiversity?

_____

_____

_____

2. Describe two aesthetic benefits of maintaining biodiversity: _____

_____

_____

3. (a) What is a genetic resource? _____

_____

(b) Many medicines are derived from plants. How does tropical rainforest destruction reduce genetic resources?

_____

_____

© 2016 **BIOZONE** International
ISBN: 978-1-927309-32-2
Photocopying Prohibited

Economic reasons for maintaining biodiversity

A variety of economic benefits (goods and services) are generated by biodiversity. These benefits are commonly called **ecosystem services** and are split into four categories: provisioning, regulating, and cultural services, which directly affect people, and supporting services, which maintain the other three services. The provisioning services are sometimes referred to as goods because they can be sold and their economic value can easily be calculated as they have a monetary value. Estimating the total economic value of total ecosystem services is difficult and contentious, but some estimates place their value at £81 trillion per year.

Provisioning services

(Products obtained from ecosystems)

- Food
- Water
- Fuel wood
- Fibres
- Biochemicals
- Genetic resources

Food production

Pollination

Ecotourism

Soil formation

Regulating services

(Benefits obtained from the regulation of ecosystem processes)

- Climate regulation
- Disease regulation
- Water regulation
- Water purification
- Pollination

Cultural services

(Nonmaterial benefits people obtain from ecosystems)

- Spiritual and religious
- Recreation and ecotourism
- Aesthetic
- Inspirational
- Educational
- Cultural heritage

Supporting services

(Services necessary for the production of all other ecosystem services)

- Soil formation
- Nutrient cycling
- Primary production

The economic cost of soil depletion

Soil depletion refers to the decline in soil fertility due to the removal of nutrients. Some definitions of soil depletion also include the physical loss (erosion) of soil.

The increase of continuous monoculture farming practices has contributed to a rapid loss of nutrients from the soil over the last few decades. Farmers must make an economic choice: spend money on fertilisers to add nutrients back to the soil or do nothing and suffer the economic consequences of low crop yields.

4. The 17th century Irish potato famine is an example of how low biodiversity can threaten our food supply. Farmers planted only one potato variety with limited genetic diversity. Most potato crops were destroyed by the fungal disease late blight and, exacerbated by the political environment at the time, there was widespread famine. How could have this situation have been prevented?

Blight affected potato

_____

_____

_____

5. Summarise the economic benefits of maintaining biodiversity: _____

_____

_____

_____

_____

_____

_____

_____

171 *In-Situ* Conservation

Key Idea: *In-situ* (on site) conservation methods manage ecosystems to protect diversity within the natural environment. A variety of strategies are used to protect at-risk species and help the recovery of those that are threatened. *In-situ* conservation means conservation on site and it focusses on ecological restoration and legislation to protect ecosystems of special value. Ecological restoration is a long term process and often involves collaboration between scientific institutions and the local communities involved. Some examples of *in-situ* conservation methods in the UK are shown below.

Snake's head fritillaries

Pagham Harbour

Starlet sea anemone

National Nature Reserves (NNRs)

The UK has 364 National Nature Reserves (NNRs), which are areas designated as having wildlife, habitat, or natural formations needing protection. NNRs often contain rare or nationally important species of plants or animals. The North Meadow NNR in Wiltshire is home to snake's head fritillaries (*Fritillaria meleagris*) a plant that is now rarely found in the English countryside.

Marine Conservation Zones (MCZs)

The UK has several types of Marine Protected Areas, each giving different levels of protection. Recently, Marine Conservation Zone (MCZ) were added. MCZs aim to conserve the diversity of rare and threatened marine species or habitats. They protect nationally important marine wildlife, habitats, and geology while allowing some sustainable activities within their boundaries. Pagham Harbour, West Sussex was designated a MCZ to protect the seagrass beds, lagoon sand shrimp, Defolin's lagoon snail, and the starlet sea anemone found there.

Conservation and action plans are in place for many UK species that are at risk of extinction or their numbers are in decline. As at 2009, 1150 species and 65 habitats were identified by the UK biodiversity action plan (BAP) as needing conservation or protective measures. The natterjack toad (above left) and the New Forest cicada (top right) are two such species.

Advantages of *in-situ* conservation

- Species left in the protected area have access to their natural resources and breeding sites.
- Species will continue to develop and evolve in their natural environment thus conserving their natural behaviour.
- *In-situ* conservation is able to protect more species at once and allow them greater space than those in captivity.
- *In-situ* conservation preserves unrecognised species.
- *In-situ* conservation protects larger breeding populations.
- *In-situ* conservation is less expensive and requires fewer specialised facilities than captive breeding.

Disadvantages of *in-situ* conservation

- Controlling illegal exploitation of *in-situ* populations is difficult.
- Habitats that shelter *in-situ* populations may need extensive restoration, including pest eradication and ongoing control.
- Populations may continue to decline during restoration.

White-backed vulture   Hazel dormouse

The British and Irish Association of Zoos and Aquariums (BIAZA) is a strong supporter of *in-situ* conservation nationally and internationally, developing, managing, and funding a diverse range of field conservation projects. BIAZA supports *in-situ* management of the white backed vulture in South Africa and locally is involved in the Hazel Dormouse Recovery Programme and Biodiversity Action Plan.

In-situ conservation requires a lot of effort initially to restore sites and eradicate pests.

Source: UK Clearing House Mechanisms for Biodiversity

1. Explain why *in-situ* conservation commonly involves both ecosystem restoration and legislation to protect species:

_____

_____

_____

_____

© 2016 **BIOZONE** International
ISBN: 978-1-927309-32-2
Photocopying Prohibited

172 Hedgerow Conservation

Key Idea: Hedgerows provide food, shelter and transport corridors for many species so are important for biodiversity. Since the 1940s, many thousands of kilometres of hedgerows have been removed from the British landscape each year as traditional mixed farms have been converted to farms with larger fields. In addition, neglect and improper management have been responsible for almost half of lost hedgerows every year. Hedgerows require maintenance and management in order to remain viable, yet hedge-laying and trimming skills are rapidly becoming lost. In 1997, legislation was introduced to control the destruction of hedgerows in rural settings. In England and Wales, landowners must apply to the local authority for permission to remove a hedgerow of greater than 20 metres in length, and this can be refused if the hedge is shown to be significant in terms of its age, environmental, or historical importance.

Hedgerows are important because…

- Hedges may support up to 80% of England's birds, 50% of its mammals, and 30% of its butterflies.
- The ditches and banks associated with hedgerows provide habitat for amphibians and reptiles.
- Hedges provide habitat, nesting material and food for birds and mammals.
- Some small mammals, e.g. dormice, once used hay ricks as overwintering habitat. With the loss of hay ricks, hedgerows are virtually their only alternative.
- They act as corridors, along which animals (e.g. pheasants) can safely move between areas of woodland.
- They provide overwintering habitat for predatory insects which move into crops to control pest insects in spring.
- Hedges provide shelter for stock and crops and reduce wind speed, which prevents erosion.
- Hedges act as barriers for windborne pests.

Photo courtesy, Kimberley Mallady

Bjorn Schulz

Hazel dormouse

Hedgerows commonly comprise hawthorn, blackthorn, field maple, hazel, and bramble. A hedgerow is essentially a linear wood and many of the associated plants are woodland species. At least 30 bird species nest in hedges. Hedgerows of different heights are preferred by different bird species, so management to provide a range of hedge heights and tree densities provides the best option for increasing diversity. For example, bullfinches prefer well-treed hedgerows over 4 m tall, whereas whitethroats, linnets, and yellowhammers favour shorter hedgerows (2-3 m) with fewer trees. The hedge base is important for ground-nesting species like the grey partridge. Hedgerows are important habitat for dormice and are used as dispersal corridors linking copses that are too small to support a viable populations on their own. Crucially they also support breeding populations independent of other habitats.

1. From an environmental perspective, describe three benefits of hedgerows to biodiversity:

   (a) _____

   (b) _____

   (c) _____

2. Explain why hedgerows might be regarded as undesirable from the perspective of a modern farmer: _____

   _____

   _____

3. Outline a brief argument to convince a farmer to retain and manage hedgerows, rather than remove them:

   _____

   _____

   _____

   _____

   _____

173 *Ex-Situ* Conservation

Key Idea: *Ex-situ* conservation methods operate away from the natural environment and are useful where species are critically endangered.

Ex-situ conservation is the process of protecting an endangered species outside its natural habitat. It is used when a species has become critically low in numbers or *in-situ* methods have been, or are likely to be, unsuccessful. Zoos,

aquaria, and botanical gardens are the most conventional facilities for *ex-situ* conservation. They house and protect specimens for breeding and can reintroduce them into the wild to restore natural populations. The maintenance of seedbanks by botanic gardens and breeding registers by zoos ensures that efforts to conserve species are not impaired by problems of inbreeding.

Above: England is home to a rare sub-species of sand lizard (*Lacerta agilis*). It is restricted to southern heathlands and the coastal sand dunes of north west England. The UK Herpetological Conservation Trust is the lead partner in the action plan for this species and Chester Zoo hosts a captive breeding colony.

Right: A puppet 'mother' shelters a takahe chick. Takahe, a rare rail species native to New Zealand, were brought back from the brink of extinction through a successful captive breeding program.

In New Zealand, introduced predatory mammals, including weasels and stoats, have decimated native bird life. Relocation of birds on to predator-free islands or into areas that have been cleared of predators has been instrumental in the recovery of some species such as the North Island kokako. Sadly, others have been lost forever.

Captive breeding and relocation

Individuals are captured and bred under protected conditions. If breeding programmes are successful and there is suitable habitat available, captive individuals may be relocated to the wild where they can establish natural populations. Zoos now have an active role in captive breeding. There are problems with captive breeding; individuals are inadvertently selected for fitness in a captive environment and their survival in the wild may be compromised. This is especially so for marine species. However, for some taxa, such as reptiles, birds, and small mammals, captive rearing is very successful.

The important role of zoos and aquaria

As well as keeping their role in captive breeding programs and as custodians of rare species, zoos have a major role in public education. They raise awareness of the threats facing species in their natural environments and engender public empathy for conservation work. Modern zoos tend to concentrate on particular species and are part of global programs that work together to help retain genetic diversity in captive bred animals.

Above: The okapi is a species of rare forest antelope related to giraffes. Okapi are only found naturally in the Ituri Forest, in the northeastern rainforests of the Democratic Republic of Congo (DRC), Africa, an area at the front line of an ongoing civil war. A okapi calf was born to Bristol Zoo Gardens in 2009, one of only about 100 okapi in captivity.

1. Describe the key features of *ex-situ* conservation methods: _____

_____

_____

_____

2. Explain why some animal species are more well suited to *ex-situ* conservation efforts than others: _____

_____

_____

_____

© 2016 **BIOZONE** International
ISBN: 978-1-927309-32-2
Photocopying Prohibited

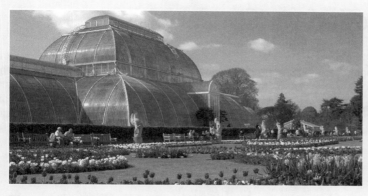

The role of botanic gardens

Botanic gardens have years of collective expertise and resources and play a critical role in plant conservation. They maintain seed banks, nurture rare species, maintain a living collection of plants, and help to conserve indigenous plant knowledge. They also have an important role in both research and education. The Royal Botanic Gardens at Kew (above) contain an estimated 25 000 species, 2700 of which are classified by the ICUN as rare, threatened, or endangered. Kew Gardens are involved in both national and international projects associated with the conservation of botanical diversity and are the primary advisors to CITES on threatened plant species. Kew's Millennium Seed Bank partnership is the largest ex situ plant conservation project in the world; working with a network in over 50 countries they have banked 10% of the world's wild plant species.

Seedbanks and gene banks

Seedbanks and gene banks around the world have a role in preserving the genetic diversity of species. A seedbank (above) stores seeds as a source for future planting in case seed reserves elsewhere are lost. The seeds may be from rare species whose genetic diversity is at risk, or they may be the seeds of crop plants, in some cases of ancient varieties no longer used in commercial production.

3. Describe three key roles of zoos and aquaria and explain the importance of each:

(a) _____

_____

(b) _____

_____

(c) _____

_____

4. Explain the importance of gene and seed banks, both to conservation and to agriculture: _____

_____

_____

_____

5. Compare and contrast *in-situ* and *ex-situ* methods of conservation, including reference to the advantages and disadvantages of each approach:

_____

_____

_____

_____

_____

_____

_____

_____

_____

_____

_____

174 Assisted Reproduction for Conservation

Key Idea: Conserving populations of endangered species may involve the use of assisted reproductive technologies. For some populations of endangered animals, reproduction depends on access to particular resources, such as suitable nest sites or high energy foods. If these resources become limited or inaccessible, these species may require assistance in order to breed successfully. For example, in New Zealand, endangered kakapo are provided with feed pellets when rimu fruit production is low. For poorly reproducing populations dominated by older individuals, assisted reproductive technologies can increase reproductive success by increasing fertilisation rates or improving embryo survival.

A primary goal in endangered species conservation is to maintain genetic diversity. This helps to ensure that the species can survive disease or environmental change. It also helps reduce the chances of inbreeding (and associated homozygosity), which increases the incidence of genetic disorders. Numerous large animals of all kinds, including the cheetah and Florida panther, have very low genetic diversity. This can cause errors in egg and sperm production and can result in poor offspring survival. Cheetah, for example, have low sperm counts and poor sperm viability, especially in captive populations.

Captive populations are invariably small and there is a need to ensure that these are as genetically diverse as possible. In order to ensure this, zoos and wildlife parks cooperate in their breeding programmes and matings are carefully documented.

The critically endangered kakapo is endemic to New Zealand. Kakapo only breed when the endemic rimu tree fruits. Fruiting is unpredictable and kakapo are fed supplementary food to help boost reproduction. Artificial insemination is sometimes used to boost genetic diversity and ensure as many females as possible produce eggs. Breeding is dominated by a few males so artificial insemination helps ensure the genetic diversity of other males is kept in the population.

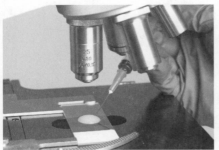

In-vitro fertilisation (IVF)
In-vitro fertilisation is a method of mixing sperm and an egg cell together in the laboratory to produce an embryo. The technique has been proposed to help boost reproductive rates in critically endangered species, including the northern white rhino. There are only three northern white rhinos remaining; two are infertile females and one is a male with low fertility. All are elderly.

Northern white rhinoceros

Surrogacy
Ordinarily, the embryo created by IVF is implanted into a female of the same species. In critically endangered species, the embryo may require implantation into a surrogate. In the case of the northern white rhino, the proposal is to use frozen sperm and eggs to produce embryos that will be implanted into southern white rhino females. This appears to be the only chance of saving the species.

Embryo transferred Charolais calves with their Angus and Hereford recipient mothers.

Embryo transfer
Embryo transfer is the transfer of embryos from the reproductive tract of one female to another. Embryos taken from a fertile female can be placed into an older female. The fertile female could then become pregnant again, boosting the reproductive population. Alternately the embryos could be transferred to closely related species, e.g southern white rhino females could be implanted with northern white rhino embryos.

1. Explain how each of the following can help in ensuring the survival of endangered species:

(a) In-vitro fertilisation: _____

_____

_____

(b) Surrogacy: _____

_____

_____

(c) Embryo transfer: _____

_____

_____

(d) Artificial insemination: _____

_____

_____

© 2016 **BIOZONE** International
ISBN: 978-1-927309-32-2
Photocopying Prohibited

175 Population Control for Conservation

Key Idea: Managing animal populations may sometimes require the removal of animals from over-populated areas to keep populations at a level that is sustainable for the system. Space for wild animals on Earth is rapidly decreasing as the expanding human population demands more space for food and other resources. Complex factors, including successful reproduction in protected areas and changes in resource distribution, can result in localised overpopulation, even by species that are threatened on a wider scale. Overpopulation increases the risk of disease and threatens population viability in the long term because it reduces the resources available to each individual.

Recent badger culls in the UK were highly controversial.

Culling is the removal of animals from a particular area (often by shooting or poisoning). It is usually done when the population increases beyond levels that are sustainable for the area or when a population poses a risk to other animals, including humans (e.g. spread of disease). Culling differs from standard pest control programmes in that the population being culled is not usually part of a formal control scheme or listed as a pest species. Culling can take the form of a hunting season (e.g. duck shooting). In this way the population is given most of the year to grow but numbers are kept in check by hunters during a specific time of year.

In some cases, threatened and protected species are culled when their populations become too high for a particular reservation. This may be done by shooting adults or by removing them to other areas. Elephants can be very destructive, pulling down trees and crushing vegetation. In South Africa, elephants in the Kruger National Park were culled up until 1994. Since then, alternative methods, such as closing water holes, have been used to control elephants. These have resulted in population growth dropping from 6.5% to 2%. Such methods also force elephants to move around more, giving parts of the park a chance to regenerate.

Culling is highly controversial. Many environmentalists argue it isn't ethical and in many cases there is little scientific data to show that it makes any difference to the environment. However park managers and some conservationists say it is better to remove some of the population than face the reality of starvation and disease spreading in an overcrowded population. Culling unprotected or pest species can also be controversial. Unless done correctly, it may actually cause the pest population to increase, as dominant adults are removed and new or younger animals invade the vacated areas.

Other methods of controlling populations include contraceptive methods such as **vasectomy** of males and **hormone treatment** of females. These methods reduce the chances of females becoming pregnant and lower the birth rate. Contraceptive methods are often used in zoos and wildlife parks. In zoos, facilities may only allow a limited number of young at any one time so only some females are allowed to breed.

Breeding in zoo animals is strictly controlled

1. List some of the reasons given for culling certain animal populations: _____

_____

_____

_____

2. List some of the reason why culling may not be the best way to control a population: _____

_____

_____

_____

3. Explain why culling is different to normal pest control: _____

_____

© 2016 **BIOZONE** International
ISBN: 978-1-927309-32-2
Photocopying Prohibited

KNOW

176 Control of Alien Species

Key Idea: Introduced (alien) species can often become pests, causing economic and environmental damage, and requiring control measures to be put in place.

Many species have been moved around the world by humans to places where they are not naturally found. This might be done for the purposes of growing food, breeding livestock, for the fur industry, or for ornamental purposes. This movement is now tightly controlled in many countries, but historically there were virtually no controls, and animals were transported between countries with little regard of their effect on the environment in which they were released. During the colonisations of the Americas, Australia, and New Zealand, many animals and plants were introduced from Europe. In the absence of their natural controls, these have become pests and have caused wide ranging damage. The cost of controlling them often runs into the billions of dollars a year.

Why control alien species?

Economics

Invasive alien species carry an economic cost, both as a result of the damage they do and because of the cost of controlling them. In the UK, it is estimated that invasive species have an economic cost of up to £2 billion a year. In New Zealand, the economic cost of invasive species (of which New Zealand has a disproportionately high number) is estimated at over NZ$2 billion a year.

Ecology

Invasive species damage the ecosystem into which they are introduced. Generally, they prey on or out-compete native species, reducing numbers of both prey and competitor species. Where they have no natural predators or other population controls, population numbers can escalate. For example, a small number of brush-tailed possums were introduced to New Zealand from Australia in 1837 for the fur trade. In 1980, the population peaked at 70 million. Possums are considered New Zealand's primary forest pest, consuming around 21 000 tonnes of vegetation a night and consuming eggs, chicks, invertebrates, and lizards. In Australia, rabbits were declared pests just 30 years after their successful introduction in 1859. In 1901, the No. 1 rabbit fence was constructed (at nearly 2000 km long it is the longest unbroken fence in the world) to try to exclude rabbits from the western agricultural areas. It was a complete failure.

Predation is an important factor in the need to control introduced species. New Zealand in particular has had major problems with introduced predators affecting native bird populations, which evolved in the absence of mammalian predators. Various mustelids (stoats, weasels, and ferrets) were introduced to control rabbits in an effort that went disastrously wrong as they quickly switched to birds as prey. Rats arrived with trading ships. Both have caused enormous damage to populations of native birds. In the UK, the American mink, which likely escaped captivity in fur farms, is now severely reducing the numbers of the native European water vole.

Disease can be carried by introduced species. The grey squirrel was introduced to the UK from America. It is larger and more aggressive than the native red squirrel and easily out competes it in certain habitats. The grey squirrel also carries the squirrelpox virus, which is fatal to red squirrels. The signal crayfish was introduced to the UK and Europe from America to boost freshwater crayfish numbers after a crayfish plague. It was only afterwards that scientists found that the signal crayfish actually carries the plague, further reducing native crayfish numbers. In New Zealand, the possum can carry bovine TB which can be spread to beef and dairy herds.

Rabbit plague, Australia

Brush tailed possum, New Zealand. New Zealand plants do not have the natural defences of Australian plants to browsing.

Economic losses from introduced pests.

Country	Estimated economic losses per year / US$
Globally	1 trillion
US	90 billion
EU	12 billion
China	11 billion
New Zealand	2 billion
UK	2 billion

Data: European commission

1. Using examples, explain why it is necessary to control alien species:

(a) _____

_____

_____

_____

(b) _____

_____

_____

_____

(c) _____

_____

_____

177 Conservation Legislation

Key Idea: There are several global conservation agreements designed specifically to protect wildlife and habitats.

One of the greatest concerns facing conservationists today is the rapidly accelerating rate at which species are being lost. To help combat this, conservation agreements have been established which typically deal with environmental and conservation issues and are designed to provide long-term protection and conservation priorities for wildlife species and their habitats. Failure to comply with the conditions of the agreement can carry legal or trading implications. The UK has signed up to several European and international conservation agreements, but also has national conservation agreements in place, such as the Countryside Stewardship Scheme, which focusses on arable environments.

International agreements

There are several international treaties and conservation agreements between governments designed to conserve biodiversity. Two such agreements are the Rio Convention on Biological Diversity and the Convention of International Trade in Endangered Species (CITES).

Rio Convention on Biological Diversity

The Convention on Biological Diversity became active in 1993. It aims to develop strategies for the conservation and sustainable use of resources while maintaining biodiversity. It has three main goals:

▶ Conservation of biodiversity
▶ Sustainable use of its (biodiversity's) components
▶ Fair and equitable sharing of the benefits arising from genetic resources.

CITES

CITES aims to ensure that trade in species animals and plants does not threaten their survival in the wild. Trade on products are controlled or prohibited depending upon the level of threat to each species. More than 35 000 species are protected under the agreement.

CITES banned trading in ivory (right) or ivory products in 1989. However poaching is still prevalent and large seizures of ivory by authorities still occur.

World Wide Fund for Nature

The World Wide Fund for Nature (WWF) is a non-governmental organisation focussed on the conservation of biodiversity and reduction of humanity's ecological footprint. It is the world's largest conservation organisation and operates in more than 100 countries. Its work currently focusses on six areas, centred around linking people with nature. The areas are climate, food, forests, fresh water, oceans, and policy influence.

One of the approaches the WWF and other NGOs use in conservation efforts is to convince governments to adopt and enforce environmentally friendly policies. One way to do this is to publicly release details when a government proposes a course of action with negative effects on the environment. For example, in 2012, WWF spoke out against the use of shale gas in the UK, saying the UK government needed to reaffirm its commitment to tackling climate change.

Domestic agreements

Most countries have a system of reserved lands focused on ecosystem conservation. These areas aim to protect and restore habitats of special importance and they may be intensively managed through pest and weed control, revegetation, reintroduction of threatened species, and site specific management practices.

1. State the main objectives of the following conservation agreements:

   (a) Rio Convention on Biological Diversity: _____

   _____

   _____

   (b) CITES: _____

   _____

   _____

2. Describe the aims of the WWF and explain its strategies for achieving these: _____

   _____

   _____

   _____

KNOW ◀

178 Chapter Review

Summarise what you know about this topic under the headings and sub-headings provided. You can draw diagrams or mind maps, or write short notes to organise your thoughts. Use the images and hints to help you and refer back to the introduction to check the points covered:

Biodiversity
HINT: How do we quantify biodiversity and how can we evaluate the distribution and abundance of populations.

Classification
HINT: Classification systems: features of the three domains and the eukaryotic kingdoms.

Conservation
HINT: What is biodiversity, why do we need it, what affects it, and how can we conserve it?

© 2016 **BIOZONE** International
ISBN: 978-1-927309-32-2
Photocopying Prohibited

179 KEY TERMS AND IDEAS: Did You Get?

1. Test your vocabulary by matching each term to its definition, as identified by its preceding letter code.

abundance

belt transect

biodiversity

conservation

diversity indices

domain

ex situ conservation

in-situ conservation

line transect

mark and recapture

quadrat

A Statistics used to quantify the heterogeneity of a system. Often used in ecological studies to assess environmental health.

B A line across a habitat along which organisms are sampled at set intervals to determine changes in community composition.

C The number of organisms in a population or area.

D The number or variety of species living within given ecosystem, biome, or on the entire Earth. Incorporates species richness as well as genetic and habitat diversity.

E A form of continuous quadrat sampling along a line.

F Sampling method used to determine the size of a population in which individuals from a population are marked and released and then recapture after a set period of time.

G Conservation methods that operate away from the natural environment (e.g. zoo breeding programmes).

H A measured and marked region used to isolate a sample area for study.

I Conservation efforts that take place on site involving whole ecosystem management.

J The act of preserving, protecting, or restoring something (e.g. an organism or habitat).

K The highest taxonomic rank in the revised classification of life based on recognition of prokaryote diversity.

2. Frigate birds are tropical seabirds. The males have a large red throat pouch which they inflate and use to attract females. Scientists wondered if the size of the pouch was related to the frequency of the drumming sound it produces when the males display. They collected the data below:

Bird	1	2	3	4	5	6	7	8	9	10	11	12
Volume of pouch / cm³	2550	2440	2740	2730	3010	3370	3080	4910	3740	5090	5090	5380
Frequency of drumming sound / Hz	461	473	532	465	485	488	527	478	485	434	468	449

(a) Use the data to calculate an r_s value: _____

_____

(b) Use the table of critical values on page 215 to determine is there is a significant correlation between the size of the pouch and the frequency of the drumming sound:

_____

_____

3. Study the data below from two hypothetical ecosystems and describe in words the species richness and evenness of ecosystem A and B (below):

Number of individuals per species in two ecosystems

Species	Ecosystem 1	Ecosystem 2
1	5	1
2	2	1
3	3	2
4	0	9
5	0	2

Ecosystem 1: _____

_____

_____

Ecosystem 2: _____

_____

_____

TEST

Topic 19 — Genetic technology

19.1 Principles of genetic technology

Learning outcomes

Activity number

☐ 1 Define the term recombinant DNA. Explain the principles of genetic engineering. — 180 181

☐ 2 Describe the principles of PCR (the polymerase chain reaction) in DNA cloning and amplification, including the role of primers and *Taq* polymerase. — 182

☐ 3 Explain how gel electrophoresis is used to analyse proteins and nucleic acids and distinguish between alleles. — 183 184

☐ 4 Describe the properties of plasmids that allow them to be used in gene cloning. — 185

☐ 5 Explain why, in genetic engineering, promoters and other control sequences must often be transferred along with the desired gene. — 185

☐ 6 Explain the use of genes for fluorescent (e.g. *gfp*) or easily stained substances as markers in gene technology. — 185

☐ 7 Explain the role of endoucleases, reverse transcriptase, and DNA ligases in genetic engineering (see #1 above). — 181 185

☐ 8 Give an outline of how microarrays (DNA chips) are used to analyse genomes and detect mRNA in studies of gene expression. — 186

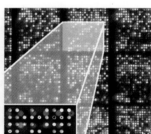

19.2 Genetic technology applied to medicine

Learning outcomes

Activity number

☐ 9 Outline the role of bioinformatics following the sequencing of genomes, such as those of humans and parasites such as the malarial parasite, *Plasmodium*. — 187 188 189

☐ 10 With reference to suitable examples, explain the advantages of producing human proteins (e.g. insulin, adenosine deaminase) using recombinant DNA technology. — 190 194

☐ 11 Outline the advantages of screening for genetic conditions. Include reference to examples, e.g. the breast cancer genes, *BRCA1* and *BRCA2*, and the genes for haemophilia, sickle cell disease, Huntington's disease, and cystic fibrosis. — 191

☐ 12 Outline how gene therapy can be used to treat genetic diseases, e.g. SCID and cystic fibrosis, and discuss the issues associated with use of different vectors. — 192 193 194

☐ 13 Discuss the social and ethical issues of genetic testing and gene therapy in medicine, including reference to IVF, therapeutic abortion, and embryo biopsy. — 195

☐ 14 Outline the use PCR and DNA testing in forensic medicine and criminal investigation. — 196-198

19.3 Genetically modified organisms in agriculture

Learning outcomes

Activity number

☐ 15 Explain the potential for genetic engineering to meet global food demands through improvements in the quality and yield of crop plants and livestock. — 199-201

☐ 16 Outline how the production of crops such as maize, cotton, tobacco, and oil seed rape may be increased by using genetically modified varieties. — 199

☐ 17 Discuss the ethical and social implications of using genetically modified organisms in the production of food. — 202

180 What is Gene Technology?

Key Idea: Gene technology involves research and exploitation of genes to benefit medicine and industry.

Gene technology is used for a wide range of applications from changing the genetic make up of an organism to finding the gene that causes a disease. Since the initial development of gene technology there has been an almost exponential growth in its use and applications due to faster, more powerful computers and faster automated production equipment.

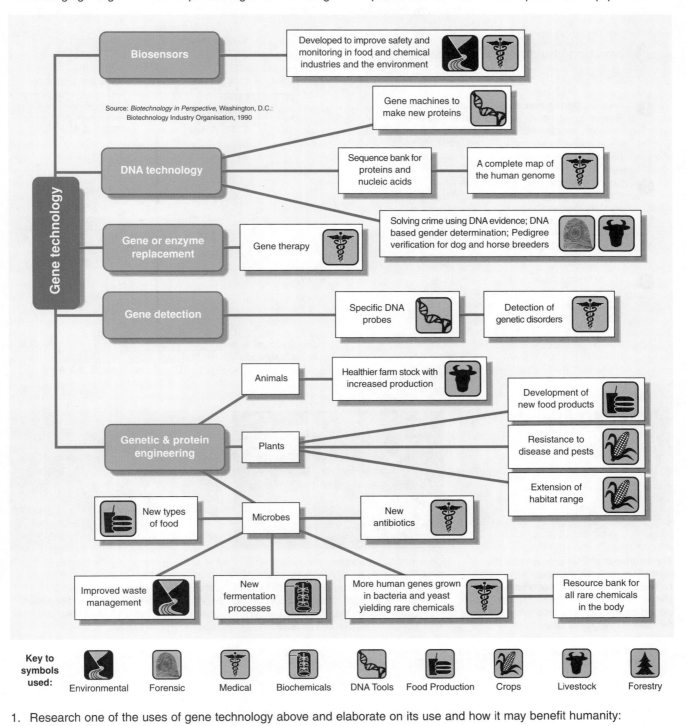

Source: *Biotechnology in Perspective*, Washington, D.C.: Biotechnology Industry Organisation, 1990

Gene technology

- Biosensors — Developed to improve safety and monitoring in food and chemical industries and the environment
- DNA technology
  - Gene machines to make new proteins
  - Sequence bank for proteins and nucleic acids — A complete map of the human genome
  - Solving crime using DNA evidence; DNA based gender determination; Pedigree verification for dog and horse breeders
- Gene or enzyme replacement — Gene therapy
- Gene detection — Specific DNA probes — Detection of genetic disorders
- Genetic & protein engineering
  - Animals — Healthier farm stock with increased production
  - Plants
    - Development of new food products
    - Resistance to disease and pests
    - Extension of habitat range
  - Microbes
    - New types of food
    - New antibiotics
    - Improved waste management
    - New fermentation processes
    - More human genes grown in bacteria and yeast yielding rare chemicals
    - Resource bank for all rare chemicals in the body

Key to symbols used: Environmental Forensic Medical Biochemicals DNA Tools Food Production Crops Livestock Forestry

1. Research one of the uses of gene technology above and elaborate on its use and how it may benefit humanity:

_____

_____

_____

_____

_____

_____

_____

KNOW

181 Making Recombinant DNA

Key Idea: Recombinant DNA (rDNA) is produced by first isolating (or synthesising) a DNA sequence, then inserting it into the DNA of a different organism.

The production of rDNA is possible because the DNA of every organism is made of the same building blocks (**nucleotides**).

rDNA allows a gene from one organism to be moved into, and expressed in, a different organism. Two important tools used to create rDNA are restriction digestion (chopping up the DNA) using **restriction endonucleases** and DNA ligation (joining of sections of DNA) using the enzyme **DNA ligase**.

Information about restriction enzymes

1 A **restriction endonuclease** (restriction enzyme) is an enzyme that cuts a double-stranded DNA molecule at a specific **recognition** site. There are many different types of restriction enzymes, each has a unique recognition site.

2 Some restriction enzymes produce DNA fragments with two **sticky ends** (right). A sticky end has exposed nucleotide bases at each end. DNA cut in such a way is able to be joined to other DNA with matching sticky ends. Such joins are specific to their recognition sites.

3 Some restriction enzymes produce a DNA fragment with two **blunt ends** (ends with no exposed nucleotide bases). The piece it is removed from is also left with blunt ends. DNA cut in such a way can be joined to any other blunt end fragment. Unlike sticky ends, blunt end joins are non-specific because there are no sticky ends to act as specific recognition sites.

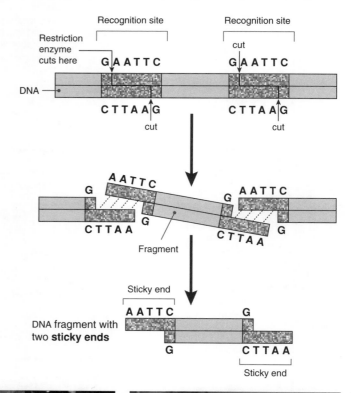

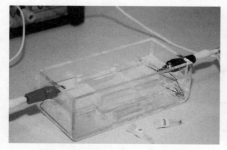

The fragments of DNA produced by the restriction enzymes are mixed with ethidium bromide, a molecule that fluoresces under UV light. The DNA fragments are then placed on an electrophoresis gel to separate the different lengths of DNA.

Once the DNA fragments are separated, the gel is placed on a UV viewing platform. The area of the gel containing the DNA fragments of the correct length is cut out and placed in a solution that dissolves the gel. This releases the DNA into the solution.

The solution containing the DNA is centrifuged at high speed to separate out the DNA. Centrifugation works by separating molecules of different densities. Once isolated, the DNA can be spliced into another DNA molecule.

1. What is the purpose of restriction enzymes in making recombinant DNA? _____

_____

_____

2. Describe the different uses of sticky ends and blunt ends: _____

_____

_____

_____

_____

3. Why is it useful to have many different kinds of restriction enzymes? _____

_____

_____

Creating a recombinant DNA plasmid

1 Two pieces of DNA are cut by the same restriction enzyme (they will produce fragments with matching **sticky ends**).

2 Fragments with matching sticky ends can be joined by base-pairing. This process is called **annealing.** This allows DNA fragments from different sources to be joined.

3 The fragments of DNA are joined together by the enzyme **DNA ligase**, producing a molecule of **recombinant DNA**.

4 The joined fragments will usually form either a linear or a circular molecule, as shown here (right) as recombinant **plasmid** DNA.

pGLO is a plasmid engineered to contain Green Fluorescent Protein (*gfp*). pGLO has been used to create fluorescent organisms, including the bacteria above (bright patches on agar plates).

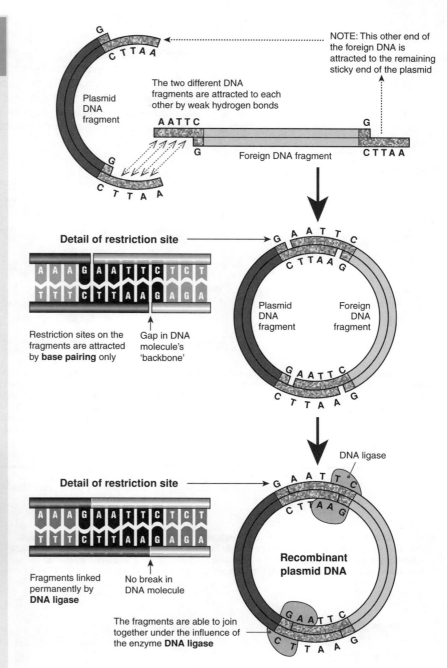

Plasmid DNA fragment

The two different DNA fragments are attracted to each other by weak hydrogen bonds

Foreign DNA fragment

NOTE: This other end of the foreign DNA is attracted to the remaining sticky end of the plasmid

Detail of restriction site

Restriction sites on the fragments are attracted by **base pairing** only

Gap in DNA molecule's 'backbone'

Plasmid DNA fragment

Foreign DNA fragment

DNA ligase

Detail of restriction site

Fragments linked permanently by **DNA ligase**

No break in DNA molecule

Recombinant plasmid DNA

The fragments are able to join together under the influence of the enzyme **DNA ligase**

4. Explain in your own words the two main steps in the process of joining two DNA fragments together:

(a) Annealing: _____

_____

(b) DNA ligase: _____

_____

5. Why can **ligation** be considered the reverse of the **restriction digestion** process? _____

_____

6. Why can recombinant DNA be expressed in any kind of organism, even if it contains DNA from another species?

_____

_____

_____

_____

182 DNA Amplification Using PCR

Key Idea: PCR uses a polymerase enzyme to copy a DNA sample, producing billions of copies in a few hours.

Many procedures in DNA technology, e.g. DNA sequencing and profiling, require a reasonable amount of well preserved DNA. However, very often, only tiny amounts are obtainable (e.g. DNA from a crime scene or from the remains of an extinct organism). The **polymerase chain reaction** (PCR) is a technique for producing large quantities of DNA from a sample. For this reason, it is also called **DNA amplification**. The technique below shows a single replication cycle. Subsequent cycles replicate DNA at an exponential rate, so PCR can produce billions of copies of DNA in just a few hours.

A single cycle of PCR

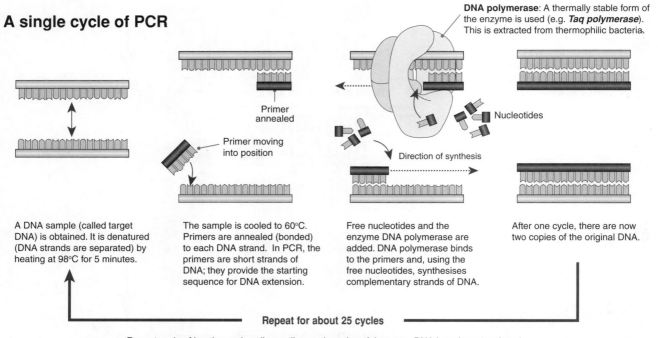

DNA polymerase: A thermally stable form of the enzyme is used (e.g. *Taq polymerase*). This is extracted from thermophilic bacteria.

Primer annealed

Primer moving into position

Nucleotides

Direction of synthesis

A DNA sample (called target DNA) is obtained. It is denatured (DNA strands are separated) by heating at 98°C for 5 minutes.

The sample is cooled to 60°C. Primers are annealed (bonded) to each DNA strand. In PCR, the primers are short strands of DNA; they provide the starting sequence for DNA extension.

Free nucleotides and the enzyme DNA polymerase are added. DNA polymerase binds to the primers and, using the free nucleotides, synthesises complementary strands of DNA.

After one cycle, there are now two copies of the original DNA.

Repeat for about 25 cycles

Repeat cycle of heating and cooling until enough copies of the target DNA have been produced

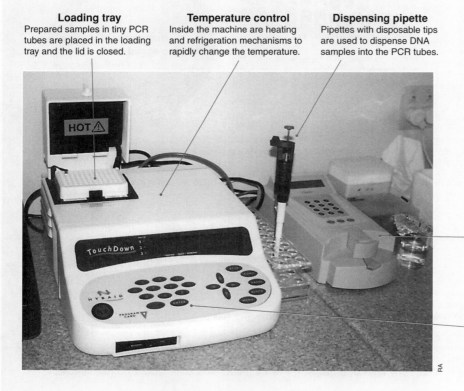

Loading tray
Prepared samples in tiny PCR tubes are placed in the loading tray and the lid is closed.

Temperature control
Inside the machine are heating and refrigeration mechanisms to rapidly change the temperature.

Dispensing pipette
Pipettes with disposable tips are used to dispense DNA samples into the PCR tubes.

Thermal cycler

Amplification of DNA can be carried out with simple-to-use machines called thermal cyclers. Once a DNA sample has been prepared, in just a few hours the amount of DNA can be increased billions of times. Thermal cyclers are in common use in the biology departments of universities, as well as other kinds of research and analytical laboratories. The one pictured on the left is typical of this modern piece of equipment.

DNA quantitation

The amount of DNA in a sample can be determined by placing a known volume in this quantitation machine. For many genetic engineering processes, a minimum amount of DNA is required.

Controls

The control panel allows a number of different PCR programmes to be stored in the machine's memory. Carrying out a PCR run usually just involves starting one of the stored programmes.

1. Explain the purpose of PCR: _____

_____

_____

© 2016 **BIOZONE** International
ISBN: 978-1-927309-32-2
Photocopying Prohibited

2. Describe how the **polymerase chain reaction** works: _____

_____

_____

_____

_____

_____

_____

_____

3. Describe two situations where only very small DNA samples may be available for sampling and PCR could be used:

(a) _____

_____

(b) _____

_____

4. After only two cycles of replication, four copies of the double-stranded DNA exist. Calculate how much a DNA sample will have increased after:

(a) 10 cycles: _____   (b) 25 cycles: _____

5. The risk of contamination in the preparation for PCR is considerable.

(a) Describe the effect of having a single molecule of unwanted DNA in the sample prior to PCR:

_____

_____

_____

(b) Describe two possible sources of DNA contamination in preparing a PCR sample:

Source 1: _____

_____

Source 2: _____

_____

(c) Describe two precautions that could be taken to reduce the risk of DNA contamination:

Precaution 1: _____

_____

Precaution 2: _____

_____

6. Describe two other genetic engineering/genetic manipulation procedures that require PCR amplification of DNA:

(a) _____

_____

_____

(b) _____

_____

_____

183 Gel Electrophoresis

Key Idea: Gel electrophoresis is used to separate DNA fragments on the basis of size.

DNA can be loaded onto an electrophoresis gel and separated by size. DNA has an overall negative charge, so when an electrical current is run through a gel, the DNA moves towards the positive electrode. The rate at which the DNA molecules move through the gel depends primarily on their size and the strength of the electric field. The gel they move through is full of pores (holes). Smaller DNA molecules move through the pores more quickly than larger ones. At the end of the process, the DNA molecules can be stained and visualised as a series of bands. Each band contains DNA molecules of a particular size. The bands furthest from the start of the gel contain the smallest DNA fragments.

Analysing DNA using gel electrophoresis

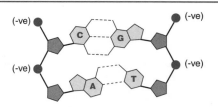

DNA is **negatively charged** because the phosphates (blue) that form part of the backbone of a DNA molecule have a negative charge.

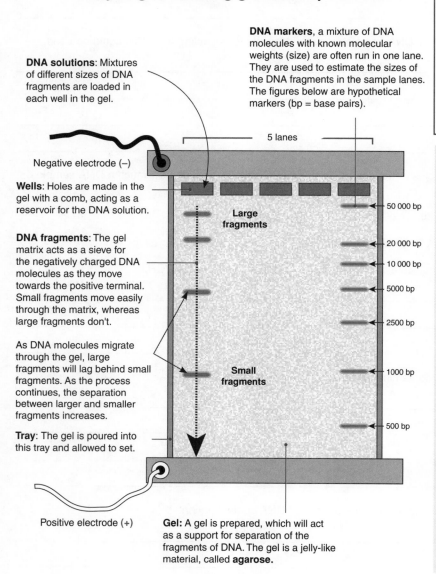

DNA solutions: Mixtures of different sizes of DNA fragments are loaded in each well in the gel.

DNA markers, a mixture of DNA molecules with known molecular weights (size) are often run in one lane. They are used to estimate the sizes of the DNA fragments in the sample lanes. The figures below are hypothetical markers (bp = base pairs).

Negative electrode (–)

Wells: Holes are made in the gel with a comb, acting as a reservoir for the DNA solution.

DNA fragments: The gel matrix acts as a sieve for the negatively charged DNA molecules as they move towards the positive terminal. Small fragments move easily through the matrix, whereas large fragments don't.

As DNA molecules migrate through the gel, large fragments will lag behind small fragments. As the process continues, the separation between larger and smaller fragments increases.

Tray: The gel is poured into this tray and allowed to set.

Positive electrode (+)

Large fragments

Small fragments

5 lanes

50 000 bp
20 000 bp
10 000 bp
5000 bp
2500 bp
1000 bp
500 bp

Gel: A gel is prepared, which will act as a support for separation of the fragments of DNA. The gel is a jelly-like material, called **agarose.**

Steps in the process of gel electrophoresis of DNA

1. A tray is prepared to hold the gel matrix.

2. A gel comb is used to create holes in the gel. The gel comb is placed in the tray.

3. Agarose gel powder is mixed with a buffer solution (this stabilises the DNA). The solution is heated until dissolved and poured into the tray and allowed to cool.

4. The gel tray is placed in an electrophoresis chamber and the chamber is filled with buffer, covering the gel. This allows the electric current from electrodes at either end of the gel to flow through the gel.

5. DNA samples are mixed with a "loading dye" to make the DNA sample visible. The dye also contains glycerol or sucrose to make the DNA sample heavy so that it will sink to the bottom of the well.

6. The gel is covered, electrodes are attached to a power supply and turned on.

7. When the dye marker has moved through the gel, the current is turned off and the gel is removed from the tray.

8. DNA molecules are made visible by staining the gel with **methylene blue** or ethidium bromide which binds to DNA and will fluoresce in UV light.

1. What is the purpose of gel electrophoresis? _____

_____

_____

2. Describe the two forces that control the speed at which fragments pass through the gel:

(a) _____

(b) _____

3. Why do the smallest fragments travel through the gel the fastest? _____

_____

_____

© 2016 **BIOZONE** International
ISBN: 978-1-927309-32-2
Photocopying Prohibited

184 Interpreting Electrophoresis Gels

Key Idea: The banding pattern on an electrophoresis gel can give information about genetic variation and relationships. Once made, an electrophoresis gel must be interpreted. If a specific DNA base sequence was being investigated, then the band pattern can be used to determine the DNA sequence and the protein that it encoded. Alternatively, depending on how the original DNA was treated, the banding pattern may be used as a profile for a species or individual. Commonly, the gene for cytochrome oxidase I (COXI), a mitochondrial protein, is used to distinguish animal species. The genetic information from this gene is both large enough to measure differences between species and small enough to have the differences make sense (i.e. the differences occur in small regions and aren't hugely varied).

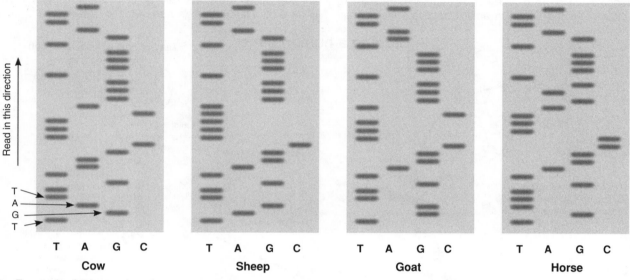

1. For each of the species above:

   (a) Determine the sequence of **synthesised DNA** in the gel in the photographs above. The synthesised DNA is what is visible on the gel. It is complementary to the sample DNA.
   (b) Convert it to the complementary sequence of the sample DNA. This is the DNA that is being investigated.

   Cow: **synthesised DNA**: _____

             sample DNA: _____

   Sheep: **synthesised DNA**: _____

             sample DNA: _____

   Goat: **synthesised DNA**: _____

             sample DNA: _____

   Horse: **synthesised DNA**: _____

             sample DNA: _____

   Based on the number of differences in the DNA sequences:

   (c) Identify the two species that are most closely related: _____

   (d) Identify the two species that are the least closely related: _____

2. Determine the relatedness of each individual (A-E) using each banding pattern on the set of DNA profiles (left). When you have done this, complete the phylogenetic tree by adding the letter of each individual.

Calibration A   B   C   D   E

LINK LINK
187 183 **KNOW**

185 Plasmids and Gene Cloning

Key Idea: *In vivo* cloning describes the insertion of a gene into an organism and using the replication machinery of that organism to multiply the gene or produce its protein product. Recombinant DNA techniques (restriction digestion and ligation) are used to insert a gene of interest into the DNA of a vector (e.g. plasmid or viral DNA). This produces a recombinant DNA molecule called a **molecular clone** that can transmit the gene of interest to another organism. To be useful, all vectors must be able to replicate inside their host organism, they must have one or more sites at which a restriction enzyme can cut, and they must have some kind of **genetic marker** that allows them to be identified. Bacterial plasmids are commonly used vectors because they are easy to manipulate, their restriction sites are well known, and they are readily taken up by cells in culture. Once the molecular clone has been taken up by bacterial cells, and those cells are identified, the gene can be replicated (cloned) many times as the bacteria grow and divide in culture.

Cloning a human gene

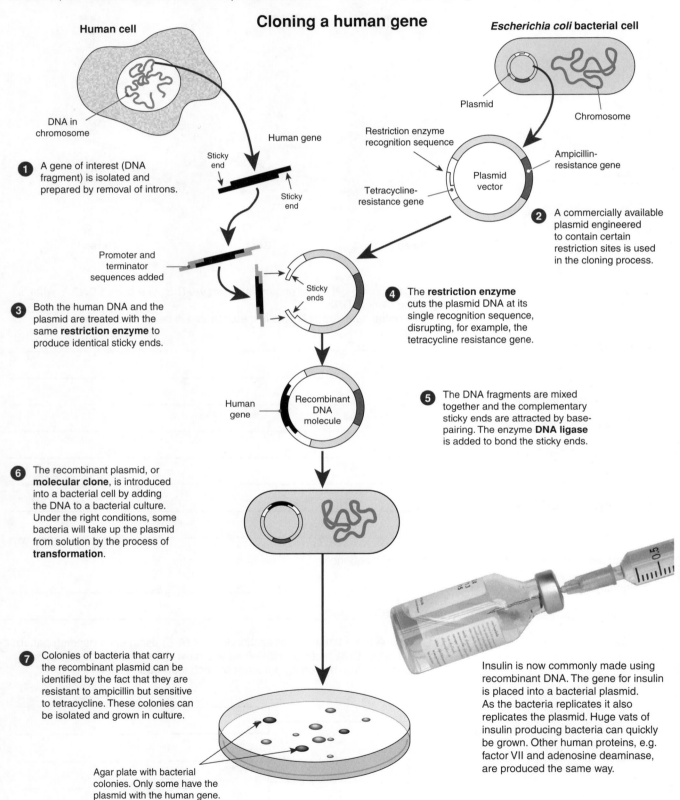

Human cell

DNA in chromosome

Human gene

Sticky end

Sticky end

1 A gene of interest (DNA fragment) is isolated and prepared by removal of introns.

Promoter and terminator sequences added

3 Both the human DNA and the plasmid are treated with the same **restriction enzyme** to produce identical sticky ends.

Escherichia coli bacterial cell

Plasmid

Chromosome

Restriction enzyme recognition sequence

Plasmid vector

Ampicillin-resistance gene

Tetracycline-resistance gene

2 A commercially available plasmid engineered to contain certain restriction sites is used in the cloning process.

Sticky ends

4 The **restriction enzyme** cuts the plasmid DNA at its single recognition sequence, disrupting, for example, the tetracycline resistance gene.

Human gene

Recombinant DNA molecule

5 The DNA fragments are mixed together and the complementary sticky ends are attracted by base-pairing. The enzyme **DNA ligase** is added to bond the sticky ends.

6 The recombinant plasmid, or **molecular clone**, is introduced into a bacterial cell by adding the DNA to a bacterial culture. Under the right conditions, some bacteria will take up the plasmid from solution by the process of **transformation**.

7 Colonies of bacteria that carry the recombinant plasmid can be identified by the fact that they are resistant to ampicillin but sensitive to tetracycline. These colonies can be isolated and grown in culture.

Insulin is now commonly made using recombinant DNA. The gene for insulin is placed into a bacterial plasmid. As the bacteria replicates it also replicates the plasmid. Huge vats of insulin producing bacteria can quickly be grown. Other human proteins, e.g. factor VII and adenosine deaminase, are produced the same way.

Agar plate with bacterial colonies. Only some have the plasmid with the human gene.

© 2016 **BIOZONE** International
ISBN: 978-1-927309-32-2
Photocopying Prohibited

Antibiotic resistance as a marker

Antibiotic resistant marker genes may be used to identify the bacteria that have taken up the foreign (e.g. human) DNA. The plasmid used often carries two genes that provide the bacteria with resistance to the antibiotics **ampicillin** and **tetracycline**. Without this plasmid, the bacteria have no antibiotic resistance genes. A single restriction enzyme recognition sequence lies within the tetracycline resistance gene. A foreign gene, spliced into this position, will disrupt the tetracycline resistance gene, leaving the bacteria vulnerable to this antibiotic. It is possible to identify the bacteria that successfully take up the recombinant plasmid by growing the bacteria on media containing ampicillin, and transferring colonies to media with both antibiotics.

gfp as a gene marker

Most often today, another gene acts as a marker instead of the tetracycline resistance gene. The gene for Green Fluorescent Protein (*gfp* above), isolated from the jellyfish *Aequorea victoria*, has become well established as a marker for gene expression in the recombinant organism. The *gfp* gene is recombined with the gene of interest and transformed cells can then be detected by the presence of the fluorescent product (cells with *gfp* present glow green under fluorescent light).

1. Explain why it might be desirable to use *in vivo* methods to clone genes rather than PCR:

2. Explain when it may not be desirable to use bacteria to clone genes:

3. Explain how a human gene is removed from a chromosome and placed into a plasmid:

4. A bacterial plasmid replicates at the same rate as the bacteria. If a bacteria containing a recombinant plasmid replicates and divides once every thirty minutes, calculate the number of plasmid copies there will be after twenty four hours:

5. When cloning a gene using **plasmid vectors**, the bacterial colonies containing the recombinant plasmids are mixed up with colonies that have none. All the colonies look identical, but some have taken up the plasmids with the human gene, and some have not. Explain how the colonies with the recombinant plasmids are identified:

6. Explain why the *gfp* marker is a more desirable gene marker than genes for antibiotic resistance:

186 Microarrays

Key Idea: DNA chips (also called microarrays or gene chips) are a progression of the technology in DNA probes. They allow thousands of DNA sequences to be probed at once.

DNA chips allow researchers to study which genes are expressed (turned on) in a cell. It is done by probing the mRNA content of a cell. If certain mRNA is present, then a specific gene is turned on and being expressed. The mRNA is extracted from a cell and then copied into **complementary**

DNA (cDNA) using the enzyme reverse transcriptase. The DNA chip itself is covered with thousands of dots each containing thousands of copies of a unique DNA sequence which corresponds to a known gene from the genome being probed. When the cDNAs are applied to the chip, they will only bind to their complementary sequence. Computer analysis of the chip determines which dots have DNA bound, and this tells researchers which genes are being expressed.

What is a DNA chip?

A **DNA chip** consists of DNA probes fixed to a small solid support such as a glass slide or a nylon filter. Each spot on the DNA chip has thousands to millions of copies of a different **DNA probe**. The probes are single stranded DNA molecules, each representing a gene.

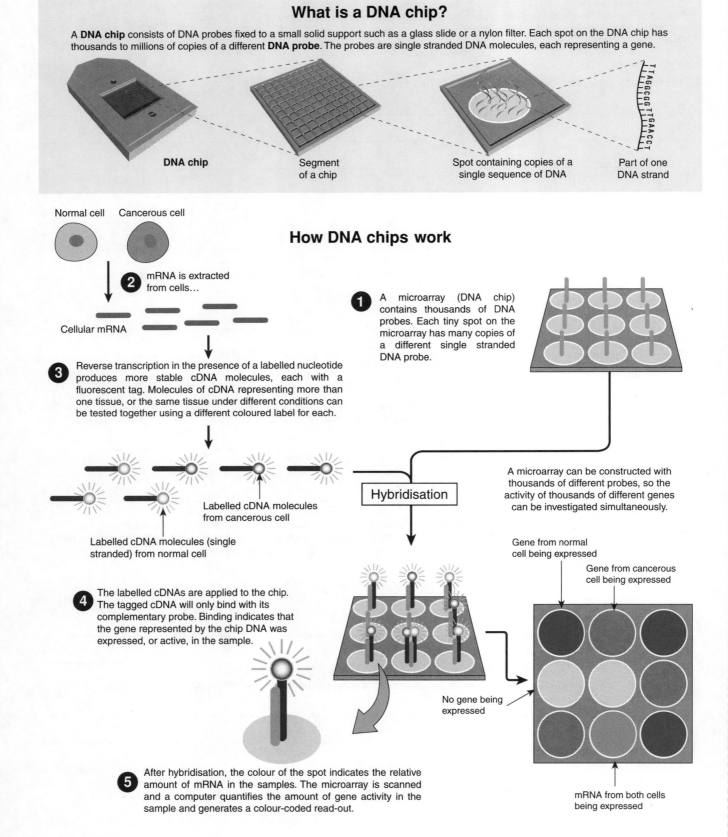

DNA chip

Segment of a chip

Spot containing copies of a single sequence of DNA

Part of one DNA strand

How DNA chips work

Normal cell   Cancerous cell

2 mRNA is extracted from cells...

Cellular mRNA

3 Reverse transcription in the presence of a labelled nucleotide produces more stable cDNA molecules, each with a fluorescent tag. Molecules of cDNA representing more than one tissue, or the same tissue under different conditions can be tested together using a different coloured label for each.

Labelled cDNA molecules from cancerous cell

Labelled cDNA molecules (single stranded) from normal cell

1 A microarray (DNA chip) contains thousands of DNA probes. Each tiny spot on the microarray has many copies of a different single stranded DNA probe.

A microarray can be constructed with thousands of different probes, so the activity of thousands of different genes can be investigated simultaneously.

Hybridisation

4 The labelled cDNAs are applied to the chip. The tagged cDNA will only bind with its complementary probe. Binding indicates that the gene represented by the chip DNA was expressed, or active, in the sample.

Gene from normal cell being expressed

Gene from cancerous cell being expressed

No gene being expressed

5 After hybridisation, the colour of the spot indicates the relative amount of mRNA in the samples. The microarray is scanned and a computer quantifies the amount of gene activity in the sample and generates a colour-coded read-out.

mRNA from both cells being expressed

© 2016 **BIOZONE** International
ISBN: 978-1-927309-32-2
Photocopying Prohibited

1. Describe one purpose of DNA chips: _____

_____

_____

2. (a) Identify the basic principle by which DNA chips work: _____

_____

_____

(b) Identify the role of reverse transcription in DNA chip technology: _____

_____

3. DNA chips (microarrays) can be used to determine which genes are being expressed in a cell. In one type of microarray, hybridisation of the cDNA from cell 1 turns the dot red while hybridisation of the cDNA from cell 2 turns the dot green. Hybridisation of cDNA from both cells turns the dot yellow. In an experiment, cDNA derived from a strain of antibiotic resistant bacteria (cell 1) was labelled with a red fluorescent tag and cDNA derived from a non-resistant strain of the same bacterium (cell 2) was labelled with a green fluorescent tag. The cDNAs were mixed and hybridised to a chip containing spots of DNA from genes 1-25. The results are shown on the right.

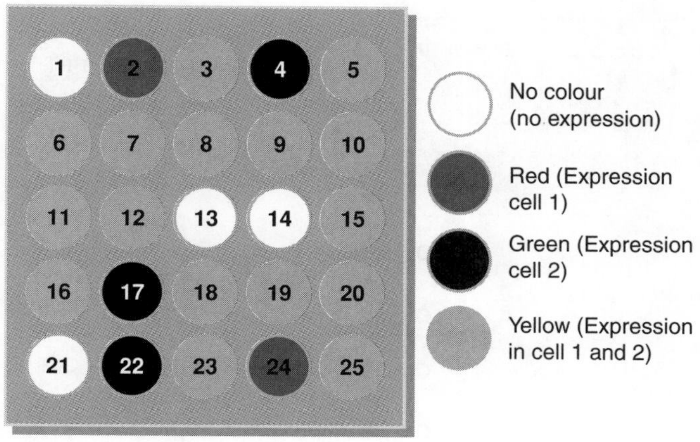

(a) Discuss the conclusions you could make about which genes might be implicated in antibiotic resistance in this case:

_____

_____

_____

(b) Suggest how this information could be used to design new antibiotics that are less vulnerable to resistance:

_____

_____

_____

4. DNA chips are frequently used in diagnostic medicine to compare gene expression in cancerous and non-cancerous tissue. Suggest how this information could be used:

_____

_____

_____

_____

5. Suggest how the study of gene expression might help a genetic engineer produce new crops or manipulate model animals for further research:

_____

_____

_____

_____

_____

187 Comparing DNA Sequences

Key Idea: Bioinformatics is the science of collecting, storing and analysing biological data using computer science.
Bioinformatics involves the collection, analysis, and storage of biochemical information (e.g. DNA sequences) using computer science and mathematics. The advancement of techniques in molecular biology is providing increasingly large amounts of information about the genetic makeup of organisms. Bioinformatics allows this information to be stored in databases where it can be easily retrieved, analysed, and compared. Comparison of DNA or protein sequences between species enables researchers to investigate and better understand their evolutionary relationships.

An overview of the bioinformatics process

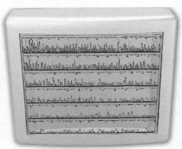

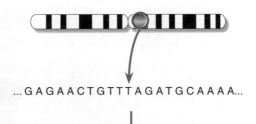

...GAGAACTGTTTAGATGCAAAA...

A gene of interest is selected for analysis.

High throughput 'Next-Gen' sequencing technologies allow the DNA sequence of the gene to be quickly determined.

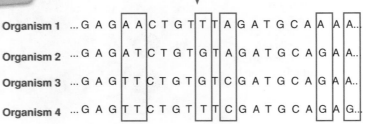

Organism 1 ...GAGAACTGTTTAGATGCAAAA...
Organism 2 ...GAGATCTGTGTAGATGCAGAA...
Organism 3 ...GAGTTCTGTGTCGATGCAGAA...
Organism 4 ...GAGTTCTGTTTCGATGCAGAG...

Powerful computer software can quickly compare the DNA sequences of many organisms. Commonalities and differences in the DNA sequence can help to determine the evolutionary relationships of organisms. The blue boxes indicate differences in the DNA sequences.

Once sequence comparisons have been made, the evolutionary relationships can be displayed as a phylogenetic tree. The example (right) shows the evolutionary relationships of the whales to some other land mammals.

Bioinformatics has played an important role in determining the origin of whales and their transition from a terrestrial (land) form to a fully aquatic form. This phylogenetic tree was determined by comparing retropositional events in whales and some of their closest relatives. Retroposons are repetitive DNA fragments that are inserted into chromosomes after they have been reverse transcribed from a mRNA molecule. Retroposons and their locations are predictable and stable, so they make reliable markers for determining species relationships. If two species have the same retroposons in the same location, they probably share a common ancestor.

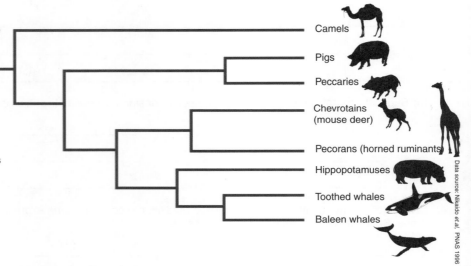

1. How has bioinformatics helped scientists determine the evolutionary relationship of organisms? _____

2. The diagram above shows the relatedness of several mammals as determined by DNA sequencing of 10 genes:

   (a) Which land mammal are whales most related to? _____

   (b) Mark with an arrow on the diagram above where whales and the organism in (a) last shared a common ancestor.

   (c) Pigs were once considered to be the most closely related land ancestor to the whales. Use the phylogenetic tree above to describe the currently accepted relationship.

© 2016 **BIOZONE** International
ISBN: 978-1-927309-32-2
Photocopying Prohibited

188 Genome Projects

Key Idea: A genome is the complete haploid set of genetic material in an organism, including all its genes. The genomes of many organisms have been sequenced and the information compiled in searchable gene databases.

The aim of genome projects is to determine the DNA sequence of an organism's entire genome. Among the thousands of species that have now had their genomes sequenced are species that are important because they are model organisms (e.g. mice), important in agriculture (e.g. honeybee, wheat), or are pests or pathogens (e.g. *Plasmodium*). Genome sizes and the number of genes per genome vary, and are not necessarily correlated with the size and complexity of the organism. Once completed, genome sequences are analysed by computer to identify genes. Gene sequences and details are entered into searchable online databases, which can be used to compare the same genes across different species.

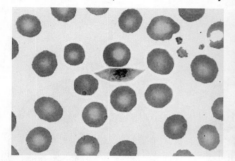

Plasmodium

Plasmodium falciparum is responsible for a particularly severe form of malaria which kills at least a million people a year. The genome for *P. falciparum* was sequenced in 2002 and consists of 23 million bases (Mb) and 5369 genes. Analysis shows that a high proportion of the genes are dedicated to immune evasion. Drugs targeting these genes could produce new kinds of vaccines.

Humans

Sequencing of the human genome was fully completed in 2003. It found that the human genome comprises about 3000 Mb and 22 500 genes. Benefits of the project include advancements in cancer research, drug development, and understanding genetic disease. The project also stimulated a rapid advancement in biotechnology equipment and techniques.

Mice

Mice are a commonly used laboratory model animal. The mouse genome was initially sequenced in 2002 and consists of 2500 MB and 30 000 genes. New drugs destined for human use are often tested on mice because more than 90% of their proteins show similarities to human proteins. Understanding the role of certain genes in mice helps our understanding of similar genes in humans.

The table below outlines the progress made since the beginning of the Human Genome Project (HGP). The push to sequence the human genome drove the development of faster, more powerful sequencing machines. At a cost of US$3 billion, it has produced an estimated economic gain of US$796 billion and created 310 000 jobs.

	Human Genome Project begins	Human Genome Project ends	10 years after HGP
Cost to generate human genome equivalent	US$1 billion	US$10-50 million	US$3-5 thousand
Time to generate human genome equivalent	6-8 years	3-4 months	1-2 days
Total DNA bases in GenBank	49 million bases	31 terabases (10^{12} bp)	150 terabases
Vertebrate genomes sequenced	0	3	112
Non-vertebrate genomes sequenced	0	14	455
Prokaryote genomes sequences	1	167	8750
No. genes with known phenotype/ disease causing mutations	53	1474	2972
Drugs that can be "genetically tailored" to patients.	61	2264	4847

National Human Genome Research Institute

1. List a benefit for each of the three genome projects shown above:

   (a) _____

   (b) _____

   (c) _____

2. How has the cost and time to sequence a human genome equivalent changed since the beginning of the HGP?

   _____

   _____

   _____

3. How many genomes have been sequenced since the beginning of the HGP? _____

   _____

LINK 192   LINK 191   LINK 189   WEB 188   KNOW

189 Bioinformatics and Medicine

Key Idea: Analysis of genomic information could lead to new and more efficient ways of treating or preventing disease. Bioinformatics has the potential to greatly increase the ability of medical technologies to identify, prevent, and treat disease.

Screening a pathogen's genome for antigenic genes and comparing them to already known genes may speed up the development of vaccines and antimicrobial drugs, and extend the tools available to fight disease.

Using bioinformatics in medicine

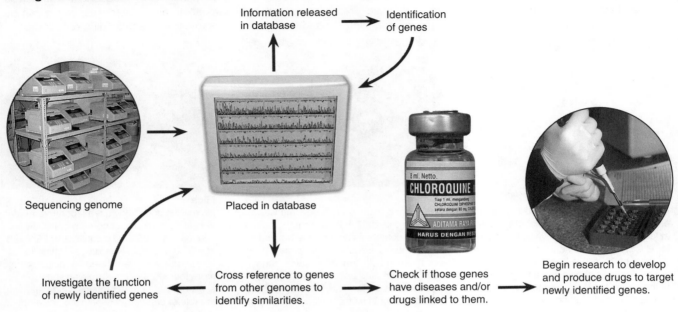

Information released in database → Identification of genes

Sequencing genome

Placed in database

Investigate the function of newly identified genes ← Cross reference to genes from other genomes to identify similarities. → Check if those genes have diseases and/or drugs linked to them. → Begin research to develop and produce drugs to target newly identified genes.

One of the new directions of research in medicine is the development of drugs targeting the gene function or gene products (proteins) of a pathogen. This begins with sequencing a genome (e.g. *Plasmodium*) and adding it to the database of already sequenced genomes. Genes are identified, cross referenced with other known similar genes, and their functions investigated. Any existing drugs targeting similar genes or gene products can then be identified and their effectiveness against the newly identified genes and their products tested. Novel genes can be identified and ways of exploiting them for medical purposes can be investigated.

Malaria and bioinformatics

Reverse vaccinology is a bioinformatics technique in which the entire genome of a pathogen is screened for genes that may produce antigenic properties, e.g. genes that code for extracellular products such as surface proteins. Once the gene is identified, the gene product (protein) is synthesised in the lab and tested in a model organism for an immune response. If successful, the product can then be used as the basis of a vaccine.

Plasmodium sporozoite

Malaria is a disease caused by the protozoan parasite *Plasmodium* of which *P. falciparum* is the most deadly. *Plasmodium* is becoming increasingly drug-resistant so a vaccine offers the best hope of controlling the disease.

The genome of *P. falciparum* was published in 2002. Fifteen loci have been identified as encoding antigens that may be useful in vaccines, including an antigen-rich region on chromosome 10. However only six of the loci appear to be similar to other *Plasmodium* species, reducing the likelihood of developing a single vaccine effective against all species.

1. Explain how bioinformatics and genome sequencing can help produce new vaccines or drugs for a disease:

_____

_____

_____

_____

2. Explain how the completion of *P. falciparum* genome has helped make the development of a malaria vaccine more likely:

_____

_____

_____

_____

© 2016 **BIOZONE** International
ISBN: **978-1-927309-32-2**
Photocopying Prohibited

190 Insulin Production

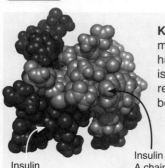

Insulin
B chain

Insulin
A chain

Key Idea: By using microorganisms to make human insulin, problematic issues of cost, allergic reactions, and ethics have been addressed.

The issue

▶ **Type I diabetes mellitus** is a metabolic disease caused by a lack of the protein hormone **insulin**. It affects around 25 in every 100 000 people.

▶ It is treatable only with injections of insulin.

▶ In the past, bovine (cow) or porcine (pig) insulin was used, but extraction and purification was expensive and some patients had severe allergic reactions to the foreign insulin or its contaminants.

▶ Many diseases, e.g. haemophilia and the immune deficiency disease SCID, also arise because an essential protein is missing. Treatment of these diseases is associated with similar problems.

Concept 1
DNA can be cut at specific sites using **restriction enzymes** and joined together using **DNA ligase**. Genes can be inserted into self-replicating bacterial **plasmids** at the point where the cuts are made.

Concept 2
Plasmids are small, circular pieces of DNA found in some bacteria. They usually carry genes useful to the bacterium. *E. coli* plasmids can carry promoters required for the transcription of genes.

Concept 3
Under certain conditions, Bacteria are able to lose or pick up plasmids from their environment. Bacteria can be readily grown in vat cultures at little expense.

Concept 4
The DNA sequences coding for the production of the two polypeptide chains (A and B) that form human insulin can be isolated from the human genome.

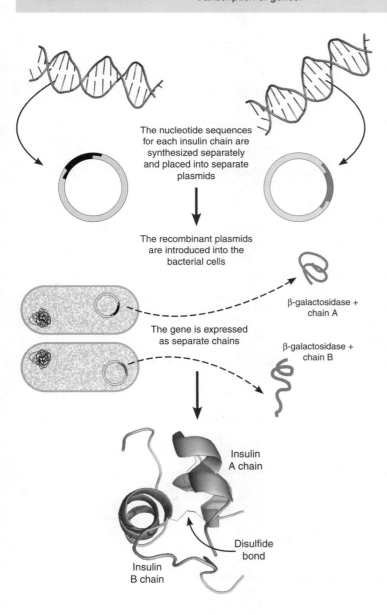

The nucleotide sequences for each insulin chain are synthesized separately and placed into separate plasmids

The recombinant plasmids are introduced into the bacterial cells

The gene is expressed as separate chains

β-galactosidase + chain A

β-galactosidase + chain B

Insulin A chain

Disulfide bond

Insulin B chain

Techniques

The **gene** is **chemically synthesised** as two nucleotide sequences, one for the **insulin A chain** and one for the **insulin B chain**. The two sequences are small enough to be inserted into a plasmid.

Plasmids are extracted from *Escherichia coli*. The gene for the bacterial enzyme β-**galactosidase** is located on the plasmid. To make the bacteria produce insulin, the insulin gene must be linked to the β-**galactosidase** gene, which carries a promoter for transcription.

Restriction enzymes are used to cut plasmids at the appropriate site and the A and B insulin sequences are inserted. The sequences are joined with the plasmid DNA using **DNA ligase**.

The **recombinant plasmids** are inserted back into the bacteria by placing them together in a culture that favours plasmid uptake by bacteria.

The bacteria are then grown and multiplied in vats under carefully controlled growth conditions.

Outcomes

The product consists partly of β-galactosidase, joined with either the A or B chain of insulin. The chains are extracted, purified, and mixed together. The A and B insulin chains connect via **disulfide cross linkages** to form the functional insulin protein. The insulin can then be made ready for injection in various formulations.

Further applications

The techniques used to produce human insulin from genetically modified bacteria can be applied to a range of human proteins and hormones. Proteins produced include factor VIII to treat haemophilia and adenosine deaminase to treat SCID.

258

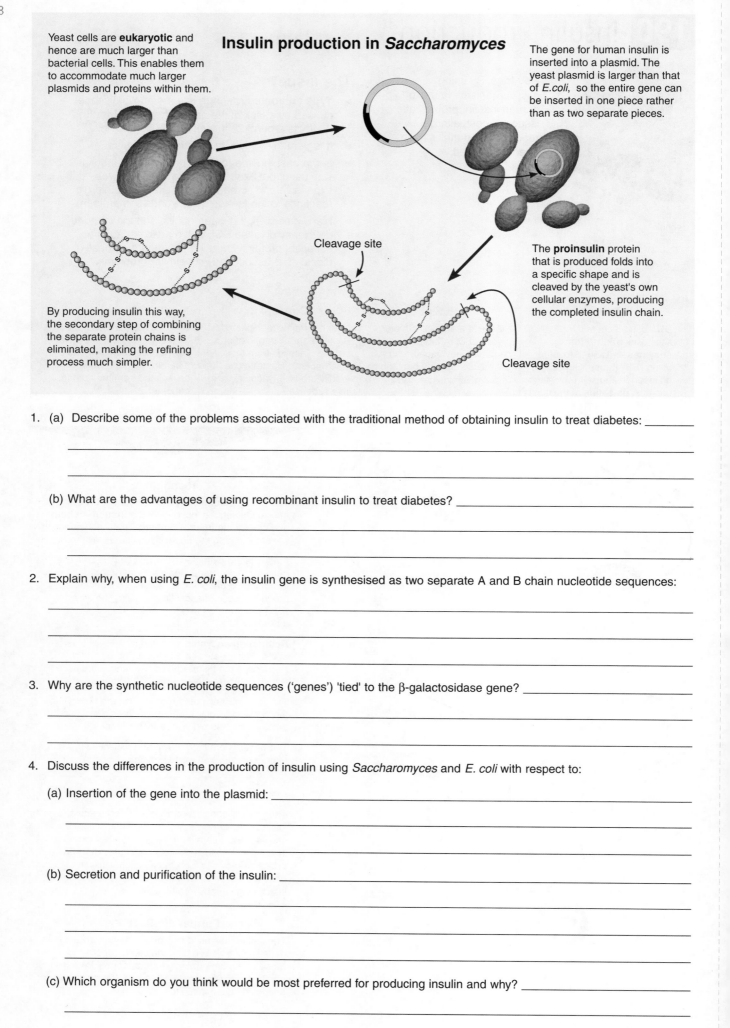

Insulin production in *Saccharomyces*

Yeast cells are **eukaryotic** and hence are much larger than bacterial cells. This enables them to accommodate much larger plasmids and proteins within them.

The gene for human insulin is inserted into a plasmid. The yeast plasmid is larger than that of *E.coli*, so the entire gene can be inserted in one piece rather than as two separate pieces.

Cleavage site

The **proinsulin** protein that is produced folds into a specific shape and is cleaved by the yeast's own cellular enzymes, producing the completed insulin chain.

By producing insulin this way, the secondary step of combining the separate protein chains is eliminated, making the refining process much simpler.

Cleavage site

1. (a) Describe some of the problems associated with the traditional method of obtaining insulin to treat diabetes: _____

_____

_____

(b) What are the advantages of using recombinant insulin to treat diabetes? _____

_____

_____

2. Explain why, when using *E. coli*, the insulin gene is synthesised as two separate A and B chain nucleotide sequences:

_____

_____

_____

3. Why are the synthetic nucleotide sequences ('genes') 'tied' to the β-galactosidase gene? _____

_____

_____

4. Discuss the differences in the production of insulin using *Saccharomyces* and *E. coli* with respect to:

(a) Insertion of the gene into the plasmid: _____

_____

_____

(b) Secretion and purification of the insulin: _____

_____

_____

_____

(c) Which organism do you think would be most preferred for producing insulin and why? _____

_____

191 Screening for Genes

Key Idea: Gene screening uses DNA probes to identify the presence and location of specific genes. It can be used to detect the presence of mutations associated with disease. Once a gene sequence is known, DNA probes can be used to determine if an individual has that specific gene (or a specific mutation). A DNA probe is a fragment of DNA or RNA, which is complementary to a known DNA sequence (the target sequence) and so will bind to it. The probe has a radioactive or fluorescent label so it can be visualised (e.g. under UV light) when it is bound to its target sequence. This technique is called **genetic screening** and is used to screen individuals for gene mutations associated with specific diseases.

Why screen for disease?

Many diseases are caused by specific gene mutations, and there are many reasons people choose to undergo gene screening tests.

▶ Identify people who may be at an increased risk of developing a certain disease.

▶ Determine the severity of a known disease.

▶ Identify carriers of certain diseases and determine the likelihood of the disease developing in their future children.

▶ Help doctors decide the best medicines or treatment to use on an individual.

Screening can be carried out at different times, for example on gametes, embryos, children, or adults.

Many diseases have a genetic origin and they often run in families. If one person has a heritable genetic mutation associated with a certain disease, this Information can be useful to other family members. It can raise awareness of the condition and allow others who may not be showing symptoms of the disease to seek testing and treatment if required.

Genetic screening can also be useful for couples making a decision about whether to have a child or not. Genetic testing may be offered when someone in the family is a carrier for a particular condition. The couple can then analyse and discuss the risks of their children developing the disease, and make an informed decision about whether or not to have children.

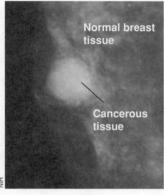
Normal breast tissue / Cancerous tissue

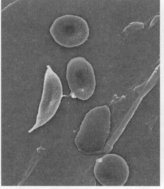

CF patients need therapy to clear the lungs of mucus

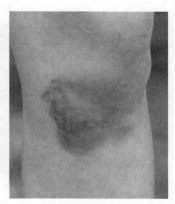

People with the **BRCA** gene mutation have an increased risk of developing breast cancer. Some families with a history of breast cancer screen for the BRCA gene. If the test is positive, a number of steps can be taken to reduce the risk of cancer developing. These include increased screening for early detection, drug therapies, and surgical removal of the breasts.

Sickle cell disease is caused by a mutation in the haemoglobin gene. The disease can be detected using a blood test, but a genetic test will determine the nature of the mutation (e.g. HbS or the milder HbC). It can also determine if a person has one copy of the gene or two. Additionally genetic testing can be done prenatally using a sample of amniotic fluid.

Cystic fibrosis (CF) is caused by a mutation to the CFTR gene. It causes excess mucus production, which affects breathing, and endocrine and gastrointestinal function. Gene testing for the most common mutation can identify carriers (people with one copy of the mutation and no symptoms). People with two copies of the mutation will have CF.

The most common forms of haemophilia are haemophilia A and B. They are caused by mutations in the genes for clotting factor VIII and XI on the X chromosome. Haemophilia A is most commonly caused by an inversion mutation, which can be detected relatively easily with genetic screening. However, more than 1000 mutations can cause haemophilia.

1. (a) How can genetic screening help in the early detection of disease? _____

_____

_____

(b) What are the advantages of early disease detection? _____

_____

_____

2. A family has a history of a certain genetic disease. Why might members of this family want to be screened for the disease before they start a family of their own?

_____

_____

_____

© 2016 **BIOZONE** International
ISBN: 978-1-927309-32-2
Photocopying Prohibited

LINK 194   LINK 95   LINK 94   WEB 191   KNOW

192 Gene Therapy

Key Idea: Gene therapy aims to replace faulty genes by using a vector to transfer the correctly functioning gene into a patient's DNA.

Gene therapy uses gene technology to treat disease by correcting or replacing faulty genes. Although the details vary, all gene therapies are based around the same technique. The correct non-faulty gene is inserted into a vector, a carrier which transfers the DNA into the patient's cells (**transfection**). The vector is introduced into a sample of the patient's cells, and these are cultured to amplify the correct gene. The cultured

cells are then transferred back to the patient. The use of altered stem cells instead of mature somatic cells has achieved longer lasting results in many patients. The treatment of somatic cells or stem cells is therapeutic (provides a benefit) but the changes are not inherited. **Germline therapy** (modification of the gametes) would enable genetic changes to be passed on. Gene therapy has had limited success because transfection of targeted cells is inefficient, and the side effects can be severe or even fatal. However, gene therapy to treat SCID, a genetic disease affecting the immune system, has had some success.

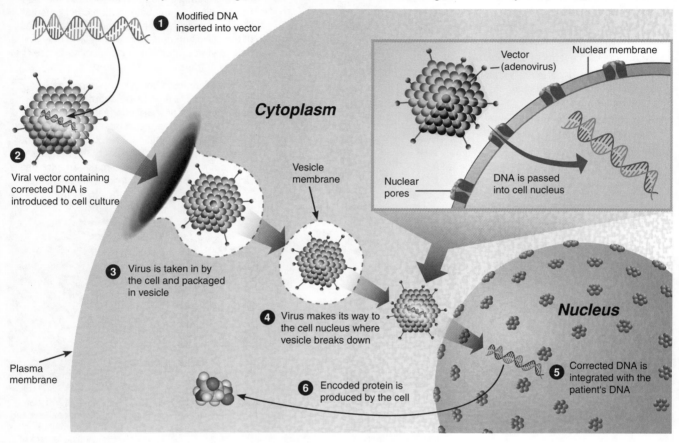

1. (a) Describe the general principle of gene therapy: _____

_____

_____

(b) Describe the medical areas where gene therapy might be used: _____

_____

_____

2. Explain the significance of transfecting **germline cells** rather than **somatic cells**: _____

_____

_____

_____

3. Explain the purpose of **gene amplification** in gene therapy: _____

_____

_____

193 Vectors for Gene Transfer

Key Idea: Several different carriers, called vectors, can be used to introduce a gene into the cell of another organism. There are advantages and problems associated with each. The transfer of a gene to the cell of another organism (e.g. in gene therapy) usually requires a **vector** (carrier), which is first engineered to carry the gene of interest. The vector may be able to transfer the gene to cultured host cells directly or the vector may be delivered by transfection (below).

Viruses

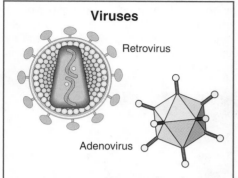

Retrovirus

Adenovirus

Viruses are well known for their ability to insert DNA into a host cell. For this reason they have become a favoured tool in transgenesis. Different types of viruses integrate their DNA into the host in different ways. This allows scientists to control where and for how long the new DNA is expressed in the host. However, the size of the piece of DNA that can be transferred is limited to about 8 kb. Also, integration of the DNA into the host DNA can cause unexpected side effects depending on where in the host's chromosome the DNA inserts itself.

Liposomes

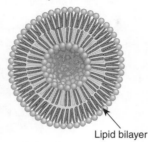

Lipid bilayer

Liposomes are spherical bodies of lipid bilayer. They can be quite large and targeted to specific types of cell by placing specific receptors on their surfaces. Because of their size, liposomes can carry plasmids 20 kb or more. They also do not trigger immune responses when used in gene therapy, but are less efficient than viruses at transferring the plasmid into a target cell.

Plasmids

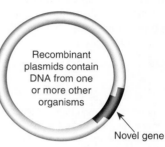

Recombinant plasmids contain DNA from one or more other organisms

Novel gene

Plasmids are circular lengths of DNA that can be up to 1000 kb long (1 kb = 1000 bp). Recombinant plasmids are frequently used to produce transgenic organisms, especially bacteria. The bacteria maybe the final target for the recombinant DNA (e.g. transgenic *E. coli* producing insulin) or it can be used as a vector to transfer the DNA to a different host (e.g. *Agrobacterium tumefaciens* is used to transfer the *Ti* plasmid to plants). In gene therapy, plasmids by themselves, as naked DNA, are unstable and not particularly efficient at integrating DNA into a target cell.

Transferring the DNA

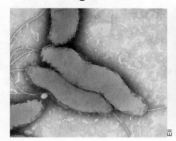
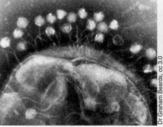

Electroporation cuvettes

Transformation is the direct uptake of foreign DNA and is common in bacteria. Recombinant DNA plasmids are mixed with bacteria and the bacteria that take up the DNA are used.

Transduction is the transfer of DNA into a bacterium by a virus. Bacteriophages (viruses that infect bacteria) are commonly used to integrate recombinant DNA into a target bacterium.

Transfection is the deliberate, introduction of foreign DNA into a cell, often in a liposome vector. There are numerous methods including electroporation and the use of the gene gun (above).

Electroporation is a method in which an electric field is applied to cells, causing the plasma membrane to become more permeable. This allows DNA to cross the plasma membrane.

1. (a) Describe a feature of viruses that make them well suited as **vectors** for DNA transfer: _____

_____

_____

(b) Identify two problems with using viral vectors for DNA transfer: _____

_____

_____

2. (a) Describe some advantages of using liposomes to deliver genes: _____

_____

_____

(b) Which method do you think would be most suitable for transfer of a liposome vector to a host and why? _____

_____

194 Gene Delivery Systems

Key Idea: The delivery of genes into target cells and then into patients has proved technically difficult, limiting the use of gene therapy.

It remains technically difficult to deliver genes successfully to a patient, limiting the success rate of gene therapy treatments. Any improvements have been mostly short-lived, or counteracted by adverse side effects. The inserted genes may reach only about 1% of target cells. Those that reach their target may work inefficiently and produce too little protein, too slowly to be of benefit. Many patients also have immune reactions to the vectors used in gene transfer. One of the first gene therapy trials was for cystic fibrosis (CF). CF was an obvious candidate for gene therapy because, in most cases, the disease is caused by a single, known gene mutation. However, despite its early promise, gene therapy for this disease has been disappointing (below right). Severe Combined Immune Deficiency (SCID) is another candidate for gene therapy, again because the disease is caused by single, known mutation (below left). Gene therapies for this disease have so far proved promising.

Treating SCID using gene therapy

The most common form of **SCID** (Severe Combined Immune Deficiency) is **X-linked SCID**, which results from mutations to a gene on the X chromosome encoding the **common gamma chain**, a protein forming part of a receptor complex for numerous types of leucocytes. A less common form of the disease, (**ADA-SCID**) is caused by a defective gene that codes for the enzyme adenosine deaminase (ADA).

Both of these types of SCID lead to immune system failure. A common treatment for SCID is bone marrow transplant, but this is not always successful and runs the risks of infection from unscreened viruses. **Gene therapy** appears to hold the best chances of producing a cure for SCID because the mutation affects only one gene whose location is known. DNA containing the corrected gene is placed into a **gutted retrovirus** and introduced to a sample of the patient's **bone marrow.** The treated cells are then returned to the patient.

In some patients with ADA-SCID, treatment was so successful that supplementation with purified ADA (produced using genetically modified bacteria) was no longer required. The treatment carries risks though. In early trials, two of ten treated patients developed leukaemia when the corrected gene was inserted next to a gene regulating cell growth.

Samples of bone marrow being extracted prior to treatment with gene therapy.

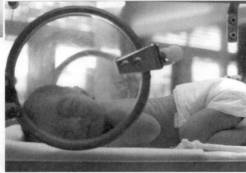

Detection of SCID is difficult for the first months of an infant's life due to the mother's antibodies being present in the blood. Suspected SCID patients must be kept in sterile conditions at all times to avoid infection.

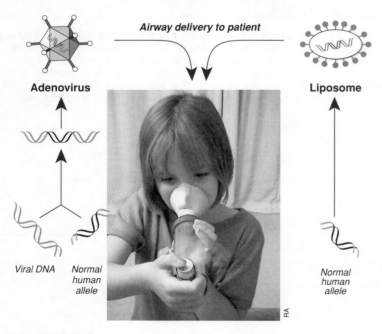

Airway delivery to patient

Adenovirus

Viral DNA   *Normal human allele*

An **adenovirus** that normally causes colds is genetically modified to make it safe and to carry the normal (unmutated) CFTR ('cystic fibrosis') gene.

Liposome

Normal human allele

Liposomes are tiny fat globules. Normal CF genes are enclosed in liposomes, which fuse with plasma membranes and deliver the genes into the cells.

Gene therapy - potential treatment for cystic fibrosis?

Cystic fibrosis (CF) is caused by a mutation to the gene coding for a chloride ion channel important in creating sweat, digestive juices, and mucus. The dysfunction results in abnormally thick, sticky mucus that accumulates in the lungs and intestines. The identification and isolation of the CF gene in 1989 meant that scientists could look for ways in which to correct the genetic defect rather than just treating the symptoms using traditional therapies.

The main target of CF gene therapy is the lung, because the progressive lung damage associated with the disease is eventually lethal.

In trials, normal genes were isolated and inserted into patients using vectors such as **adenoviruses** and **liposomes**, delivered via the airways (left). The results of trials were disappointing: on average, there was only a 25% correction, the effects were short lived, and the benefits were quickly reversed. Alarmingly, the adenovirus used in one of the trials led to the death of one patient.

Source: Cystic Fibrosis Trust, UK.

© 2016 **BIOZONE** International
ISBN: 978-1-927309-32-2
Photocopying Prohibited

1. A great deal of current research is being devoted to discovering a gene therapy solution to treat **cystic fibrosis** (CF):

    (a) Describe the symptoms of CF: _____

    _____

    _____

    (b) Why has this particular genetic disease been so eagerly targeted by geneticists? _____

    _____

    _____

    _____

    _____

    (c) Outline some of the problems so far encountered with gene therapy for CF: _____

    _____

    _____

    _____

    _____

    _____

    _____

2. Identify two vectors for introducing healthy CFTR genes into CF patients.

    (a) Vector 1: _____

    (b) Vector 2: _____

3. (a) Describe the difference between X-linked SCID and ADA-SCID: _____

    _____

    (b) Identify the vector used in the treatment of SCID: _____

    _____

4. Briefly outline the differences in the gene therapy treatment of CF and SCID:_____

    _____

    _____

    _____

    _____

5. Changes made to chromosomes as a result of gene therapy involving somatic cells are not inherited. Germ-line gene therapy has the potential to cure disease, but the risks and benefits are still not clear. For each of the points outlined below, evaluate the risk of germ-line gene therapy relative to somatic cell gene therapy and explain your answer:

    (a) Chance of interfering with an essential gene function: _____

    _____

    _____

    _____

    (b) Misuse of the therapy to selectively alter phenotype: _____

    _____

    _____

    _____

195 Ethics of Gene Technology in Medicine

Key Idea: Gene technology can be used to identify and in some cases repair specific (often harmful) mutations in genes in embryos, children, and adults. It raises many ethical issues, especially for embryo testing.

The genetic screening of gametes, embryos, children, and adults for some diseases is now possible. Genetic screening has many applications including in the detection and treatment of diseases. Whilst genetic screening has many positive applications, it raises a number of ethical issues. This is particularly the case for the screening of embryos and fetuses because it may result in the destruction of embryos and fetuses if they have genetic defects, or even an undesirable genotype (e.g. the wrong sex). Gene therapy raises separate issues, including the assessment of risk if inserted genes disrupt other genes, and the issues surrounding the correction of germline cells.

Genetic screening and gene therapy

Carrier testing: A person with a family history for a disease may want to be tested to see if they carry the gene for that disease. The result may influence whether or not they choose to have children.

Diagnostic testing: A person may have symptoms typical of a particular genetic disorder. Genetic screening is used to determine if the person has the gene associated with a particular disease or not.

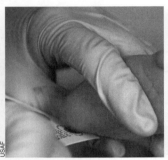

Newborn screening: Newborns are screened for a range of metabolic disorders (e.g. phenylketonuria). If a disease is detected, treatment can begin immediately and the child's prognosis is improved.

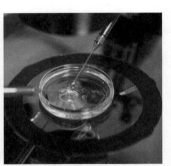

Gene therapy: Somatic cells with faulty genes can have corrected genes inserted into them, alleviating the symptoms of disease in an individual. If the correction is made to germline cells (gametes), the correction will be inherited.

Arguments for gene technology

▸ Testing allows potential carriers to be screened for a disease so they can decide whether they have children or not. This is important for diseases that do not show any symptoms until later in life (e.g. Huntington's disease).

▸ Researchers can study individuals with the gene(s) associated with a disease and this may help them to develop a treatment or cure for that disease.

▸ Knowing a person's genetic make-up can be used to optimise drug therapies and improve treatment outcomes.

▸ Knowing the risk of developing a disease allows informed decisions to be made about medical options. For example, breast cancer can be treated, so an individual may decide to increase screening to increase the chance of early detection. They may choose to reduce risk factors (e.g. breast removal if they are at high risk of developing breast cancer).

▸ Gene therapy can be used to place corrected genes into cells that are unable to make specific proteins due to faulty genes. The corrected cells can then produce the correct proteins.

Arguments against gene technology

▸ Genetic tests can only tell you if you carry a gene for an associated disorder. They cannot predict when and if you will develop the disease, or to what extent. Testing therefore carries the risk of causing unnecessary anxiety.

▸ An individual's privacy may be compromised by testing. The knowledge that you may develop a genetic disorder in the future could be used against you (e.g. medical insurance could be declined or an employer may no longer want to employ you).

▸ Designer babies could be produced where parents pick certain characteristics they want their child to have. This is already seen in countries where more value is placed on the birth of a boy child than a girl, and unwanted female fetuses are terminated.

▸ The discovery of a genetic defect in an unborn child may lead to the decision to terminate the pregnancy, an action some people believe is morally wrong because they feel it devalues human life.

▸ Corrected genes insert randomly into DNA. They can trigger cancer if they disrupt other important genes.

1. Describe advantages and disadvantages of gene technology for gene screening and gene therapy:

_____

_____

_____

© 2016 **BIOZONE** International
ISBN: 978-1-927309-32-2
Photocopying Prohibited

196 DNA Profiling Using PCR

Key Idea: Short units of DNA that repeat a different number of times in different people can be used to produce individual genetic profiles.

In chromosomes, some of the DNA contains simple, repetitive sequences. These non-coding nucleotide sequences repeat over and over again and are found scattered throughout the genome. Some repeating sequences, called **microsatellites** or **short tandem repeats** (STRs), are very short (2-6 base pairs) and can repeat up to 100 times. The human genome has many different microsatellites. Equivalent sequences in different people vary considerably in the numbers of the repeating unit. This phenomenon has been used to develop

DNA profiling, which identifies the natural variations found in every person's DNA. Identifying these DNA differences is a useful tool for forensic investigations. DNA testing in the UK is carried out by the Forensic Science Service (FSS). The FSS targets 10 STR sites; enough to guarantee that the odds of someone else sharing the same result are extremely unlikely; about one in a thousand million (a billion). DNA profiling has been used to help solve previously unsolved crimes and to assist in current or future investigations. DNA profiling can also be used to establish genetic relatedness (e.g. in paternity disputes or pedigree disputes), or when searching for a specific gene (e.g. screening for disease).

Microsatellites (short tandem repeats)

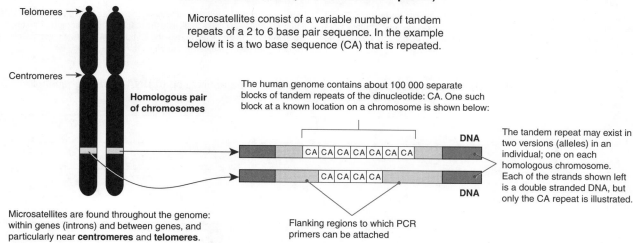

Microsatellites consist of a variable number of tandem repeats of a 2 to 6 base pair sequence. In the example below it is a two base sequence (CA) that is repeated.

Telomeres →

Centromeres →

Homologous pair of chromosomes

The human genome contains about 100 000 separate blocks of tandem repeats of the dinucleotide: CA. One such block at a known location on a chromosome is shown below:

CA CA CA CA CA CA CA   **DNA**

CA CA CA CA   **DNA**

The tandem repeat may exist in two versions (alleles) in an individual; one on each homologous chromosome. Each of the strands shown left is a double stranded DNA, but only the CA repeat is illustrated.

Microsatellites are found throughout the genome: within genes (introns) and between genes, and particularly near **centromeres** and **telomeres**.

Flanking regions to which PCR primers can be attached

How short tandem repeats are used in DNA profiling

This diagram shows how three people can have quite different microsatellite arrangements at the same point (locus) in their DNA. Each will produce a different DNA profile using gel electrophoresis:

1 **Extract DNA from sample**

A sample collected from the tissue of a living or dead organism is treated with chemicals and enzymes to extract the DNA, which is separated and purified.

2 **Amplify microsatellite using PCR**

Specific primers (arrowed) that attach to the flanking regions (light grey) either side of the microsatellite are used to make large quantities of the micro-satellite and flanking regions sequence only (no other part of the DNA is amplified/replicated).

3 **Visualise fragments on a gel**

The fragments are separated by length, using **gel electrophoresis**. DNA, which is negatively charged, moves toward the positive terminal. The smaller fragments travel faster than larger ones.

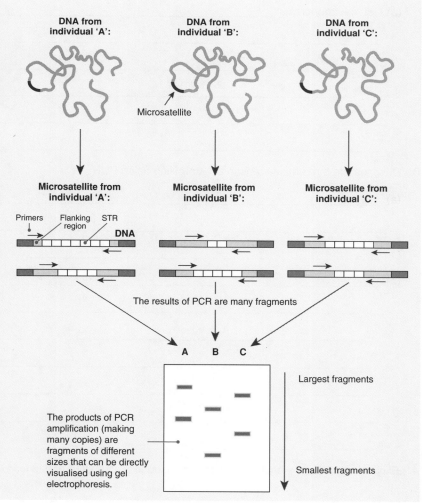

DNA from individual 'A':

DNA from individual 'B':

DNA from individual 'C':

Microsatellite

Microsatellite from individual 'A':

Microsatellite from individual 'B':

Microsatellite from individual 'C':

Primers   Flanking region   STR   **DNA**

The results of PCR are many fragments

A   B   C

Largest fragments

The products of PCR amplification (making many copies) are fragments of different sizes that can be directly visualised using gel electrophoresis.

Smallest fragments

LINK 197   LINK 182   WEB 196   KNOW

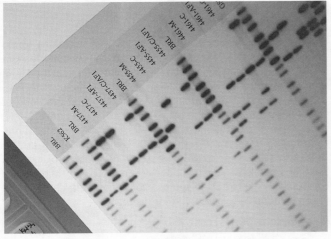
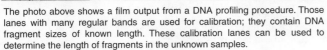

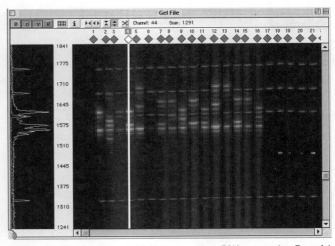

The photo above shows a film output from a DNA profiling procedure. Those lanes with many regular bands are used for calibration; they contain DNA fragment sizes of known length. These calibration lanes can be used to determine the length of fragments in the unknown samples.

DNA profiling can be automated in the same way as DNA sequencing. Powerful computer software is able to display the results of many samples that are run at the same time. In the photo above, the sample in lane 4 has been selected and displays fragments of different length on the left of the screen.

1. Describe the properties of **short tandem repeats** that are important to the application of **DNA profiling** technology:

_____

_____

_____

_____

_____

_____

2. Explain the role of each of the following techniques in the process of DNA profiling:

(a) Gel electrophoresis: _____

_____

_____

(b) PCR: _____

_____

_____

3. Describe the three main steps in DNA profiling using PCR:

(a) _____

_____

_____

(b) _____

_____

_____

(c) _____

_____

_____

4. Explain why as many as 10 STR sites are used to gain a DNA profile for forensic evidence: _____

_____

197 Forensic Applications of DNA Profiling

Key Idea: DNA profiling has many forensic applications, from identifying criminal offenders to saving endangered species. The use of DNA as a tool for solving crimes such as homicide is well known, but it can also has several other applications.

DNA evidence has been used to identify body parts, solve cases of industrial sabotage and contamination, for paternity testing, and even in identifying animal products illegally made from endangered species.

1

DNA left behind when offender drunk from a cup in the kitchen.

Offender was wearing a cap but lost it when disturbed. DNA can be retrieved from flakes of skin and hair.

Bloodstain. DNA can be extracted from white blood cells in the sample

Hair. DNA can be recovered from cells at the base of the strand of hair.

During the initial investigation, samples of material that may contain DNA are taken for analysis. At a crime scene, this may include blood and body fluids as well as samples of clothing or objects that the offender might have touched. Samples from the victim are also taken to eliminate them as a possible source of contamination.

2 DNA is isolated and profiles are made from all samples and compared to known DNA profiles such as that of the victim.

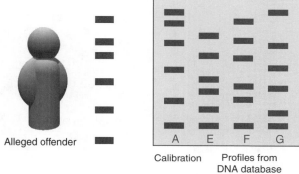

| A | B | C | D |

Calibration   Profiles of collected DNA   Investigator (C)   Victim (D)

3 Unknown DNA samples are compared to DNA databases of convicted offenders and to the DNA of the alleged offender.

Alleged offender

| A | E | F | G |

Calibration   Profiles from DNA database

4 Although it does not make a complete case, DNA profiling, in conjunction with other evidence, is one of the most powerful tools in identifying offenders or unknown tissues.

The role of frequency and probability

Every person has two copies of each chromosome and therefore two copies (alleles) of every testable DNA marker. For example, the short tandem repeat (STR) known as CSF1PO contains between 7 and 15 repeats of GATA and has 9 possible alleles. Some alleles (and therefore genotypes) are more common in the population that others. For the CSF1PO STR, the frequency of the genotype 10,11 (allele 10 and allele 11) is 0.1270, i.e. it appears in 12.7% of the population. When DNA is tested, a number of STRs are sampled (the exact number varies between countries). When the data from all STRs is considered, levels of probability that the DNA came from a certain person can be calculated to 1 in 500 trillion.

Allele frequencies of the CSF1PO STR

Allele (number of repeats)	Frequency	Allele (number of repeats)	Frequency
7	0.0232	12	0.3446
8	0.0212	13	0.0656
9	0.0294	14	0.0092
10	0.2321	15	0.0010
11	0.2736		

1. Why are DNA profiles obtained for both the victim and investigator? _____

_____

_____

2. Use the evidence to decide if the alleged offender is innocent or guilty and explain your decision:

_____

_____

3. What is the frequency of the following CSF1PO alleles:

(a) 9: _____ (b) 12: _____

(c) The 9, 12 genotype (*hint, use the Hardy-Weinberg equation*): _____

198 Finding the Connection

Key Idea: Using specific DNA sequences to identify breeds and the relationships between them can be useful in developing future livestock.

In the UK there are a number of different sheep breeds, each of which has been bred for a specific purpose (e.g. meat of wool production). While some of these breeds are very old, others are recent developments. As new sheep breeds are

developed by selective breeding, older breeds become less profitable and are eventually replaced. These older breeds are important because they carry traits that could be valuable but are now absent in more recent breeds. The relationships between the older and newer breeds are important as they show the development of breeds and help farmers and breeders to plan for the future development of their livestock.

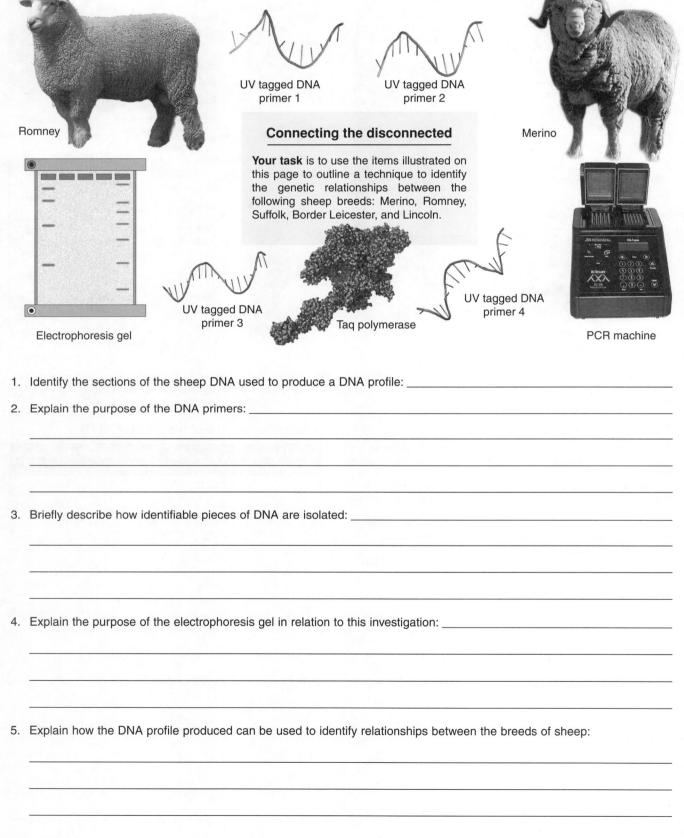

Romney

UV tagged DNA primer 1

UV tagged DNA primer 2

Merino

Connecting the disconnected

Your task is to use the items illustrated on this page to outline a technique to identify the genetic relationships between the following sheep breeds: Merino, Romney, Suffolk, Border Leicester, and Lincoln.

UV tagged DNA primer 3

Taq polymerase

UV tagged DNA primer 4

Electrophoresis gel

PCR machine

1. Identify the sections of the sheep DNA used to produce a DNA profile: _____

2. Explain the purpose of the DNA primers: _____

_____

_____

_____

3. Briefly describe how identifiable pieces of DNA are isolated: _____

_____

_____

_____

4. Explain the purpose of the electrophoresis gel in relation to this investigation: _____

_____

_____

_____

5. Explain how the DNA profile produced can be used to identify relationships between the breeds of sheep:

_____

_____

_____

© 2016 **BIOZONE** International
ISBN: 978-1-927309-32-2
Photocopying Prohibited

199 Applications of Genetic Engineering

Key Idea: Transgenesis is the insertion of a gene from one species into another, so its protein product is expressed in the second species. Transgenesis has many applications including agriculture, and food and medical technologies. Transgenesis refers to the specific genetic engineering technique of inserting a gene from one species into another that does not normally contain the gene. It allows direct modification of a genome so that novel traits can be introduced to an organism. Organisms that have undergone transgenesis are called transgenic organisms. The genes are inserted using vectors or by direct insertion of the DNA. Applications of transgenesis include enhancing desirable features in livestock and crops, producing human proteins, and treating genetic defects with gene therapy. Cloning transgenics, or using them in selective breeding programmes, ensures the introduced gene is inherited in following generations.

Creating transgenic Bt maize

1 The Bt gene from the bacterium *Bacillus thuringiensis* is extracted and amplified by PCR.

2 Promoter and terminator sequences are added so the gene can be expressed in the target plant cell.

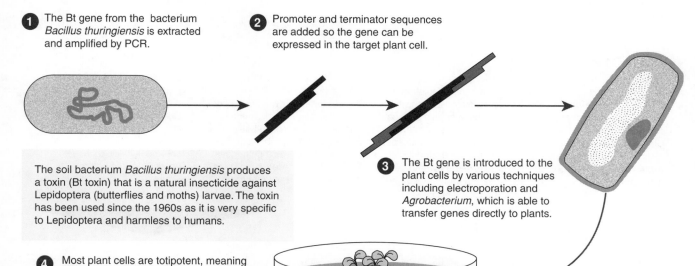

The soil bacterium *Bacillus thuringiensis* produces a toxin (Bt toxin) that is a natural insecticide against Lepidoptera (butterflies and moths) larvae. The toxin has been used since the 1960s as it is very specific to Lepidoptera and harmless to humans.

3 The Bt gene is introduced to the plant cells by various techniques including electroporation and *Agrobacterium*, which is able to transfer genes directly to plants.

4 Most plant cells are totipotent, meaning they can be used to grow new plants. Those displaying Bt toxin production are matured in a greenhouse and bred. The seeds will also contain the Bt gene.

Applications of transgenesis

Modifying crops

Transgenesis has been used to modify the genome of Bt cotton (above) and maize to include genes that produce insecticides. Herbicide resistant rapeseed has also been produced. Studies show the herbicide resistance genes are now found in wild rapeseed.

Medical research

By inserting genes into model animals, the effect of a gene can be studied. Rhesus macaques have been engineered to provide models for the effects and potential treatments of diseases such as Huntington's and Parkinson's.

Livestock improvement

Transgenic sheep have been used to enhance wool production. The keratin protein of wool contains large amounts of the amino acid cysteine. Injecting developing sheep with the genes for the enzymes that generate cysteine produces woollier sheep.

Animals as biofactories

Transgenic animals can be used as biofactories to produce certain proteins. Transgenic sheep with the human α-1-antitrypsin gene produce the protein in their milk from which it can be extracted and used to treat hereditary emphysema.

1. What is transgenesis? _____

_____

2. Describe an application of transgenesis: _____

_____

_____

3. Describe a possible problem with transgenesis:_____

_____

_____

© 2016 **BIOZONE** International
ISBN: 978-1-927309-32-2
Photocopying Prohibited

LINK 202 LINK 200 KNOW

200 Transgenic Plant: Golden Rice

Key Idea: The use of recombinant DNA to build a new metabolic pathway has greatly increased the nutritional value of a variety of rice.

The issue

▶ **Beta-carotene** (β-carotene) is a precursor to **vitamin A** which is involved in many functions including vision, immunity, fetal development, and skin health.

▶ Vitamin A deficiency is common in developing countries where up to 500 000 children suffer from night blindness, and death rates due to infections are high due to a lowered immune response.

▶ Providing enough food containing useful quantities of β-carotene is difficult and expensive in many countries.

Concept 1
Rice is a staple food in many developing countries. It is grown in large quantities and is available to most of the population, but it lacks many of the essential nutrients required by the human body for healthy development. It is low in β-carotene.

Concept 2
Rice plants produce β-carotene but not in the edible rice endosperm. Engineering a new biosynthetic pathway would allow β-carotene to be produced in the endosperm. Genes expressing enzymes for carotene synthesis can be inserted into the rice genome.

Concept 3
The enzyme **carotene desaturase** (CRT1) in the soil bacterium *Erwinia uredovora*, catalyses multiple steps in carotenoid biosynthesis. **Phytoene synthase** (PSY) overexpresses a colourless carotene in the daffodil plant *Narcissus pseudonarcissus*.

Concept 4
DNA can be inserted into an organism's genome using a suitable vector. *Agrobacterium tumefaciens* is a tumour-forming bacterial plant pathogen that is commonly used to insert novel DNA into plants.

The development of golden rice

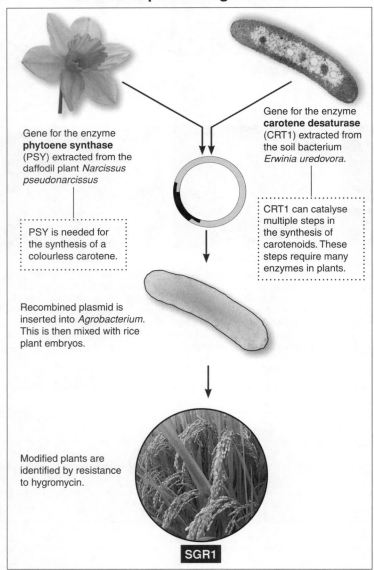

Gene for the enzyme **phytoene synthase** (PSY) extracted from the daffodil plant *Narcissus pseudonarcissus*

PSY is needed for the synthesis of a colourless carotene.

Gene for the enzyme **carotene desaturase** (CRT1) extracted from the soil bacterium *Erwinia uredovora*.

CRT1 can catalyse multiple steps in the synthesis of carotenoids. These steps require many enzymes in plants.

Recombined plasmid is inserted into *Agrobacterium*. This is then mixed with rice plant embryos.

Modified plants are identified by resistance to hygromycin.

SGR1

Techniques

The **PSY** gene from daffodils and the **CRT1** gene from *Erwinia uredovora* are sequenced.

DNA sequences are synthesised into packages containing the CRT1 or PSY gene, terminator sequences, and **endosperm specific promoters** (these ensure expression of the gene only in the edible portion of the rice).

The *Ti* plasmid from *Agrobacterium* is modified using restriction enzymes and DNA ligase to delete the tumour-forming gene and insert the synthesised DNA packages. A gene for resistance to the antibiotic **hygromycin** is also inserted so that transformed plants can be identified later. The parts of the *Ti* plasmid required for plant transformation are retained.

Modified *Ti* plasmid is inserted into the bacterium.

Agrobacterium is incubated with rice plant embryo. Transformed embryos are identified by their resistance to hygromycin.

Outcomes

The rice produced had endosperm with a distinctive yellow colour. Under greenhouse conditions golden rice (**SGR1**) contained 1.6 µg per g of carotenoids. Levels up to five times higher were produced in the field, probably due to improved growing conditions.

Further applications

Further research on the action of the PSY gene identified more efficient methods for the production of β-carotene. The second generation of golden rice now contains up to 37 µg per g of carotenoids. Golden rice was the first instance where a complete biosynthetic pathway was engineered. The procedures could be applied to other food plants to increase their nutrient levels.

The ability of *Agrobacterium* to transfer genes to plants is exploited for crop improvement. The tumour-inducing *Ti* plasmid is modified to delete the tumour-forming gene and insert a gene coding for a desirable trait. The parts of the *Ti* plasmid required for plant transformation are retained.

Soybeans are one of the many food crops that have been genetically modified for broad spectrum herbicide resistance. The first GM soybeans were planted in the US in 1996. By 2007, nearly 60% of the global soybean crop was genetically modified; the highest of any other crop plant.

GM cotton was produced by inserting the gene for the BT toxin into its genome. The bacterium *Bacillus thuringiensis* naturally produces BT toxin, which is harmful to a range of insects, including the larvae that eat cotton. The BT gene causes cotton to produce this insecticide in its tissues.

1. Describe the basic methodology used to create golden rice: _____

   _____

   _____

   _____

   _____

2. Explain how scientists ensured β-carotene was produced in the endosperm: _____

   _____

   _____

   _____

3. What property of *Agrobacterium tumefaciens* makes it an ideal vector for introducing new genes into plants?

   _____

   _____

   _____

   _____

4. (a) How could this new variety of rice reduce disease in developing countries? _____

   _____

   _____

   _____

   (b) Absorption of vitamin A requires sufficient dietary fat. Explain how this could be problematic for the targeted use of golden rice in developing countries:

   _____

   _____

5. As well as increasing nutrient content as in golden rice, other traits of crop plants are also desirable. For each of the following traits, suggest features that could be desirable in terms of increasing yield:

   (a) Grain size or number: _____

   (b) Maturation rate: _____

   (c) Pest resistance: _____

201 Food for the Masses

Key Idea: Genetic engineering has the potential to solve many of the world's food shortage problems by producing crops with greater yields than those currently grown.

Currently 1/6 of the world's population are undernourished. If trends continue, 1.5 billion people will be at risk of starvation by 2050 and, by 2100 (if global warming is taken into account), nearly half the world's population could be threatened with food shortages. The solution to the problem of food production is complicated. Most of the Earth's arable land has already been developed and currently uses 37% of the Earth's land area, leaving little room to grow more crops or farm more animals. Development of new fast growing and high yield crops appears to be part of the solution, but many crops can only be grown under a narrow range of conditions or are susceptible to disease. Moreover, the farming and irrigation of some areas is difficult, costly, and can be environmentally damaging. Genetic modification of plants may help to solve some of these looming problems by producing plants that will require less intensive culture or that will grow in areas previously considered not arable.

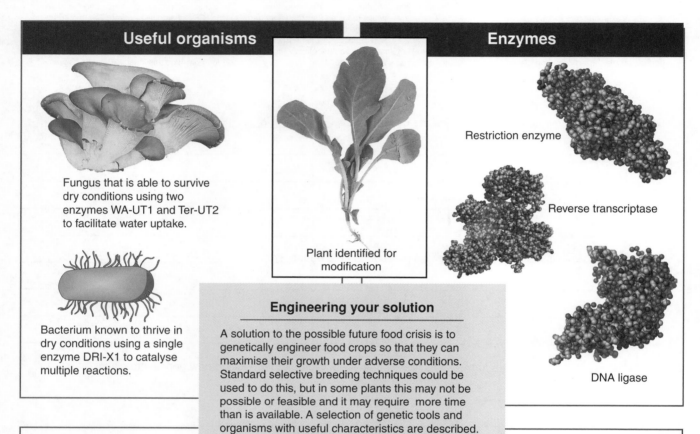

Useful organisms

Fungus that is able to survive dry conditions using two enzymes WA-UT1 and Ter-UT2 to facilitate water uptake.

Bacterium known to thrive in dry conditions using a single enzyme DRI-X1 to catalyse multiple reactions.

Plant identified for modification

Enzymes

Restriction enzyme

Reverse transcriptase

DNA ligase

Engineering your solution

A solution to the possible future food crisis is to genetically engineer food crops so that they can maximise their growth under adverse conditions. Standard selective breeding techniques could be used to do this, but in some plants this may not be possible or feasible and it may require more time than is available. A selection of genetic tools and organisms with useful characteristics are described. **Your task** is to use the items shown to devise a technique to successfully create a plant that could be successfully farmed in semi-desert environments such as sub-Saharan Africa. The following page will take you through the procedure. Not all the items will need to be used.

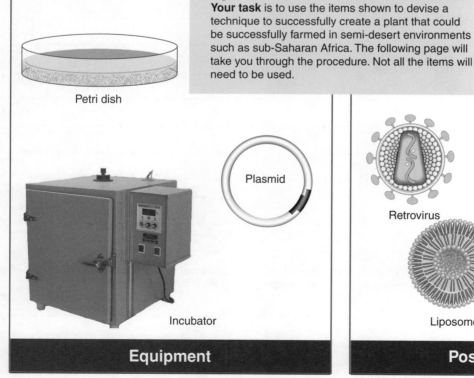

Equipment

Petri dish

Plasmid

Incubator

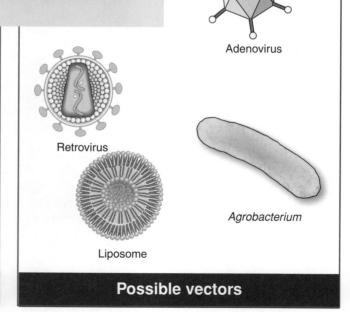

Possible vectors

Adenovirus

Retrovirus

Liposome

Agrobacterium

1. Identify the organism you would chose as a 'donor' of drought survival genes and explain your choice:

_____

_____

2. Describe a process to identify and isolate the required gene(s) and identify the tools to be used: _____

_____

_____

_____

_____

_____

_____

_____

3. Identify a vector for the transfer of the isolated gene(s) into the crop plant and explain your decision: _____

_____

4. Explain how the isolated gene(s) would be integrated into the vector's genome: _____

_____

_____

_____

_____

_____

_____

5. (a) Explain how the vector will transform the identified plant: _____

_____

_____

   (b) Identify the stage of development at which the plant would most easily be transformed. Explain your choice:

_____

_____

_____

_____

6. Explain how the transformed plants could be identified: _____

_____

_____

_____

_____

_____

7. Explain how a large number of plants can be grown from the few samples that have taken up the new DNA:

_____

_____

_____

202 Ethics of Gene Technology in Food Production

Key Idea: There are many potential benefits, risks, and ethical questions in using genetically modified organisms. Genetically modified organisms (GMOs) have many potential benefits, but their use raises a number of biological and ethical concerns. Some of these include risk to human health, animal welfare issues, and environmental safety. Currently a matter of concern to consumers is the adequacy of government regulations for the labelling of food products with GMO content. In some countries GM products must be clearly labelled, while other countries have no requirements for GM labelling. This can take away consumer choice about the types of products they buy. The use of GM may also have trade implications for countries exporting and importing GMO produce.

Potential benefits of GMOs

1. Increase in crop yields, including crops with more nutritional value and that store for longer.
2. Decrease in use of pesticides, herbicides and animal remedies.
3. Production of crops that are drought tolerant or salt tolerant.
4. Improvement in the health of the human population and the medicines used to achieve it.
5. Development of animal factories for the production of proteins used in manufacturing, the food industry, and health.

Potential risks of GMOs

1. Possible (uncontrollable) spread of transgenes into other species of plants, or animals.
2. Concerns that the release of GMOs into the environment may be irreversible.
3. Animal welfare and ethical issues: GM animals may suffer poor health and reduced life span.
4. GMOs may cause the emergence of pest, insect, or microbial resistance to traditional control methods.
5. May create a monopoly and dependence of developing countries on companies who are seeking to control the world's commercial seed supply.

Issue: Genetically modified crops

Background: Many food crops now have varieties that are genetically engineered, including maize, rice, and soybeans. Soybeans are the world's largest agricultural crop. Pests do a lot of damage to soybeans and maize crops so reducing pest damage would increase crop yields and value. Pesticide use is common and there has been a 130 fold increase in insecticide use in the US alone since 2001.

Genetic modification of crops to resist pests reduces the dependence on pesticides. This has already been successfully performed in maize (Bt maize) and soybeans (resistance against soybean cyst nematodes).

Problem: Plants that produce toxins may be toxic to humans.

Pests may become resistant to the pest-resistant properties of the engineered plant rendering it ineffective. The ultimate outcome of this is unknown.

Possible solution: Careful testing of the toxic properties of the plant under a variety of circumstances is required to ensure it is safe for human consumption.

Plans for alternative pest controls or mitigation must be in place in the event that pests become resistant to the engineered plant.

Issue: Who owns the technology?

Background: Crop seed developers and animal breeders spend large amounts of money on development. The genetic modification of plants and animals requires Government approval to develop the technology, carry out testing, and bring the product to market. This is a lengthy process that can cost millions of dollars. Companies therefore wish to make a profit or at least recoup costs on their product. This leads to patents to protect the technology and a monopoly on the product while the patent is in place. Monopolies can increase costs to farmers by dictating prices.

Problem: Biotech companies may have some leverage over farmers. For example, a seed producing company produces GE seeds, which cost hundreds of millions of dollars to develop. To ensure sales and a profit, they sell only these seeds (at great cost) to the farmer, who has little choice but to buy the seeds as there is little else to choose from. Non GE seeds may leave the farmer at a disadvantage compared to other growers as the crop yield may be less.

GE crops may be sold to overseas markets with little regulation and little choice. These markets will carry the load of potential problems, increasing the divide between developed and developing nations.

Possible solution: Legislation must be in place to ensure intellectual property is protected while also ensuring farmers have access to all available seed and stock. There must be careful consideration of the effect of GE crops on the agriculture of developing countries.

© 2016 **BIOZONE** International
ISBN: 978-1-927309-32-2
Photocopying Prohibited

1. Describe an advantage and a problem with the use of plants genetically engineered to be resistant to crop pests:

   (a) Advantage: _____

   _____

   (b) Problem: _____

   _____

2. Describe two uses of transgenic animals within the livestock industry:

   (a) _____

   (b) _____

   (c) Describe the possible problems that may occur over the ownership of genetically modified organisms.

   _____

   _____

   _____

3. Some years ago, Britain banned the import of a GM, pest resistant corn variety containing marker genes for ampicillin antibiotic resistance. Suggest why the use of antibiotic-resistance genes as markers is no longer common practice:

   _____

   _____

   _____

   _____

4. Many agricultural applications of DNA technology make use of transgenic bacteria which infect plants and express a foreign gene. Explain one advantage of each of the following applications of genetic engineering to crop biology:

   (a) Development of nitrogen-fixing *Rhizobium* bacteria that can colonise non-legumes such as corn and wheat:

   _____

   _____

   _____

   (b) Addition of transgenic *Pseudomonas fluorescens* bacteria into seeds (bacterium produces a pathogen-killing toxin):

   _____

   _____

   _____

5. Some of the public's fears and concerns about genetically modified food stem from moral or religious convictions, while others have a biological basis and are related to the potential biological threat posed by GMOs.
   (a) Conduct a class discussion or debate to identify these fears and concerns, and list them below:

   _____

   _____

   _____

   (b) Identify which of those you have listed above pose a real biological threat: _____

   _____

   _____

   _____

© 2016 **BIOZONE** International
ISBN: 978-1-927309-32-2
Photocopying Prohibited

203 Chapter Review

Summarise what you know about this topic under the headings and sub-headings provided. You can draw diagrams or mind maps, or write short notes to organise your thoughts. Use the images and hints to help you and refer back to the introduction to check the points covered:

Principles of genetic technology
HINT: Explain PCR, gel electrophoresis, microarrays, and recombinant DNA techniques.

Genetic technology in medicine
HINT: Applications of gene technology (including profiling, sequencing, screening, and gene therapy) in forensics and medicine.

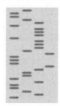

GMOs in agriculture
HINT: Using recombinant DNA technology to modify crop plants.

204 KEY TERMS AND IDEAS: Did You Get It?

1. Test your vocabulary by matching each term to its definition, as identified by its preceding letter code.

annealing

DNA amplification

DNA ligation

gel electrophoresis

GMO

marker gene

microsatellite

PCR

primer

recognition site

recombinant DNA

restriction endonuclease

sticky end

Taq polymerase

vector

A An organism or artificial vehicle that is capable of transferring a DNA sequence to another organism.

B The pairing (by hydrogen bonding) of complementary single-stranded nucleic acids to form a double-stranded polynucleotide. The term is applied to making recombinant DNA, to the binding of a DNA probe, or to the binding of a primer to a DNA strand during PCR.

C A cut in a length of DNA by a restriction enzyme that results in two strands of DNA being different lengths with one strand overhanging the other.

D A short length of DNA used to identify the starting sequence for PCR so that polymerase enzymes can begin amplification.

E An enzyme that is able to cut a length of DNA at a specific sequence or site.

F The site or sequence of DNA at which a restriction enzyme attaches and cuts.

G A gene, with an identifiable effect, used to determine if a piece of DNA has been successfully inserted into the host organism.

H A reaction that is used to amplify fragments of DNA using cycles of heating and cooling (abbreviation).

I A process that is used to separate different lengths of DNA by placing them in a gel matrix placed in a buffered solution through which an electric current is passed.

J The process of producing more copies of a length of DNA, normally using PCR.

K DNA that has had a new sequence added so that the original sequence has been changed.

L The repairing or attaching of fragmented DNA by ligase enzymes.

M A short (normally two base pairs) piece of DNA that repeats a variable number of times between people and so can be used to distinguish between individuals.

N An organism that has had part of its DNA sequence altered either by the removal or insertion of a piece of DNA.

O An enzyme that is able to replicate DNA and is commonly used in PCR to amplify a length of DNA.

2. Below is a DNA sequence of sections, A, B, C, D, and E and A', B', C', D', and E'. A scientists wants to isolate sections B, C, and D as a continuous group by PCR. Primers are B and D'. Complete the PCR process to show how B, C, and D are isolated. The first steps are done for you:

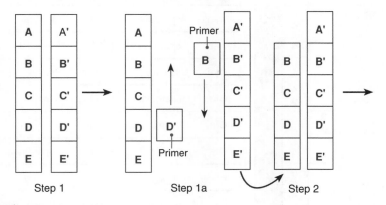

Step 1   Step 1a   Step 2

TEST

Image credits

The writing team would like to thank the following people and organisations who have kindly provided data, photographs, or illustrations for this edition:

• Don Horne for the photo of the snails • Dartmouth College for the electron micrograph images of the chloroplast • Louisa Howard Dartmouth college for the electron micrograph of the mitochondria • Wintec for the sports testing image • Ed Uthman for the image of the human fetus • Marc King for the photos of the chicken combs • Aptychus for the photo of the Tamil girl • Rita Willaert for the photo of the Nuba woman • Allan and Elaine Wilson for the photo of Harris' antelope squirrel • Dr David Wells, AgResearch • C Gemmil for the transect sampling photo • Kent Pryor for the photo of the rocky shore • Conrad Pilditch for images of rocky shore organisms • Stephen Moore for the invertebrate diversity photos • Rhys Barrier, University of Waikato or the photo and data of the black mudfish • Jonathan Wright, Bernard Field Station, Claremont College for the photo of *Hexarthra* • Ian Duggan for the *Hexarthra* data, University of Waikato • Kimberley Mallady for the photo of the hedgerow • UC Berkeley • Dr D. Cooper, University of California, San Francisco for the image of the podocyte • D. Frankhauser, University of Cincinnati, Clermont College for the photo of the Pacinian corpuscle

We also acknowledge the photographers who have made images available through **Wikimedia Commons** under Creative Commons Licences 2.0, 2.5, 3.0, or 4.0: Tangopaso • Kristian Peters • Piotr Kuczynski • it:Utente:Cits • NYWTS • Dr Graham Beards • Jpbarrass • KTBN • Aviceda • UtahCamera • Lorax • AKA • Dirk Beyer • Masur • Graham Bould • Andreas Trepte • Stemonitis • Tomoaki Horie • msdonna • C. Johnson Walker • Artem Topchiy • Meyer A. • Frances schmehel • Michael Apel • Simon Carey • Cymothoa exigua • M Betley • Cgoodwin • Bjorn Schulz • Zephyris • Jacoplane • Deuterostome • Iidar Sagdejev • RM Hunt • Pöllö • Jpogi • Roadnottaken • Noah Lehardt • Ute Frevert • Danielle Schwartz • Yathin sk • Honza beran • Piet Spaans

Contributors identified by coded credits:

BioRad: Bio-Rad Laboratories, **BH:** Brendan Hicks (Uni. of Waikato), **CDC**: Centers for Disease Control and Prevention, Atlanta, USA, **DS** Digital Stock, **EII:** Education Interactive Imaging, **FRI**: Forest and Research Industry, **NASA:** National Aeronautics and Space Administration, **NIH:** National Institute of Health, **NYSDEC**: New York State Dept of Environmental Conservation, **RA**: Richard Allan, **RCN:** Ralph Cocklin, **TG**: Tracey Greenwood, **WMRCVM**: Virginia-Maryland College of Veterinary Medicine, **WBS**: Warwick Silvester (Uni. of Waikato), **WMU**: Waikato Microscope Unit, **USDA**: United States Department of Agriculture, **USAF**: United States Air Force, DOC Department of Conservation

Image libraries:

We also acknowledge our use of royalty-free images, purchased by BIOZONE International Ltd from the following sources: **Corel** Corporation from various titles in their Professional Photos CD-ROM collection; Dollar Photo Club, dollarphotoclub.com; istock photos, istockphoto.com; **IMSI** (International Microcomputer Software Inc.) images from IMSI's MasterClips® and MasterPhotosTM Collection, 1895 Francisco Blvd. East, San Rafael, CA 94901-5506, USA; ©1996 **Digital Stock**, Medicine and Health Care collection; ©**Hemera** Technologies Inc, 1997-2001; © 2005 JupiterImages Corporation www.clipart.com; ©1994., ©**Digital Vision**; Gazelle Technologies Inc.; ©1994-1996 **Education Interactive Imaging** (UK), **PhotoDisc®**, Inc. USA, www.photodisc.com. We also acknowledge the following clipart providers: TechPool Studios, for their clipart collection of human anatomy: Copyright ©1994, TechPool Studios Corp. USA (some of these images have been modified); Totem Graphics, for clipart; Corel Corporation, for vector art from the Corel MEGAGALLERY collection.

mRNA-amino acid table

How to read the table:
Use table below to decode the genetic code as a sequence of amino acids in a polypeptide, from a given mRNA sequence.

To work out which amino acid is coded for by a codon (triplet of bases) look for the first letter of the codon in the row label on the left hand side. Then look for the column that intersects the same row from above that matches the second base. Finally, locate the third base in the codon by looking along the row from the right hand end that matches your codon.

First letter	U	C	A	G	Third letter
U	UUU Phe UUC Phe UUA Leu UUG Leu	UCU Ser UCC Ser UCA Ser UCG Ser	UAU Tyr UAC Tyr UAA STOP UAG STOP	UGU Cys UGC Cys UGA STOP UGG Trp	U C A G
C	CUU Leu CUC Leu CUA Leu CUG Leu	CCU Pro CCC Pro CCA Pro CCG Pro	CAU His CAC His CAA Gln CAG Gln	CGU Arg CGC Arg CGA Arg CGG Arg	U C A G
A	AUU Ile AUC Ile AUA Ile AUG Met	ACU Thr ACC Thr ACA Thr ACG Thr	AAU Asn AAC Asn AAA Lys AAG Lys	AGU Ser AGC Ser AGA Arg AGG Arg	U C A G
G	GUU Val GUC Val GUA Val GUG Val	GCU Ala GCC Ala GCA Ala GCG Ala	GAU Asp GAC Asp GAA Glu GAG Glu	GGU Gly GGC Gly GGA Gly GGG Gly	U C A G

Read second letter here. Read first letter here. Second letter. Read third letter here. Third letter.

Ala	Alanine	**Leu**	Leucine
Arg	Arginine	**Lys**	Lysine
Asn	Asparagine	**Met**	Methionine
Asp	Aspartic acid	**Phe**	Phenylalanine
Cys	Cysteine	**Pro**	Proline
Gln	Glutamine	**Ser**	Serine
Glu	Glutamic acid	**Thr**	Threonine
Gly	Glycine	**Trp**	Tryptophan
His	Histidine	**Tyr**	Tyrosine
Ile	Isoleucine	**Val**	Valine

Index